A Course of Lectures on

THE THEORY OF SOUND

A Course of Lectures on

THE THEORY OF SOUND

BY

S. N. RSCHEVKIN

TRANSLATED FROM THE RUSSIAN BY

O. M. BLUNN

TRANSLATION EDITED BY

P. E. DOAK

A Pergamon Press Book

THE MACMILLAN COMPANY

NEW YORK

1963

THE MACMILLAN COMPANY
60 Fifth Avenue
New York 11, N.Y.

This book is distributed by
THE MACMILLAN COMPANY
pursuant to a special arrangement with
PERGAMON PRESS LIMITED
Oxford, England

Library of Congress Number : 62-19271

This book is translated from the Russian
"*Kurs Lektsii po Teorii Zvuka*"
(published by the Moscow State University, 1960)

Printed by The Compton Printing Works (London) Ltd.
Made in England

CONTENTS

CONTENTS

PREFACE TO ENGLISH EDITION

This course of lectures translated by the Pergamon Institute was written by the author to help students in the Physics Faculty of Moscow University who wish to specialize in acoustics. Experience has shown that students and other persons beginning independent scientific work in this field experience many difficulties in the fundamentals of the theory of sound. In a general physics course acoustics is usually read at the beginning of the course as part of the mechanics section and so cannot be expounded as rigorously or as fully as other topics (magnetism, optics, molecular physics, electricity and nuclear physics).

This "textbook" has helped students to understand and assimilate the material much more quickly than formerly when they had to rely solely on lectures. It has also been possible to pay much more attention to the coaching of students in the theory of the subject during tutorials.

The author has only made slight additions and editorial corrections for the English edition. Some of the drawings have been replaced by new ones. Chapter VII now contains the derivation of the expression for the "attached mass" of an aperture in a partition across a tube, which is based on the kinetic energy of higher oscillatory modes which decay in the near zone.

The author hopes that readers of the English edition will be able to obtain useful knowledge from it in the study of the fundamentals of the theory of sound.

S.N. RSCHEVKIN

INTRODUCTION

In its classical form the theory of sound is based on the laws of motion of liquids and gases, certain special features of oscillatory motions of low amplitude being taken into account. The motion of liquids and gases is governed by the laws of hydro- and aerodynamics. Since the equations of hydro- and aerodynamics are written in the same mathematical form, it is therefore possible to confine ourselves to hydrodynamic equations if a wider meaning is imparted to the word and if we regard a liquid or gas as a fluid. Hydrodynamic equations are non-linear in their general form and their solution presents difficult problems. In order to solve individual problems it is therefore necessary to make a number of simplifying assumptions which permit a solution of the problem to some degree of approximation. Thus, it is possible to ignore viscosity in the solution of many problems of the motion of a fluid. *The hydrodynamics of an ideal fluid,* without viscosity, gives solutions which as a first approximation correspond very well with test data in a number of cases. Such an approximation is widely used in the solution of problems involved in the motion of fluids and more particularly air. The lift force on an aircraft wing can be calculated approximately without including viscosity. But without viscosity it is impossible to calculate the resistance to the motion of a body. Neither does the hydrodynamics of an ideal fluid give correct solutions for very viscous fluids.

At speeds considerably below that of sound the compressibility of fluids can be ignored. *The hydrodynamics of an incompressible fluid* is to a known extent applicable to the solution of problems in the dynamics of both gases and relatively incompressible liquids even though at first sight it does not seem possible for a gas to be regarded as incompressible. The apparent incompressibility is a consequence of the fact that at speeds less than the speed of sound any changes in pressure due to the motion of the body are propagated in the form of a wave travelling at the speed of sound in advance of the moving body itself. As a result, when the various parts of a body enter new zones of a medium, they find that the pressure there has already been changed by the motion of the body in preceding moments of time. Given that the dimensions of the moving body are limited, the deformation of the gas can be regarded as constant, which is equivalent to regarding the gas as incompressible.

At speeds near to or greater than the speed of sound fluids cannot be regarded as incompressible; moreover, in rapid processes it is necessary to take account of thermal conduction phenomena, which may be of special importance. The aerodynamics of a compressible gas is known as gas-dynamics. This branch of the mechanics of continuous media has been greatly extended with the development of jet propulsion and the flight of aircraft at supersonic speeds.

For a rigorous solution of the problem of oscillatory motion in continuous media it is necessary to regard liquids, gases and solid bodies as compressible. In oscillatory motion, bodies of sufficiently large extent experience curious phenomena known as waves which transmit deformations and pressures in all directions from the point where they arise, the disturbances being transmitted at a finite speed (the speed of sound). Each medium has a definite speed of sound depending upon its compressibility and density.

The main problems in acoustics are solved on the assumption that the oscillations are of small amplitude. The compressibility of the medium must be taken into account. Thus, it is understood that acoustics is small amplitude gas-dynamics.

INTRODUCTION

The majority of problems in the radiation and propagation of sound are governed by the *wave equation*. This equation is formed from the hydrodynamic equations of motion of an ideal fluid (Euler's equations) together with the *equation of continuity* of the medium, and the assumption that Hooke's law holds good, according to which stresses are proportional to the deformations (this is always true of small deformations).

In forming the wave equation in acoustics numerous assumptions are made which limit the extent of its application. For a more exact approach to the problem it must be borne in mind that acoustic processes take place in viscous media and that wave amplitudes frequently cannot be regarded as small. But it has been shown by experience that the wave equation gives a quite accurate description of a wide range of acoustic phenomena in gases and liquids, and that deviations from the laws governing the propagation of waves are only small corrections to the wave equation solutions in the overwhelming majority of cases. The wave equation is one of the fundamental equations of classical physics. It is used also in optics and electrodynamics in the same form as in acoustics.

The fundamentals of classical acoustics were laid in the nineteenth century, but it is only since the 1920's that the theory of sound has been further developed with improvements in experimental techniques and a wider scope for applied acoustics.

There are now several lines of development in the theory of sound which are extremely important in principle and also very valuable from the practical point of view.

In connection with the transmission of sound over long distances (in the atmosphere and at sea) there has been an extensive development of the theory of wave propagation in laminar media with different speeds of sound for each layer. A very profound theoretical study has been made of the dispersion and fluctuation of sound in turbulent media where such parameters as temperature are non-uniform. There also has been an extensive development of statistical methods of studying sound propagation in closed buildings as well as under natural conditions.

Many very difficult theoretical problems of sound radiation and diffraction have been solved. There has been an extensive development of the theory of sound propagation in ducts and buildings.

It has become important to substantiate the basic equations in acoustics from the point of view of molecular physics. This line of development has brought about a new field of molecular acoustics.

Owing to the problems of ultrasonics and architectural acoustics, a profound theoretical analysis has been made of many aspects of sound propagation in solid and plastic bodies, especially piezoelectric and ferromagnetic substances.

CHAPTER I

THE WAVE EQUATION

Hydrodynamic Equations

Consider the motion of an infinitesimal volume element of a fluid medium $dv = dx\,dy\,dz$ having the shape of a rectangular parallelepiped with sides dx, dy, and dz (Fig. 1). It is assumed that there is a steady pressure $P_0(x, y, z)$ within the fluid on which certain changes in pressure δP are imposed which are functions of time t and the coordinates x, y, z. The total pressure is

$$P(x, y, z, t) = P_0(x, y, z) + \delta P(x, y, z, t) = P_0 + \delta P.$$

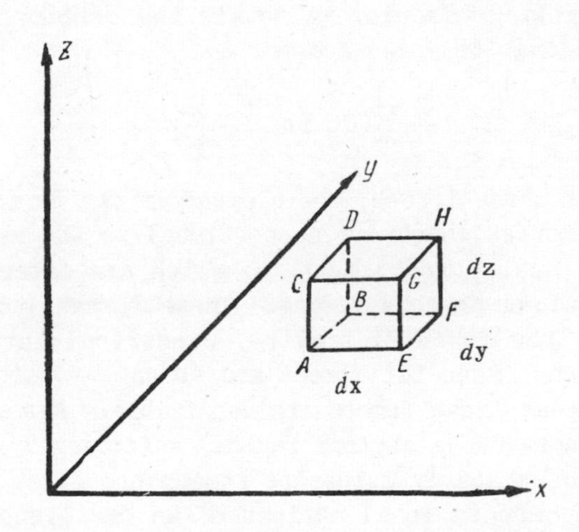

Fig. 1

We will put p for the quantity δP, which is usually small compared with P_0 in acoustic processes in gases,* and refer to it as the excess or *acoustic pressure*. The portion of the medium dv is affected by acoustic forces from the surrounding medium: the face $ABCD$ of element dv is affected by the force $P(x, y, z, t)\,dydz$ along the positive x axis, where $P(x, y, z, t)$ is the mean pressure over the face $ABCD$; the face $EFGH$ is affected by the force $P(x+dx, y, x, t)\,dydz$ along the negative x axis where $P(x+dx, y, z, t)$ is the mean pressure over the face $EFGH$. Owing to the smallness of dx it can be assumed that

$$P(x+dx, y, z, t)=P(x, y, z, t)+\frac{\partial P}{\partial x}dx=$$
$$=P(x, y, z, t)+\frac{\partial p}{\partial x}dx.$$

The total force in the x-direction affecting the portion of fluid is:

$$P(x, y, z, t)dy\,dz-P(x+dx, y, z, t)\,dy\,dz=$$
$$=-\frac{\partial p}{\partial x}dx\,dy\,dz=-\frac{\partial p}{\partial x}dv.$$

By similar reasoning we obtain the components of the forces along the y and z axes:

$$-\frac{\partial p}{\partial y}dv \text{ and } -\frac{\partial p}{\partial z}dv.$$

Besides these forces, the element dv can be affected by certain forces which are proportional to the mass of the element *(mass forces)* X, Y, Z, which are often referred to as spatial or body forces. These forces include, for example, the force of gravity, electrical forces in an ionized gas, magnetic forces and so on. It often can be assumed that these forces are negligible. As a simple real example consider a certain region, sufficiently large in extent, of a nearly quiescent atmosphere (i.e. no wind), in which certain local motions of an oscillatory nature

---

* In the propagation of sound in liquids p may often be comparable with P_0, or $>P_0$.

take place. The effect of the force of gravity is compensated by the pressure gradient in a still medium, so that it cannot be a cause of movement. Its only effect is to make the steady pressure P_0 a function of the coordinate z. The quantity P_0 increases constantly along the axis of the force of gravity, and the density ρ of the medium increases together with it. Since changes in P_0 take place slowly with distance, it can be assumed that the quantity P_0 is constant in a certain limited region and, consequently, that the density of the medium is also constant. Therefore, in considering local oscillatory processes (sound) in a nearly quiescent medium, it is possible to neglect steady mass forces of the gravitational type in the equation of motion. It is also assumed in the following analysis that there are no fluctuating spatial forces in that part of the medium where the wave motion is being considered, even though such forces may generally speaking exist.

Sound waves can be extremely diverse in character depending on the initial and boundary conditions. The boundary conditions express the effect of the external forces in problems of sound excitation; if the forced (compressed) motion at a certain boundary is known, the effect of the external variable forces acting on that boundary of the medium is thereby taken into account. Thus, in investigating the radiation of sound by vibrating bodies we confine ourselves to an examination of oscillatory movements of the medium due to the movement of the boundaries, without considering directly the effects of the external forces on the medium.

It is also quite possible in many cases to solve the wave equation when one includes steady or fluctuating spatial external forces which act on the medium over the entire space in question or over a certain restricted space, but this problem will not be considered here. Thus, to form the wave equation, it is presupposed that the motion of each portion of the fluid takes place without external forces.

On an element dv of an actual fluid in motion there arise forces of friction which are proportional at low velocities to the velocity gradients. We will consider first wave motion in an ideal fluid, i.e. it is assumed that there is no viscosity in the medium.

The equation of motion will contain the acceleration of the particle. The velocity of an element of fluid varies with time at each point in space. Suppose that the velocity at point O is equal to $\mathbf{u}_1$ at the instant t_1, and $\mathbf{u}_2$ at the instant t_2. After a period of time $\Delta t = t_2 - t_1$ the portion of the medium in question moves from point O to point O' over a distance $\Delta s = u \Delta t$ in the direction of the velocity of motion. Since velocity varies not only in time, but also in space, it follows that the velocity at point O' is different from that at point O at the same instant. Thus, at the instant t_2 the velocity of the particle which was at point O at the instant t_1 will be $\mathbf{u}_2$ and the change in velocity of this particle will be $\mathbf{u}_2 - \mathbf{u}_1$. The acceleration will then equal $(\mathbf{u}_2 - \mathbf{u}_1)/(\mathbf{u}_2 - \mathbf{u}_1)$. This expression can be put in the form:

$$\frac{\mathbf{u}_2 - \mathbf{u}_1}{t_2 - t_1} + \frac{\mathbf{u}_2' - \mathbf{u}_2}{t_2 - t_1}.$$

In the limit of very small Δt the first term gives a partial derivative with respect to time $\frac{\partial \mathbf{u}}{\partial t}$, which in this case can be called the *local derivative*. The quantity $(\mathbf{u}_2' - \mathbf{u}_2)/(t_2 - t_1)$ takes into account the change in velocity due to a movement Δs through space and in the limit gives a quantity called the *convective acceleration*, or *acceleration of transport*. We can put

$$\mathbf{u}_2' - \mathbf{u}_2 = \frac{\partial \mathbf{u}}{\partial s} \Delta s = \frac{\partial \mathbf{u}}{\partial s} u \Delta t.$$

The convective acceleration is $u\frac{\partial \mathbf{u}}{\partial s}$. The total acceleration of the element can be expressed by the total or *substantial* derivative and is:

$$\frac{d\mathbf{u}}{dt} = \frac{\partial \mathbf{u}}{\partial t} + \frac{\partial \mathbf{u}}{\partial s}u. \tag{1-1}$$

The name *substantial derivative* has been used to indicate that the acceleration refers to a moving element of matter (substance). In steady motion $\frac{\partial \mathbf{u}}{\partial t} = 0$; but there is always acceleration of a moving portion of a medium owing to the effect of the second term $\frac{\partial \mathbf{u}}{\partial s}u$.

The velocity $\mathbf{u}$ is the sum of the steady velocity $\mathbf{u}_0$ (wind, artificially created flows) and an additional oscillatory velocity $\mathbf{u}'$. Equation (1-1) takes the form:

$$\frac{d\mathbf{u}}{dt} = \frac{\partial \mathbf{u}}{\partial t} + \left|\mathbf{u}_0 + \mathbf{u}'\right| \frac{\partial(\mathbf{u}_0 + \mathbf{u}')}{\partial s}. \tag{1-2}$$

In forming the simplest wave equation it is assumed that there are no large steady velocities in the medium, so that u_0 is small. We also limit the oscillatory velocities $\mathbf{u}'$ and assume that they are small.

The velocity $\mathbf{u}$ can have a large gradient $\left(\frac{\partial \mathbf{u}}{\partial s}\right)$ (for example, at the boundary of rapidly flowing jets or in the propagation of explosive waves). To start with, we will confine ourselves to simple cases when there are no large gradients of steady or oscillatory velocity. The second term in equation (1-2) contains the product of two small quantities and is itself small. It therefore can be assumed that the following condition is satisfied:

$$\left|\mathbf{u}_0 + \mathbf{u}'\right| \frac{\partial(\mathbf{u}_0 + \mathbf{u}')}{\partial s} \ll \frac{\partial \mathbf{u}}{\partial t}, \tag{1-3}$$

which, as we shall see (in Chapter II), implies that the velocity u must be much less than the speed of sound. If this condition is satisfied we can equate, quite accurately, the total derivative of the velocity with respect to time to its partial derivative with respect to time:

$$\frac{d\mathbf{u}}{dt} \approx \frac{\partial \mathbf{u}}{\partial t}.$$

We now write the equations of motion of an element dv of the fluid, putting ρ for the density of the medium, ξ, η and ζ for the displacements of the element along the coordinate axes, and $\dot{\xi}$, $\dot{\eta}$ and $\dot{\zeta}$ for its velocities. The equation of motion along the x axis has the form:

$$\rho \frac{\partial \dot{\xi}}{\partial t} dv = -\frac{\partial p}{\partial x} dv.$$

Cancelling dv and forming similar equations for motion along the y and z axes, we get:

$$\begin{aligned} \rho \frac{\partial \dot{\xi}}{\partial t} &= -\frac{\partial p}{\partial x}, \\ \rho \frac{\partial \dot{\eta}}{\partial t} &= -\frac{\partial p}{\partial y}, \\ \rho \frac{\partial \dot{\zeta}}{\partial t} &= -\frac{\partial p}{\partial z}. \end{aligned} \qquad (1\text{-}4)$$

Equations (1-4) are the components of the equation of motion along the x, y and z axes. They are an approximate form of the general non-linear hydrodynamic equations (Euler equations). These linearized equations of motion are used below to form the wave equation. If condition (1-3) is not fulfilled, the equations of motion become non-linear.

Hooke's Law

It can be assumed in acoustics that the quantity ρ varies only slightly about its constant value ρ_0 in a still medium. Suppose we put:

$$\rho = \rho_0 + \delta\rho, \quad \text{where} \quad \frac{\delta\rho}{\rho_0} \ll 1. \qquad (1\text{-}5)$$

A change in density is related to a change in volume. Suppose that a certain portion of fluid of density ρ_0 occupies a volume v_0. If its volume changes slightly and becomes equal to $v_0 + \delta v$, then the density will be $\rho_0 + \delta\rho$. For the mass of the fluid in question, we have:

$$v_0\rho_0 = (v_0 + \delta v)(\rho_0 + \delta\rho) = v_0\rho_0 + v_0\,\delta\rho + \rho_0\,\delta v + \delta v\,\delta\rho.$$

Ignoring the small second order quantity $\delta v\,\delta\rho$, we get:

$$v_0\,\delta\rho + \rho_0\,\delta v = 0,$$

or

$$\frac{\delta\rho}{\rho_0} = -\frac{\delta v}{v_0}.$$

The quantity $\frac{\delta\rho}{\rho_0}$ is called the *condensation*, whilst the quantity $\frac{\delta v}{v_0}$ is called the *strain* or *volume deformation*. Considering expression (1-5) we assume that Hooke's law is applicable and accordingly hypothesize that for small deformations, the acoustic (excess) pressure causing the deformation is proportional to the amount of deformation:

$$\delta P = p = \varkappa\frac{\delta\rho}{\rho_0} = -\varkappa\frac{\delta v}{v_0}. \tag{1-6}$$

The quantity $\varkappa$ will be referred to as the *bulk modulus*. To form the wave equation it is essential to assume that Hooke's law is applicable, i.e. that the deformation is a linear function of the stress.

The Velocity Potential and the Equation of Motion

We now integrate the equations of motion (1-4) with respect to time. From the first equation we get:

$$\dot{\xi} = -\int_0^t \frac{1}{\rho}\frac{\partial p}{\partial x}\,dt.$$

It is easily seen that

$$\frac{\partial}{\partial x}\left(\frac{p}{\rho}\right)=\frac{1}{\rho}\frac{\partial p}{\partial x}-\frac{p}{\rho^2}\frac{\partial \rho}{\partial x}.$$

The second term in this expression is small compared with the first. In fact

$$\frac{\frac{p}{\rho^2}\frac{\partial \rho}{\partial x}}{\frac{1}{\rho}\frac{\partial p}{\partial x}}=\frac{p}{\rho}\frac{\partial \rho}{\partial p}.$$

According to equation (1-6),

$$\frac{\partial \rho}{\partial p}=\frac{\rho_0}{\varkappa};$$

Hence

$$\frac{p}{\rho}\frac{\partial \rho}{\partial p}=\frac{\varkappa}{\rho_0}\frac{\delta\rho}{\rho}\frac{\rho_0}{\varkappa}=\frac{\delta\rho}{\rho}.$$

In accordance with relation (1-5), this is a very small quantity. Thus, if we substitute $\frac{1}{\rho}\frac{\partial p}{\partial x}$ for $\frac{\partial}{\partial x}\left(\frac{p}{\rho}\right)$, we then get from the three equations (1-4) by transposing the operations of differentiation and integration:

$$\dot{\xi}=-\frac{\partial}{\partial x}\int_0^t\left(\frac{p}{\rho}\right)\partial t;\quad \dot{\eta}=-\frac{\partial}{\partial y}\int_0^t\left(\frac{p}{\rho}\right)dt;\quad \dot{\zeta}=-\frac{\partial}{\partial z}\int_0^t\left(\frac{p}{\rho}\right)dt.$$

In integration certain arbitrary constants $\dot{\xi}_0, \dot{\eta}_0,$ and $\dot{\zeta}_0$, appear which are obviously functions only of the coordinates and not of time; they are the components of the velocity at the initial moment of time $t = 0$. It is assumed that these velocities are the negative derivatives with respect to the coordinate axes of a certain point function $\Phi_0(x, y, z)$:

$$\dot{\xi}_0=-\frac{\partial \Phi_0}{\partial x};\quad \dot{\eta}_0=-\frac{\partial \Phi_0}{\partial y};\quad \dot{\zeta}_0=-\frac{\partial \Phi_0}{\partial z}. \tag{1-7}$$

This signifies that *the motion at the initial moment is potential.* The following condition is satisfied for such motion:

$$\operatorname{rot} \dot{\mathbf{u}}/_{t=0}=0,$$

i.e. the motion is eddyless. We find the function Φ_0 in the form of a curvilinear integral:

$$\Phi_0(x, y, z)=\int\left(\frac{\partial\Phi_0}{\partial x}dx+\frac{\partial\Phi_0}{\partial y}dy+\frac{\partial\Phi_0}{\partial z}dz\right).$$

The integrand is the complete differential of the function Φ_0. If condition (1-7) is fulfilled, we can write

$$\dot{\xi}=-\frac{\partial}{\partial x}\left[\int_0^t\frac{p}{\rho}dt+\Phi_0\right];\quad \dot{\eta}=-\frac{\partial}{\partial y}\left[\int_0^t\frac{p}{\rho}dt+\Phi_0\right];$$

$$\dot{\zeta}=-\frac{\partial}{\partial z}\left[\int_0^t\frac{p}{\rho}dt+\Phi_0\right],$$

or, putting

$$\int_0^t\frac{p}{\rho}dt+\Phi_0=\Phi(x, y, z, t), \qquad (1\text{-}8)$$

we get:

$$\dot{\xi}=-\frac{\partial\Phi}{\partial x};\quad \dot{\eta}=-\frac{\partial\Phi}{\partial y};\quad \dot{\zeta}=-\frac{\partial\Phi}{\partial z}. \qquad (1\text{-}9)$$

Thus conditions (1-7) are fulfilled at any instant and the motion is potential.

Moreover, it is seen that

$$\frac{\partial\dot{\zeta}}{\partial y}-\frac{\partial\dot{\eta}}{\partial z}=0;\quad \frac{\partial\dot{\xi}}{\partial z}-\frac{\partial\dot{\zeta}}{\partial x}=0;\quad \frac{\partial\dot{\eta}}{\partial x}-\frac{\partial\dot{\xi}}{\partial y}=0,$$

i.e. the components rot $\mathbf{u}$ are equal to zero and the velocity field will remain *eddyless*. Thus, if the acoustic field is eddyless at the initial moment, then it will also possess this same property later. The function Φ, as defined by equation (1-8), is called the *velocity potential*. Suppose we now take the derivative with respect to time of (1-8). This gives

$$\frac{\partial\Phi}{\partial t}=\frac{p}{\rho}, \text{ whence } p=\rho\frac{\partial\Phi}{\partial t}. \quad (1\text{-}10)$$

This expression is a single equation of motion for acoustic oscillations in a fluid which is equivalent to the three equations in (1-4). If the velocity potential Φ is found for the problem in question the particle velocity and pressure at each given point at any instant can be found by (1-9) and (1-10).

The Equation of Continuity

We shall now formulate the second important relationship in the theory of motion of a fluid, namely, the *equation of continuity*. In essence it expresses the law governing the conservation of mass and mathematically formulates the obvious fact that if there is a resultant flow of matter across the boundary of any volume element the amount of matter in this element will change and this will cause a corresponding change in density. If the homogeneous structure of the medium is disturbed (for example, if vapour condenses into a droplet as a result of compression inside the element, or if a discontinuity, i.e. cavitation, occurs when the pressure in the fluid is reduced), it is obviously impossible to define the change in the amount of any one particular type of matter in the given element simply by the flow of matter across its boundary. In forming the equation of continuity in its simplest form it is presupposed that the aggregate state of the substance does not change during *motion, i.e. the medium is continuous and uniform.*

The total amount of matter leaving an infinitesimal volume element dv per unit time equals $\operatorname{div}(\rho\mathbf{u})dv$. The density is thereby reduced and there is a corresponding reduction in mass equal to $-\frac{\partial\rho}{\partial t}dv$ per unit time. Since these two quantities are equal the equation of continuity takes the form

$$\operatorname{div}(\rho \mathbf{u}) = -\frac{\partial \rho}{\partial t}$$

or

$$\frac{\partial(\rho \dot{\xi})}{\partial x} + \frac{\partial(\rho \dot{\eta})}{\partial y} + \frac{(\partial \rho \dot{\zeta})}{\partial z} = -\frac{\partial \rho}{\partial t}. \quad (1\text{-}11)$$

The second and third terms in the partial derivative

$$\frac{\partial(\rho \dot{\xi})}{\partial x} = \rho_0 \frac{\partial \dot{\xi}}{\partial x} + \delta\rho \frac{\partial \dot{\xi}}{\partial x} + \dot{\xi} \frac{\partial \rho}{\partial x}$$

can be ignored since $\delta\rho, \dot{\xi}$ and their derivatives with respect to x are small quantities; we also proceed in the same way with the other terms on the left hand side of equation (1-11). Then

$$\rho_0 \left(\frac{\partial \dot{\xi}}{\partial x} + \frac{\partial \dot{\eta}}{\partial y} + \frac{\partial \dot{\zeta}}{\partial z} \right) = -\frac{\partial \rho}{\partial t}, \quad (1\text{-}12)$$

but since $\frac{\partial \rho}{\partial t} = \frac{\partial(\delta\rho)}{\partial t}$, it follows that

$$\operatorname{div} \mathbf{u} = -\frac{\partial\left(\frac{\delta\rho}{\rho_0}\right)}{\partial t}. \quad (1\text{-}13)$$

It is quite permissible to write the equations of continuity in their linear form (1-12) or (1-13) if the deformations are very small. But the equation of continuity (1-11) is non-linear in its general form.

We wish to rewrite the equation of continuity (1-13) in a slightly different form. Using relationship (1-6), we write $\frac{p}{\varkappa}$ instead of $\frac{\delta\rho}{\rho_0}$, so that (1-13) becomes

$$\operatorname{div} \mathbf{u} = -\frac{1}{\varkappa} \frac{\partial p}{\partial t}.$$

Using formula (1-10) we substitute $\rho \frac{\partial^2 \Phi}{\partial t^2}$, for the derivative of p with respect to t, and the second derivatives of Φ with respect to coordinates x, y and z for the derivatives of the velocities $\dot{\xi}$, $\dot{\eta}$ and $\dot{\zeta}$ with respect to x, y and z. Then, according to equation (1-9):

$$\frac{\partial^2 \Phi}{\partial x^2} + \frac{\partial^2 \Phi}{\partial y^2} + \frac{\partial^2 \Phi}{\partial z^2} = \frac{\rho}{\varkappa} \frac{\partial^2 \Phi}{\partial t^2}. \tag{1-14}$$

We write $\nabla^2 \Phi$ for the Laplacian differential operator on the left-hand side and introduce the notation

$$c^2 = \frac{\varkappa}{\rho} \approx \frac{\varkappa}{\rho_0}. \tag{1-15}$$

We then get the following equation:

$$c^2 \nabla^2 \Phi = \frac{\partial^2 \Phi}{\partial t^2}. \tag{1-14a}$$

This equation is known as *the wave equation*. It contains only one unknown function of the coordinates and time, $\Phi(x, y, z, t)$. By solving this equation we can find all the main quantities of the acoustic field, i.e. the particle velocity and the acoustic pressure.

If we take the derivative with respect to t of both sides of equation (1-14) and take into account on the basis of expressions (1-8) and (1-10) that

$$\frac{\partial}{\partial t}\left(\frac{\partial^2 \Phi}{\partial t^2}\right) = \frac{1}{\rho} \frac{\partial^2 p}{\partial t^2} \text{ and } \frac{\partial}{\partial t}\left(\nabla^2 \Phi\right) = \nabla^2\left(\frac{p}{\rho}\right) \approx \frac{1}{\rho} \nabla^2 p,$$

we then obtain the wave equation in a different and often

used form:

$$c^2 \nabla^2 p = \frac{\partial^2 p}{\partial t^2}. \quad (1\text{-}16)$$

The wave equation can be interpreted physically as follows. The Laplacian of a quantity may be regarded as a measure of the difference between the concentration of some quantity in the neighbourhood of a point and its concentration at the point itself. The wave equation states that an excess concentration causes a decrease in the rate at which the concentration increases, and a defect in concentration results in an increase in this rate.

For example, consider the familiar case of transverse waves on a stretched string. Here the wave equation is $T\partial^2 y/\partial x^2 = m\partial^2 y/\partial t^2$, where T is tension in the string, y its transverse displacement, x distance along the string, and m its mass per unit length. The Laplacian has reduced to $\partial^2 y/\partial x^2$, the instantaneous curvature of the string at the point x, which is clearly a measure of the amount a representative value of y at points near x exceeds its value at x. Thus the wave equation states that the acceleration of the string at x (or the force per unit length acting on it due to neighbouring portions of the string) is proportional to its curvature. Alternatively, in the more general terminology used above, we can say that an excess value of y at x ($\partial^2 y/\partial x^2$ negative) causes a decrease in the rate at which y increases (a decrease in the velocity $\partial y/\partial t$), and vice versa.

After solving equation (1-16) we can find Φ by integrating p with respect to time $\left(\Phi = \int_0^t \frac{p}{\rho} dt\right)$, and then find the particle velocity by formula (1-9). It is evident from (1-6) and (1-16) that the density fluctuations satisfy the wave equation. Similarly from (1-9) and (1-14a) it can be seen that the Cartesian particle velocity components (and the corresponding displacement components) each satisfy the wave equation independently. But velocity and displacement *components* in other coordinate systems (e.g. spherical polar coordinates) do not necessarily satisfy the wave equation (1-16) (see Chapter IV, eq. (4-3) and following).

As we have seen, a number of simplifying assumptions were made in forming the wave equation:

1. The medium was assumed to be inviscid.
2. The mean pressure and density of the medium were assumed to be constant.
3. Steady and fluctuating spatial forces were neglected. The external forces were assumed to affect the medium only at its boundaries.
4. The steady velocity components and their gradients were assumed to be small.
5. The oscillatory velocity components and their gradients were also assumed to be small.
6. The motion was assumed to be eddyless (potential).
7. Only small deformations of the medium were assumed to occur, the deformations and stresses being directly proportional (Hooke's law).
8. It was assumed that the wave is propagated in a uniform medium, and that there is no change of phase (state of matter) during the wave motion.

Despite the large number of assumptions, the simple form of the wave equation (1-15) gives a very good description of the main properties of acoustic waves. This indicates that the stated assumptions are valid within fairly wide limits.

Reference should be made to an important property of solutions of the wave equation. If the functions Φ_1, $\Phi_2 \ldots \Phi_n$

are solutions of the wave equation, then the following function is also its solution owing to the linearity of the equation:

$$\Phi = \sum_{i=1}^{n} a_i \Phi_i,$$

where the a_i are constant quantities.

Thus, the individual solutions can be superposed one on the other and their sum will be a solution of the wave equation. Individual wave processes which are governed by the wave equation (1-15) are simply added in the event of simultaneous existence; this property of the solution is called the *principle of superposition*.

If the oscillatory process is governed by a harmonic law, we can then put

$$\Phi(x, y, z, t) = \Psi(x, y, z) \cdot e^{j\omega t}$$

where $\Psi(x, y, z)$ is a function solely of the coordinates, ω is the angular frequency of the process $\left(\omega = \frac{2\pi}{T}\right.$, where T is the period of the oscillation), and $j = \sqrt{-1}$. Since

$$\nabla^2 \Phi = \nabla^2 \Psi e^{j\omega t}, \text{ and } \frac{\partial^2 \Phi}{\partial t^2} = -\omega^2 \Psi e^{j\omega t},$$

a simpler equation can be obtained from (1-15):

$$\nabla^2 \Psi + k^2 \Psi = 0,$$

where $k = \frac{\omega}{c}$.

This is the fundamental equation for waves having simple harmonic time dependence and is called the *Helmholtz equation*. It will be seen later that the constants c and k have a quite definite physical meaning.

CHAPTER II

THE PLANE WAVE

The Plane Wave Equation

It is supposed that all the quantities defining the wave motion at the *moment of time in question* are identical in any plane transverse to the x axis and that a change in the state of motion occurs only on transition from one plane to another. Then the derivatives $\frac{\partial^2 \Phi}{\partial y^2}$ and $\frac{\partial^2 \Phi}{\partial z^2}$ in equation (1-14) are zero, whilst Φ depends solely on x and t. The wave process is described by the equation:

$$c^2 \frac{\partial^2 \Phi}{\partial x^2} = \frac{\partial^2 \Phi}{\partial t^2}. \tag{2-1}$$

This is the *wave equation for a plane wave*. The form of this equation shows that all the motions occur only along the x axis, since the velocities $\dot{\eta} = -\frac{\partial \Phi}{\partial y}$ and $\dot{\zeta} = -\frac{\partial \Phi}{\partial z}$ are always zero. To solve equation (2-1) we introduce, according to D'Alembert's method, new variables:

$$u = ct - x,$$
$$v = ct + x.$$

Then

$$\frac{\partial^2 \Phi}{\partial x^2} = \frac{\partial^2 \Phi}{\partial u^2} - 2 \frac{\partial^2 \Phi}{\partial u \partial v} + \frac{\partial^2 \Phi}{\partial v^2},$$

$$\frac{\partial^2 \Phi}{\partial t^2} = c^2 \left(\frac{\partial^2 \Phi}{\partial u^2} + 2 \frac{\partial^2 \Phi}{\partial u \partial v} + \frac{\partial^2 \Phi}{\partial v^2} \right)$$

and after cancellings, equation (2-1) takes the form

$$\frac{\partial^2\Phi}{\partial u\partial v}=\frac{\partial}{\partial u}\left(\frac{\partial\Phi}{\partial v}\right)=0.$$

Integrating it, we find that $\frac{\partial\Phi}{\partial v}=F(v)$ is an arbitrary function of v. A second integration gives:

$$\Phi(u,v)=\int F(v)\,dv+\Phi_1(u)=\Phi_1(u)+\Phi_2(v),$$

where $\int F(v)\,dv$ is denoted by $\Phi_2(v)$, and the arbitrary function $\Phi_1(u)$ is a constant of integration with respect to v. Returning to variables x and t, we get:

$$\Phi(x,t)=\Phi_1(ct-x)+\Phi_2(ct+x). \qquad (2\text{-}2)$$

where Φ_1 and Φ_2 are quite *arbitrary functions with arguments of a characteristic type*. Thus, the general solution of the wave equation is characterized not by a particular type of function, but by a particular type of argument $(ct \mp x)$, formed from the variables x and t.

From equation (2-2), in accordance with formulae (1-9) and (1-10):

$$\left.\begin{aligned}\dot{\xi}&=\Phi_1'(ct-x)-\Phi_2'(ct+x),\\ p&=\rho c\Phi_1'(ct-x)+\rho c\Phi_2'(ct+x),\end{aligned}\right\} \qquad (2\text{-}3)$$

where Φ_1' and Φ_2' are derivatives of the functions with respect to their arguments. Consequently, p and $\dot{\xi}$ can be expressed by formulae of the same type as Φ with two arbitrary functions.

Suppose that at the initial instant ($t = 0$) a disturbance is created in the medium in the region from $x = 0$ to $x = a$ such that the velocities in this region are zero, whilst the pressure equals $2p_0$. (The conditions at the initial instant can be most diverse; they are called *the initial conditions.*) The first equation in (2-3) makes it possible to draw the conclusion that $\Phi_2'(x)=\Phi_1'(-x)$ in the region from $x = 0$ to $x = a$ when $t = 0$. Consequently, according to the second equation in (2-3), $p(x)$ when $t = 0$ consists of two equal parts in the region from $x = 0$ to $x = a$

$$p=2\rho c\,\Phi_1'(-x)=2p_0.$$

The first part of the pulse, $p_1=\rho c\,\Phi_1'(ct-x)$, at the moment $t = t_1$ gives $p_1=p_0$ and $\dot{\xi}=\frac{p_0}{\rho c}$ at values of the argument $ct_1 - x$, lying in the region from $ct_1 - x = -a$ to $ct_1-x=0$, i.e. between points with abscissae $x=ct_1+a$ and $x = ct$, (Fig. 2). In other words, the first part of the pulse moves forward without changing shape through a distance ct_1 along the positive x axis. The second part of the pulse, $p_2=\rho c\,\Phi_2'(ct+x)$ gives $p_2=p_0$ and $\dot{\xi}=-\frac{p_0}{\rho c}$ in the region from $ct_1+x=a$ to $ct_1+x=0$, i.e. from $x=-ct_1+a$ to $x=-ct_1$; this part of the pulse without changing shape moves through a distance ct_1 along the negative x axis. The velocity $\dot{\xi}$ will have values $\frac{p_0}{\rho c}$ and $-\frac{p_0}{\rho c}$ in the regions that each of the two pulses occupy separately and will be zero in that part of space where the pulses are superposed one on the other. Figure 2 shows the position and the magnitude of the components of the resultant pressure pulse at the initial instant and at two subsequent instants.

If there is an arbitrarily shaped pulse of pressure p_0 (or velocity $\dot{\xi}_0$) at the initial instant, defined as a function of x, we can similarly find both arbitrary functions Φ_1 and Φ_2, from equations (2-3); in general these functions are not equal. During the course of time the pulses of type Φ_1 and Φ_2 will move out without changing shape, the first along the positive x axis, and the second along the negative x axis.

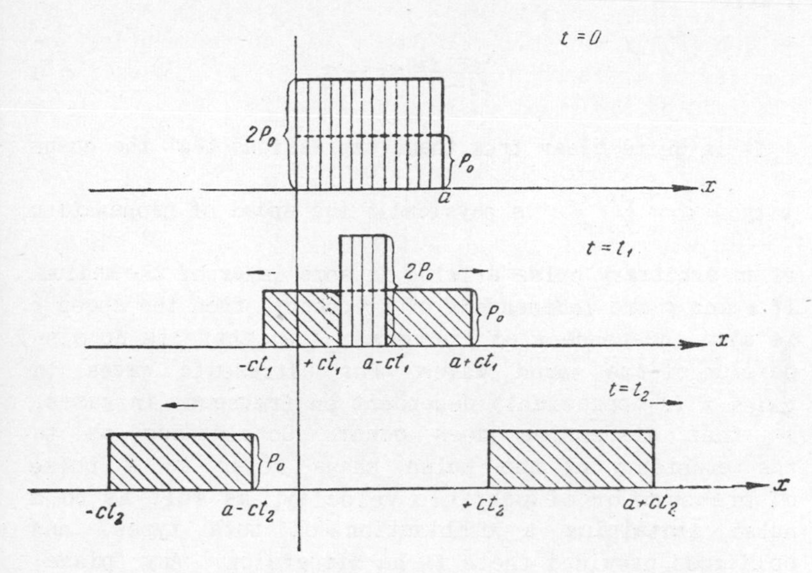

Fig. 2.

It is quite clear from this reasoning that for any pulse the *phase* corresponding to the value a of the arguments of the functions Φ_1 or Φ_2 (the beginning, end, maximum or other typical point in the case of pulses of complex shape) moves from the position $x_1 = ct_1 - a$ to the position $x_2 = ct_2 - a$ during the time between t_1 and t_2 for the first part of the pulse, expressed by the function Φ_1 of argument $ct - x$, and from the position $x_1' = -ct_1 + a$ to the position $x_2' = -ct_2 + a$ for the second part expressed by the function Φ_2 of argument $ct + x$.

Thus, for the first part of the pulse which is propagated along the positive x axis, we have:

$$\frac{x_2 - x_1}{t_2 - t_1} = +c,$$

whilst for the second part of the pulse along the negative

x axis

$$\frac{x'_2 - x'_1}{t_2 - t_1} = -c.$$

It is quite clear from these expressions that the quantity $c = \sqrt{\frac{\varkappa}{\rho}}$ is physically the speed of propagation of an arbitrary pulse arising in some layer of the medium. If $\varkappa$ and ρ are independent of frequency, then the speed c is also independent of frequency, i.e. there is no dispersion of the sound waves. For ultrasonic waves in gases $\varkappa$ is appreciably dependent on frequency in gases, so that dispersion does occur. Conclusions as to the constancy of the pulse shape refer to a pulse of pressure or of particle velocity, as well as to a pulse containing a combination of both types, and hold good provided there is no dispersion. Any (plane) deformation of the medium in a certain layer at the initial instant is transmitted in the form of two pulses which travel in opposite directions at speed c, and there is no change in the shape of the pulses on propagation, i.e. no change in the functions Φ_1 and Φ_2 (or p and $\dot{\xi}$). This process of propagation of deformation in an elastic medium is known as a *plane wave*. In this case we have *longitudinal waves*, since the velocity of oscillation of the particles is in the same direction as the propagation of the waves.

Consider a gas occupying the region $x > 0$ bounded by a rigid wall which coincides with the plane $x = 0$. When a pulse originates in the gas very near the wall the wave process cannot be propagated in the negative x direction and the solution of the wave equation can then be written in the form:

$$\Phi = \Phi_1 \ (ct - x), \tag{2-4}$$

$$\dot{\xi} = \Phi'_1 \ (ct - x), \tag{2-5}$$

$$p = \rho c \, \Phi_1' \, (ct - x). \tag{2-6}$$

If the pressure in the medium at the solid boundary $x = 0$, (or the form of the function $\dot{\xi}$ at $x = 0$), is given as a function of time, then the form of the functions Φ_1' and $\Phi_1 \ (ct - x)$ will be known and the wave process is thus determined at all other points of the medium at any moment of time. Thus, in the case in question, the full definition of the form of the wave process does not require two independent initial conditions for the pressure and particle velocity, for it is sufficient to define one boundary condition either for $\dot{\xi}$, or for p, since these quantities are inter-related as can be seen from equations (2-5) and (2-6).

If the function Φ is periodic, for example, cos $(ct - x)$ or sin $(ct - x)$, we then get a periodic wave train which travels out from the excitation plane at a speed c.

Equation (2-4) describes a wave which is propagated in only one direction. Such a wave is called a plane *progressive* wave. Dividing equations (2-6) by (2-5), we get:

$$p = \rho c \dot{\xi}. \tag{2-7}$$

In a plane progressive wave *for any pulse shape (as well as for periodic waves), the pressure at any point is proportional to the particle velocity and is in the same phase.*

The Speed of Sound

For small deformations use may be made of Hooke's law (see Chapter I):

$$\delta P = p = -\varkappa \frac{\delta v}{v_0} = \varkappa \frac{\delta \rho}{\rho_0},$$

where $\varkappa$ is the bulk modulus. When the medium undergoes acoustic vibrations, then when it is compressed heating takes place, and when it is rarefied cooling occurs. Since it can be supposed that the temperature does not balance out during the vibration, we can infer that $\varkappa$ is the adiabatic bulk modulus, which is greater than the isothermal modulus.

Passing to the limit, for infinitesimal deformations we get:

$$\frac{\delta p}{\delta \rho} \approx \frac{\partial p}{\partial \rho} = \frac{\varkappa}{\rho_0} = c^2,$$

or

$$c = +\sqrt{\left(\frac{\partial p}{\partial \rho}\right)_{\mathrm{ad}}} = \sqrt{\left(\frac{\varkappa_{\mathrm{ad}}}{\rho_0}\right)}. \qquad (2\text{-}8)$$

The speed of sound c can therefore be determined if the relationship between density and pressure is known, i.e. the equation of state of the substance. It is clear from equation (2-8) that the *speed of sound is a certain constant* typical of the given substance under definite conditions; c may be a function of temperature and pressure of the medium.

Using Poisson's adiabatic law for gases we can write:

$$Pv^{\gamma} = \frac{P}{\rho^{\gamma}} = \text{const} \quad \text{or} \quad \frac{P_0 + p}{P_0} = \left(\frac{\rho_0 + \delta\rho}{\rho_0}\right)^{\gamma}, \qquad (2\text{-}9)$$

where P_0 is the constant pressure in the gas, and $\gamma = \frac{c_p}{c_v}$.

Expanding the right-hand side as a series, we have:

$$1 + \frac{p}{P_0} = \left(1 + \frac{\delta\rho}{\rho_0}\right)^{\gamma} = 1 + \gamma\frac{\delta\rho}{\rho_0} + \frac{\gamma(\gamma-1)}{2}\left(\frac{\delta\rho}{\rho_0}\right)^2 + \dots$$

Ignoring small terms of order higher than the first, we

get:

$$p \approx \gamma P_0 \frac{\delta\rho}{\rho_0}.$$

Since this expression has the form of Hooke's law, we can conclude that

$$\varkappa \approx \gamma P_0. \qquad (2\text{-}10)$$

It will be clear that this relationship is fulfilled only for oscillations of small amplitude. For the speed of sound with small amplitudes we get:

$$c_0 = \sqrt{\left(\frac{\varkappa}{\rho_0}\right)} \approx \sqrt{\left(\frac{\gamma P_0}{\rho_0}\right)}. \qquad (2\text{-}11)$$

A more exact expression is obtained by using formulae (2-8) and (2-9):

$$\frac{\partial p}{\partial \rho} = \gamma \frac{P_0}{\rho_0{}^{\gamma}} \rho^{\gamma-1} = \frac{\gamma P_0}{\rho_0}\left(\frac{\rho}{\rho_0}\right)^{\gamma-1}$$

Hence,

$$c = \sqrt{\left(\frac{\gamma P_0}{\rho_0}\right)} \cdot \left(\frac{\rho}{\rho_0}\right)^{\frac{\gamma-1}{2}} = c_0\left(\frac{\rho}{\rho_0}\right)^{\frac{\gamma-1}{2}} \approx c_0\left(1 + \frac{\gamma-1}{2\rho_0 c_0^2} p + \ldots\right), \qquad (2\text{-}12)$$

i.e. the speed of sound in a gas depends on the amplitude of the oscillations. For large amplitudes the speed of wave propagation will be greater in regions of compression ($p > 0$) than in regions of rarefaction ($p < 0$). This leads to a change in wave shape: the shape of a sinusoidal wave will be distorted and harmonics will arise. For waves of the pulse type where p has a constant positive sign, $c > c_0$.

It could be supposed that the adiabatic law is not valid for slow acoustic oscillations, since the temperature between the hot and cold sections of the medium will succeed in balancing out during the period of vibration. But this conclusion is not correct. The balancing of the temperature has to take place between parts of an acoustic wave with different temperatures, but parts of a wave with the maximum difference in temperature lie a half wavelength apart, and even though there is an increase in the time during which the temperature can be balanced if the frequency is reduced, the distance between layers with appreciably different temperatures increases to the same extent. As a result, if the frequency is reduced the adiabatic condition will be fulfilled no less rigorously than at high frequencies.

It has been shown by an analysis of the phenomena of thermal conduction that small deviations from the adiabatic law occur in a wave* not at low frequencies, but, on the contrary, at extremely high frequencies. Deviations from the adiabatic conditions also occur when a wave is propagated in tubes with metallic walls, but this has no great effect on the speed of sound.

The adiabatic bulk modulus for liquids can be calculated only from empirical equations of state. The isothermal bulk modulus can be found experimentally from static measurements, whereas the adiabatic modulus is usually determined by measuring the speed of sound and then using formula (2-8).

At normal atmospheric pressure ($P_0 = 1.016 \times 10^6$ dyne/cm^2) and a temperature 0°C, the speed of sound in air ($\rho_0 = 1.29 \times 10^{-3}$ g/cm^3, $\gamma = 1{\cdot}41$) will be:

$$c_0 = 3.33 \times 10^4 \text{ cm/sec} = 333 \text{ m/sec}.$$

The average of a large number of measurements gives a very close approximation to the theoretical value $c_0 = 331{\cdot}5$ m/sec. If it is supposed that the acoustic vibra-

* Lord Rayleigh, *Theory of Sound* vol. II. Constable, London, 1945 (see Sect. 247).

tions are governed by the isothermal law (Pv = const), then in forming relationship (2-10) we should put $\gamma = 1$ and the speed of sound in air would be $1 \cdot 79 \times 10^4$ cm/sec. This quantity, which is not in accordance with experimental results, was found theoretically by Newton. The Laplace correction taking into account the adiabatic nature of acoustic vibrations resolved the contradiction between theory and experiment. Thus, experiment very convincingly confirmed the supposition about the adiabatic nature of the process of acoustic vibrations. The calculated speed also is in excellent agreement with experiment for other gases.

Using the ideal gas equation (Clapeyron's equation) $P_0 v_0 = \frac{P_0}{\rho_0} = RT$ (where T is absolute temperature, v_0 specific volume, R the gas constant per gram of gas, equal to $8 \cdot 315 \times 10^7\ m^{-1}$ erg/deg, where m is the molecular weight),

$$c = \sqrt{(\gamma RT)} = \sqrt{\left(\frac{8 \cdot 315 \times 10^7}{m} \gamma T\right)}.$$

It will be seen from this formula first that c is independent of the magnitude of the steady (atmospheric) pressure P_0. This is a corollary of the fact that for an isothermal atmosphere ρ_0 increases proportionally to P_0, whilst c, depending on the ratio of P_0 to ρ_0, remains unchanged. Secondly, since c varies in proportion to $\sqrt{T}$, we can write for the speed of sound at the temperature θ

$$c_\theta = c_0 \sqrt{(1 + \alpha\theta)} \approx c_0 + \frac{c_0 \alpha}{2} \theta,$$

where $\alpha = \frac{1}{273}$ per °C is a coefficient of gas expansion, and $c_0 = \sqrt{\gamma \cdot R \cdot 273}$ (the velocity of sound at 0°C). At room temperature (20°C) $C_{20} = 3 \cdot 43 \times 10^4$ cm/sec. The speed of sound increases by about 60 cm/sec for each degree and at 1000°C it equals $C_{1000} = 7 \cdot 20 \times 10^4$ cm/sec.

In other diatomic gases γ has the same value as air and, consequently, for hydrogen with a density $0 \cdot 09 \times 10^3$ g/cm ^{3}, the speed of sound will be $\sqrt{\frac{1 \cdot 29}{0 \cdot 09}} = 3 \cdot 8$ times larger than for air, and at 0^oC is about $12 \cdot 6 \times 10^4$ cm/sec = 1260 m/sec.

For liquids it is necessary to base the calculations on experimental values of the adiabatic bulk modulus $\varkappa_{ad}$. Thus, for water at 17^oC, $\varkappa_{17} = 2 \cdot 12 \times 10^{10}$ dyne/cm ^{2}, $\rho_{17} = 0 \cdot 999$ g/cm^3, and $\gamma \approx 1$; hence $c_{17} = 1 \cdot 431 \times 10^5$cm/sec, which agrees closely with experiment. Despite the large thermal conductance of liquids compared with gases, no effective balancing of the temperature in the acoustic wave occurs, and as in gases the propagation of sound in liquids is also an adiabatic process. The speed of sound in water increases with temperature roughly by $4 \cdot 5$ m/sec. for one degree, and with pressure by approximately $0 \cdot 05$ m/sec per atm or $0 \cdot 005$ m/sec meter of depth. At depths of 100 to 200 m (in warm sea water) and 1 to $1 \cdot 5$ km (in oceans) the speed of sound is at a minimum. Thus, in the Pacific and Atlantic oceans c_{min} = 1490 m/sec, whereas on the surface of the ocean in the tropics c = 1530 m/sec. The speed of sound in water as a function of temperature and salinity is found by the empirical formula*:

$$C = 1448 \cdot 6 + 4 \cdot 618\ \theta - 0 \cdot 0523\ \theta^2 + 2 \cdot 3 \times$$
$$\times 10^{-4}\ \theta^3 + (1 \cdot 301 - 0 \cdot 009\ \theta)\ (S - 35) + 0 \cdot 018\ P$$

where σ is the salinity in milligrams per litre, and P the pressure in atmospheres.

The speed of sound in solid bars is expressible by a formula similar to $c = \sqrt{\frac{\varkappa}{\rho}}$, derived for gases and liquids. In this formula it is necessary to put $\varkappa = E$, where E is Young's modulus. For *longitudinal waves* in a continuous elastic solid

$$\varkappa = E \frac{1 - \mu}{(1 + \mu)(1 - 2\mu)},$$

* K.V. Mackenzie, *J. Acoust. Soc. Amer.* 32, 100, 1960.

where μ is Poisson's ratio, so that the speed of longitudinal waves is

$$c_l=\sqrt{\left(\frac{E}{\rho}\right)}\cdot\sqrt{\left[\frac{1-\mu}{(1+\mu)(1-2\mu)}\right]}$$

The speed of transverse waves in a continuous elastic solid is

$$c_t=\sqrt{\left(\frac{G}{\rho}\right)}.$$

where G is the rigidity modulus. The speed of torsional waves in circular bars has the same value.

Table 1 shows the density ρ, the adiabatic bulk modulus $\varkappa$, the speed of sound c and the acoustic impedance ρc for various media.

TABLE 1

Substance	ρ	$\varkappa$	c	ρc
Air, 0° and 760 mm Hg	$1{\cdot}29\times10^{-3}$	$1{\cdot}43\times10^{6}$	$3{\cdot}33\times10^{4}$	43
Air, 20° and 760 mm Hg	$1{\cdot}20\times10^{-3}$	$1{\cdot}43\times10^{6}$	$3{\cdot}43\times10^{4}$	41
Hydrogen, 0° and 760 mm Hg	$0{\cdot}09\times10^{-3}$	$1{\cdot}43\times10^{6}$	$12{\cdot}6\times10^{4}$	11
Carbon dioxide, 0° and 760 mm Hg	$1{\cdot}98\times10^{-3}$	$1{\cdot}43\times10^{6}$	$2{\cdot}58\times10^{4}$	51
Distilled water, 0°	0·999	$2{\cdot}04\times10^{10}$	$1{\cdot}43\times10^{5}$	$1{\cdot}43\times10^{5}$
Sea water, 10°	1·03	$2{\cdot}32\times10^{10}$	$1{\cdot}5\times10^{5}$	$1{\cdot}5\times10^{5}$
Mercury	13·6	$25{\cdot}6\times10^{10}$	$1{\cdot}46\times10^{5}$	$19{\cdot}8\times10^{5}$
Ethyl alcohol	0·79	$1{\cdot}3\times10^{10}$	$1{\cdot}18\times10^{5}$	$0{\cdot}93\times10^{5}$
Steel (The speed of longitudinal waves in bars is given)	7·8	$1{\cdot}8\times10^{12}$	$5{\cdot}05\times10^{5}$	$39{\cdot}3\times10^{5}$
Brass (The speed of longitudinal waves in bars is given)	8·5	$1{\cdot}05\times10^{12}$	$3{\cdot}42\times10^{5}$	$29{\cdot}0\times10^{5}$
Lead (The speed of longitudinal waves in bars is given)	11·4	$0{\cdot}5\times10^{12}$	$1{\cdot}2\times10^{5}$	$13{\cdot}7\times10^{5}$

The Sinusoidal Plane Wave

Consider a harmonic wave propagated along the positive x axis. Suppose that the velocity potential is in the form of a cosine function with an argument proportional to $(ct - x)$. Since the cosine must have a dimensionless argument the constant of proportionality, which we shall call k, must have the dimension of length in the minus first degree. The quantity $k\,(ct - x)$ must change by 2π at the point in question during the period T, whence

$$kcT = 2\pi \quad \text{or} \quad k = \frac{2\pi}{cT} = \frac{\omega}{c},$$

where ω is the angular frequency of the oscillations. The quantity k is called the *wave number*. The velocity potential for a periodic wave can be written in the form:

$$\Phi = A\cos k\,(ct - x) = A\cos(\omega t - kx). \tag{2-13}$$

Here A is an arbitrary constant giving the amplitude of the process.

We wish to find the distance, λ, through which a certain phase of the process (for example, the maximum) moves during time T, i.e. the *wavelength*.

It will be seen from formula (2-13) that $k\lambda = kcT = 2\pi$, whence

or

$$\left.\begin{aligned} \lambda &= \frac{2\pi}{k} = cT \\ k &= \frac{2\pi}{\lambda} = \frac{\omega}{c}. \end{aligned}\right\}$$

The direction of propagation of the wave can be ascribed to the wave number and thus a vector wave number can be defined.

It is convenient to write the velocity potential in exponential form:

$$\Phi = Ae^{j(\omega t - kx)}, \qquad (2\text{-}14)$$

where $j = \sqrt{-1}$. The quantity Φ is a complex quantity here, but if necessary it is always possible to take its real part $\mathrm{Re}\Phi$, which is given by equation (2-13). The amplitude of the process is also represented as a complex quantity:

$$A = |A| e^{j\varphi},$$

where φ is a certain phase angle defining the phase of the process when $t = 0$ and $x = 0$. Equation (2-14) then takes the form:

$$\Phi = |A| e^{j(\omega t - kx + \varphi)}. \qquad (2\text{-}15)$$

We will use Φ in the form (2-15) instead of (2-14) only in those cases when this is necessary. When using formula (2-14) it is necessary to remember that the quantity A contains the phase multiplier $e^{j\varphi}$.

The particle velocity and acoustic pressure are:

$$\dot{\xi} = -\frac{\partial \Phi}{\partial x} = jkAe^{j(\omega t - kx)}, \qquad (2\text{-}16)$$

$$p = \rho \frac{\partial \Phi}{\partial t} = j\omega\rho Ae^{j(\omega t - kx)} \qquad (2\text{-}17)$$

and are identical in phase. In those regions of the wave where pressure is maximum, velocity in the positive x direction is also a maximum at the same time, whilst in regions of the wave with the minimum pressure velocity is a maximum in the negative x direction. Thus, the phases of compression travel in the wave and always coincide in space with the phase of the positive particle velocity, whilst the phase of rarefaction coincides with the phase of the negative particle velocity.

It is easy to see that there is every justification for using the condition $\frac{du}{dt} \approx \frac{\partial u}{\partial t}$ which we used in forming the wave equation of an acoustic wave, even for very loud sounds. It is found from relationships (2-16) that the amplitude of u equals kA, whilst the amplitudes of $\frac{d\dot{\xi}}{dx}$ and $\frac{\partial \dot{\xi}}{\partial t}$ equal k^2A and $k\omega A$ respectively; consequently, the maximum value of the ratio of the convective to the local acceleration is:

$$\frac{\dot{\xi}\,\frac{\partial \dot{\xi}}{\partial x}}{\frac{\partial \dot{\xi}}{\partial t}} = \frac{kA \cdot k^2 A}{k\omega A} = \frac{kA}{c} = \frac{\dot{\xi}_m}{c}.$$

For a very intense sound which is too unbearable to hear $p_m = 10{,}000$ bar and $\dot{\xi}_m = \frac{10000}{41} = 244$ cm/sec; $\frac{\dot{\xi}_m}{c} = \frac{2{\cdot}44 \times 10^2}{3{\cdot}43 \times 10^4} \approx \frac{1}{141}$. Thus, for the majority of sounds, with which acoustics is concerned in practice, $u\frac{\partial u}{\partial x} \ll \frac{\partial u}{\partial t}$ and the condition $\frac{du}{dt} \approx \frac{\partial u}{\partial t}$ is satisfied with great accuracy.

The general expression $p = \rho c \dot{\xi}$ (2-7) naturally holds for harmonic waves also, as can easily be found by formulae (2-16) and (2-17).

It is also obvious that the expression holds good for amplitudinal values p_m and $\dot{\xi}_m$ as well as for effective values p_e and $\dot{\xi}_e$

$$p_m = \rho c \dot{\xi}_m,$$
$$p_e = \rho c \dot{\xi}_e.$$

In acoustic analysis, as in electrical engineering, use is often made of effective values p_e and $\dot{\xi}_e$ without bothering to say so specifically each time. Thus, if it is said that the acoustic pressure equals p, it is then understood that the effective pressure is given and that the maximum pressure in this case equals $\sqrt{2}p$.

For a progressive wave propagated in the negative x-direction, we can take the expression:

$$\Phi = A'e^{j(\omega t+kx)}.$$

Calculating p and $\dot{\xi}$, we find that

$$p = -\rho c\dot{\xi}. \qquad (2\text{-}18)$$

For waves in the negative x-direction the phase of compression coincides with the maximum particle velocity in the negative x-direction, whilst the phase of rarefaction coincides with the maximum particle velocity in the positive x-direction. The conclusion can therefore be drawn that the direction *in which a wave is propagated is the direction of the particle velocity in the zone of compression.* It can also be inferred from formulae (2-17) and (2-18) that the expression $p = \rho c\dot{\xi}$ is suitable for forward waves as well as for reverse waves, if we ascribe the sign $+$ or $-$ to the speed c according to the direction of propagation of the wave.

The expression $p = \rho c\dot{\xi}$ can be regarded in a way common in electrical circuit theory. Suppose that a current I flows in an a.c. circuit with a voltage E and a total impedance Z. These quantities are connected by Ohm's law for alternating current.

$$E = ZI.$$

If Z is a pure resistance R, then

$$E = RI.$$

By analogy, if we consider that

p is analogous to E,

$\dot{\xi}$ " I,

ρc " R,

then the relationship between p and $\dot{\xi}$ is analogous to Ohm's law for a purely active load.

The quantity

$$R = \rho c \tag{2-19}$$

is called the *specific acoustic resistance of the medium.*

Acoustic resistance is measured in acoustic ohms per cm^2. One acoustic ohm (ac. ohm) is the resistance at which a force of 1 dyne causes a velocity of 1 cm/sec.

Acoustic resistance is a characteristic constant of the medium (the quantity ρc is given in Table 1 for certain media). Later, when we consider the flow of energy in a wave, it will be seen how a quantity which is analogous to electrical resistance and is connected with the dissipation of energy comes to appear in all our expressions for a medium without friction.

Our analogy with an electrical circuit is only superficial since it would be more correct to compare a plane wave with waves along an electrical transmission line, and not with current in a circuit with lumped constants. However, our analogy with Ohm's law and the rest of the analogies with electrical circuits which we shall draw are useful, if only from the point of view of helping to remember the formulae.

Temperature Changes in Sound Waves

We know from thermodynamics that when changes in gas pressure are adiabatic, changes in absolute temperature T are governed by the law:

$$\frac{T_0 + \delta T}{T_0} = \left(\frac{P}{P_0}\right)^{\frac{\gamma - 1}{\gamma}}.$$

For small acoustic pressures $p = P - P_0$ we can write:

$$1 + \frac{\delta T}{T_0} = \left(1 + \frac{p}{P_0}\right)^{\frac{\gamma - 1}{\gamma}} \approx 1 + \frac{\gamma - 1}{\gamma} \frac{p}{P_0} + \dots$$

or

$$\delta T \approx \frac{\gamma - 1}{\gamma} \frac{p}{P_0} T_0.$$

Variations in temperature appear to be small in the transmission of sound waves. By way of example we will consider the case of a very intense sound with a pressure amplitude $p_m = 10^4$ bar; then, if $P_0 \approx 10^6$ *bar*

$$\delta T_m \approx \frac{0{\cdot}41}{1{\cdot}41} \times \frac{10^4}{10^6} 293 = 0{\cdot}85°C \left(\text{if} \quad t° = 20°C\right).$$

For sounds near the threshold of audibility ($p_m \approx 10^{-4}$ bar) we get $\delta T_m \approx 0{\cdot}85 \times 10^{-8}$ °C. It is quite possible to take direct measurements of temperature changes in intense sound waves. Temperature changes are very difficult to measure directly, not only for very feeble sounds which lie on the threshold of hearing, but even for fairly loud sounds ($p_m \approx 1$ bar).

The Energy of Sound Waves

In order to calculate the energy carried by an area S of a wave front when a plane wave is propagated, we will take an element of mass Δm of the medium, having a volume bounded by the side surface of a cylinder of arbitrary section S (with generatrices parallel to the x axis) and two planes transverse to the x axis, defined by the abscissae x and $x + \Delta x$ (Fig. 3). Here Δx is small compared with the wavelength ($\Delta x \ll \lambda$). For the volume of the element at the initial moment we have $\Delta v = S\Delta x$, and for its mass $\Delta m = \rho \Delta v$. Suppose that the volume of the element of mass Δm changes by dv during a small period of time. The potential energy in the volume of this element is increased by

$$\Delta U = -\int_{P_0}^{P_0+p} P dv$$

when the pressure changes from P_0 to $P_0 + p$.

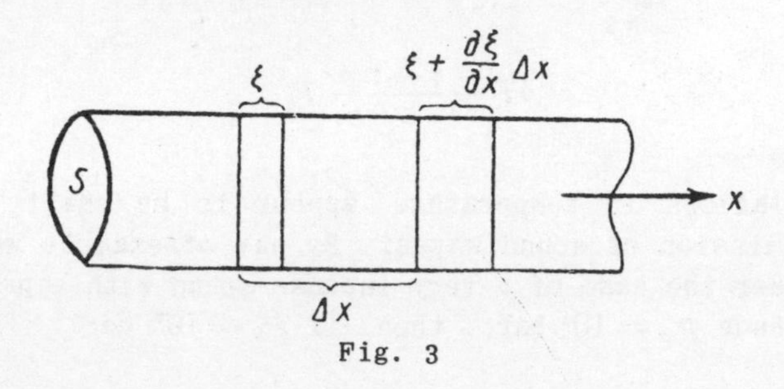

Fig. 3

The change in volume (dv) of the element Δv and the change in pressure inside it are related, as we know, by:

$$dP = -\varkappa \frac{dv}{\Delta v} = -\rho c^2 \frac{dv}{\Delta v}.$$

Hence

$$dv = -\frac{S\Delta x}{\rho c^2} dP.$$

Substituting dv in the expression for potential energy and integrating with respect to P, we get:

$$\Delta U = \frac{S\Delta x}{\rho c^2} \int_{P_0}^{P_0+p} P dP = \frac{S\Delta x}{\rho c^2} \Big|_{P_0}^{P_0+p} \frac{P^2}{2} = \frac{1}{2} \frac{S\Delta x}{\rho c^2} p^2 + \frac{S\Delta x}{\rho c^2} P_0 p.$$

The kinetic energy of the element Δm is:

$$\Delta T = \frac{1}{2} (S\Delta x \rho) \dot{\xi}^2 = \frac{1}{2} \frac{S\Delta x}{\rho c^2} p^2.$$

The total oscillatory energy of the element Δm is:

$$\Delta W = \Delta U + \Delta T = \frac{S\Delta x}{\rho c^2} p^2 + \frac{S\Delta x}{\rho c^2} P_0 p.$$

Suppose that the acoustic pressure is expressed by the law:

$$p = p_m \cos(\omega t - kx).$$

We require to calculate the total energy in the interval from x_1 to $x_1+n\lambda$. Regarding Δx as a sufficiently small quantity compared with λ and considering its differential dx, we get:

$$W=\frac{S}{\rho c^2}\int_{x_1}^{x_1+n\lambda} p^2 dx+\frac{SP_0}{\rho c^2}\int_{x_1}^{x_1+n\lambda} p\,dx=$$

$$=\frac{Sp_m^2}{\rho c^2}\int_{x_1}^{x_1+n\lambda}\cos^2(\omega t-kx)\,dx+\frac{SP_0 p_m}{\rho c^2}\int_{x_1}^{x_1+n\lambda}\cos(\omega t-kx)\,dx.$$

It is easy to see that the second integral equals zero, and that the first equals $\frac{n\lambda}{2}$. For the volume of the entire cylinder we get the energy $W=\frac{Sn\lambda}{2\rho c^2}p_m^2$. As follows from the calculation, its value is independent of the abscissa x_1. For the acoustic energy per unit volume, i.e. the *acoustic energy density*, we have:

$$W_1=\frac{W}{Sn\lambda}=\frac{1}{2}\frac{p_m^2}{\rho c^2}=\frac{p_e^2}{\rho c^2}.$$

It is obvious that the energy moves along the x axis at the speed of sound c and that after one second the flow of acoustic energy from a continuously radiating source occupies the volume of a cylinder with a base S cm^2 and a height c. The flow of acoustic energy J carried by a unit area of the wave front, i.e. the *energy density flux*, or *intensity*, is found by multiplying the density of the energy W_1 by the speed of sound c, this product being the total energy in the cylinder occupied by the acoustic energy radiated across a fixed unit area in unit time:

$$J=W_1 c=\frac{1}{2}\frac{p_m^2}{\rho c}=\frac{p_e^2}{\rho c}=\frac{p_e^2}{R}.$$

The quantity J is a vector. Expressing p_m in terms of $\dot{\xi}_m$, we have:

$$J = \frac{1}{2}\frac{\rho^2 c^2 \dot{\xi}_m^2}{\rho c} = \frac{1}{2}\rho c \dot{\xi}_m^2 = \rho c \dot{\xi}_e^2 = R\dot{\xi}_e^2;$$

we can also write:

$$J = \frac{1}{2} p_m \dot{\xi}_m = p_e \dot{\xi}_e.$$

In the U.S.S.R. the vector J is known as the *Umov vector* after N.A. Umov who introduced the notion of a flux of mechanical energy in bodies in 1874*. The direction of the energy flux vector is the same as the direction of propagation of the wave. The flux of acoustic energy density is known in acoustics as the *sound intensity*. The sound intensity is measured in ergs per cm^2 per second or in watts per cm^2.

The transmission of the energy of a sound wave into regions not previously traversed by the wave requires continuous expenditure of energy on the part of the source exciting the sound. In those zones which the wave has already reached, the energy is continuously being transmitted on further at the speed of sound. The variable pressures occurring in any one part of the medium continuously do work transmitting energy on to other parts of the medium, so that an active resistance R arises during oscillatory motions of the elements of the medium. The formulae for the sound intensity are written in the form

$$J = \frac{p_e^2}{R} = R\dot{\xi}_e^2, \tag{2-20}$$

and are quite like the Joule-Lenz law, except that the power expended under the action of pressure is used for the transmission of energy to the previously undisturbed particles of the medium and not in the creation of heat.

* In Great Britain the vector J is known as the *intensity vector* and this name is accordingly used in the translation.

For these reasons, the acoustic impedance of the medium $R = \rho c$ is often known as the *radiation resistance of the medium*.

To illustrate these relationships, we will find the conditions under which the acoustic intensity is the same in air as in water. Suppose we put subscript 1 for quantities relating to air, and subscript 2 for those referring to water. We then get:

$$\frac{p_1^2}{\rho_1 c_1} = \frac{p_2^2}{\rho_2 c_2},$$

whence

$$\frac{p_2}{p_1} = \sqrt{\left(\frac{\rho_2 c_2}{\rho_1 c_1}\right)} = \sqrt{\left(\frac{1 \cdot 43 \times 10^5}{41}\right)} \approx 58.$$

For equal sound intensity, the pressure in water is 58 times greater than in air. It is easy to calculate that the particle velocity in water is accordingly 58 times less than in air.

The Logarithmic Scale of Sound Intensity - Decibel Scale

Values of the sound intensity in air that are commonly met in practice vary widely, roughly between 2×10^{-10} erg/cm^2 · sec and 2×10^6 erg/cm^2 · sec, which correspond to acoustic pressures from about 10^{-4} bar to 10^4 bar. It would often be necessary to write numerical values with a large number of figures before or after the decimal point and this is very inconvenient. It is therefore better to measure sound intensity J on a logarithmic scale. We fix a certain reference level of sound intensity J_0 and introduce the quantity

$$\beta = 10 \log_{10} \frac{J}{J_0} = 20 \log_{10} \frac{p}{p_0}, \qquad (2\text{-}21)$$

which we refer to as the *intensity level*.

If the intensities of two sounds are J_1 and J_2 respectively, then the difference between their intensity levels is

$$\Delta\beta = 10 \log \frac{J_1}{J_2} = 10 \log \frac{J_1}{J_0} - 10 \log \frac{J_2}{J_0} = \beta_1 - \beta_2. \quad (2\text{-}21a)$$

The logarithmic unit of measure for the intensity in equation (2-21) is known as the *decibel* (dB). If $\log \frac{J_1}{J_2} = 0{\cdot}1$, i.e. if $\frac{J_1}{J_2} = 1{\cdot}26$, we then get $\Delta\beta = 1$ dB. The level $\Delta\beta = 10$ decibel = 1 bel is obtained if $\frac{J_1}{J_2} = 10$; other relationships between $\frac{J_1}{J_2}$ and $\frac{p_1}{p_2}$ respectively are shown in Table 2.

TABLE 2

J_1/J_2	1	1·26	2	4	5	10	10^2	10^3	10^4	10^6	10^{10}	10^{14}
p_1/p_2	1	1·12	1·41	2	2·24	3.16	10	31·6	10^2	10^3	10^5	10^7
$\Delta\beta$	0	1	3	6	7	10	20	30	40	60	100	140

The quantity J_0 is best fixed slightly below the mean threshold of audibility for normal hearing at 1000 c/s, namely,

$$J_0 = 10^{-9} \frac{\text{erg}}{\text{cm}^2 \text{ sec}} = 10^{-16} \frac{\text{W}}{\text{cm}^2},$$

which corresponds to a pressure

$$p_0 = 2{\cdot}04 \times 10^{-4} \text{ bar. eff.}$$

if $\theta = 20^0 C$ at 760 mm Hg.

The level 140 dB roughly corresponds to the noise one would hear close to the motor of an aeroplane; the pressure level of ordinary speech is 60 to 65 dB; at the threshold of audibility of sounds of frequency 1000 c/s the intensity level of sound is close to zero.

Thus, all the intensity levels of sound which are encountered in practice are expressible in numbers from 0 dB to about 140 dB, and it is usually sufficient to round off the quantities β to whole numbers, since a change $\Delta\beta$ of 0·5 dB will not be detected by the ear as an appreciable difference in sound intensity. In order to calculate the ratios of sound intensity from the difference in levels, formulae (2-21) and (2-21a) can be rewritten as follows:

$$\frac{J_1}{J_2} = 10^{\frac{\Delta\beta}{10}}; \quad \frac{p_1}{p_2} = 10^{\frac{\Delta\beta}{20}};$$

$$J = J_0\, 10^{\frac{\beta}{10}}; \; p = p_0\;\, 10^{\frac{\beta}{20}}.$$

The decibel scale has come to be used very extensively indeed in acoustics and the applied sciences associated with it. For example, decibels are used to express the reduction of sound intensity in trunk telephones lines, the reduction of voltage and current in radio communication lines and links, the decay in sound intensity due to a partition between two buildings, the attenuation of electromagnetic waves in screening and so on. *Loudness,* or the subjective intensity of sound, is not measured by the quantity β; sounds of a different frequency but with the same intensity level β may differ in loudness when heard and, conversely, equally loud noises of different frequencies may differ in intensity level.

Intensity of Sound for Waves in Opposite Directions

Suppose that there are two waves proceeding in opposite directions. This can happen, for example, on reflection from a partially sound-absorbing surface. The resultant particle velocity is expressible in the form:

$$\dot{\xi} = \dot{\xi}_1 e^{j(\omega t - kx)} + \dot{\xi}_2 e^{j(\omega t + kx)}.$$

Then

$$p = \rho c \dot{\xi}_1 e^{j(\omega t - kx)} - \rho c \dot{\xi}_2 e^{j(\omega t + kx)} = p_1 e^{j(\omega t - kx)} - p_2 e^{j(\omega t + kx)}$$

(It is assumed that $p_1 > p_2$ and $\dot{\xi}_1 > \dot{\xi}_2$).

These expressions can be transformed as follows:

$$\dot{\xi} = \dot{\xi}_2 [e^{j(\omega t - kx)} + e^{j(\omega t + kx)}] + (\dot{\xi}_1 - \dot{\xi}_2) e^{j(\omega t - kx)} =$$

$$= 2 \dot{\xi}_2 e^{j\omega t} \cdot \frac{e^{jkx} + e^{-jkx}}{2} + (\dot{\xi}_1 - \dot{\xi}_2) e^{j(\omega t - kx)} =$$

$$= 2\dot{\xi}_2 e^{j\omega t} \cdot \cos kx + (\dot{\xi}_1 - \dot{\xi}_2) e^{j(\omega t - kx)};$$

$$p = -2p_2 e^{j\omega t} \cdot \frac{e^{jkx} - e^{-jkx}}{2} + (p_1 - p_2) e^{j(\omega t - kx)} =$$

$$= 2p_2 e^{j(\omega t - \frac{\pi}{2})} \cdot \sin kx + (p_1 - p_2) e^{j(\omega t - kx)}.$$

Changing over to their real form, we get

$$\left.\begin{aligned} \dot{\xi} &= 2\dot{\xi}_2 \cos kx \cdot \cos \omega t + (\dot{\xi}_1 - \dot{\xi}_2) \cos(\omega t - kx), \\ p &= 2p_2 \sin kx \cdot \sin \omega t + (p_1 - p_2) \cos(\omega t - kx). \end{aligned}\right\} \quad (2\text{-}22)$$

The first terms in these equations represent a *standing wave*, and the second terms a *progressive wave*. If the amplitudes of the two original waves are equal, then planes fixed in space occur on which there is a maximum velocity amplitude (antinodes), at $kx = n\pi$ $(x = n\frac{\lambda}{2})$, and others on which there is a zero velocity amplitude (nodes), at $kx = (n + \frac{1}{2})\pi$; $(x = n\frac{\lambda}{2} + \frac{\lambda}{4})$. Conversely, the pressure has maxima at the nodes, and equals zero at the antinodes. As can easily be found from (2-22), with unequal amplitudes the total wave has velocity amplitude $(\dot{\xi}_1 + \dot{\xi}_2)$ and pressure amplitude $(p_1 - p_2)$ at the antinodes, and $(\dot{\xi}_1 - \dot{\xi}_2)$ and $(p_1 + p_2)$ respectively at the nodes,

The minimum amplitude of acoustic pressure due to the difference in amplitude between the two wave components occurs at the antinodes. The resultant flux of acoustic energy (sound intensity) is equal to the difference between the sound intensities of the forward and reverse waves:

$$J = \frac{1}{2}\rho c\dot{\xi}_1^2 - \frac{1}{2}\rho c\dot{\xi}_2^2 = \frac{1}{2}\frac{p_1^2}{\rho c} - \frac{1}{2}\frac{p_2^2}{\rho c}.$$

If the forward and reverse waves are equal in velocity amplitude, then the sound intensity $J = 0$. But in standing waves sound can easily be observed experimentally, and the conclusion about zero sound intensity is at first glance paradoxical. In order to detect sound in a standing wave it is necessary to use a different type of receiver at the nodes and antinodes. A receiver which reacts to acoustic pressure has to be used at the nodes, and a receiver which reacts to particle velocity (e.g. a Rayleigh disc) has to be used at the antinodes.

To clear up the contradiction it is necessary to consider the energy density in the standing wave. At the nodes of a standing wave the velocity is zero and the density of the kinetic energy is also zero, whilst the mean (time averaged) potential energy density equals $\frac{1}{4}\frac{(2p_m)^2}{\rho c^2} = 2\left(\frac{p_m^2}{2\rho c^2}\right)$. At the antinodes the mean potential energy density is zero, whilst that of the kinetic energy equals $4\left(\frac{p_m^2}{2\rho c^2}\right)$. It is easy to see that the total mean energy density at any point of the standing wave is equal to twice the energy density in each of the component waves.

$$W_1 = \left[\frac{1}{4}\cdot\frac{(2p_m)^2}{\rho c^2}\sin^2 kx + \frac{1}{4}\frac{(2p_m)^2}{\rho c^2}\cos^2 kx\right] = 2\left(\frac{1}{2}\frac{p_m^2}{\rho c^2}\right).$$

Thus, we come to the conclusion that the concept of sound intensity can be used expediently only in reference to a progressive (free) wave, but that for plane waves in opposite directions, and for standing waves in general, it is convenient to use the notion of mean sound energy density.

CHAPTER III

TRANSMISSION OF SOUND THROUGH PLANE BOUNDARIES AND LAYERS

The Reflection of Normally Incident Plane Waves at a Plane Boundary between Two Media

Suppose that there are two media I and II (Fig. 4, between which there is a plane boundary which is normal to the x axis and passes through the origin. Suppose also that the specific acoustic resistance of the first medium is $R_1 = \rho_1 c_1$, and that of the second $R_2 = \rho_2 c_2$. If a plane wave is incident on this boundary from the first medium, normal to the boundary, then part of the energy passes on into the second medium (also in the form of a plane wave) and part is reflected at the boundary and goes back into the first medium. We will use the following notation:

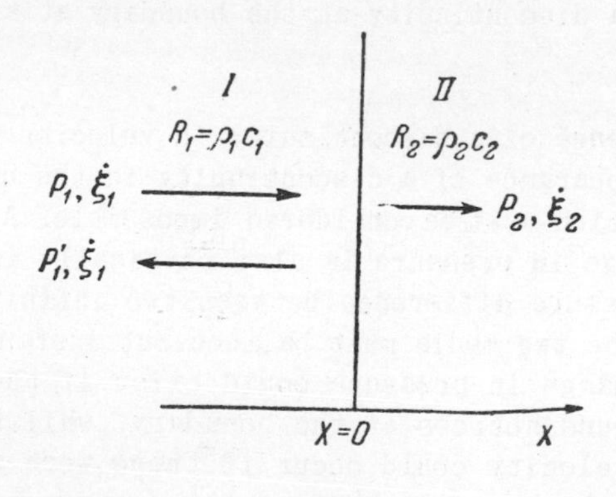

Fig. 4

For the first medium:

$\dot{\xi}_1$ and p_1 the velocity amplitude and pressure amplitude of the incident wave; $\dot{\xi}_1'$ and p_1' the velocity amplitude and pressure amplitude respectively of the reflected wave;

For the second medium:

$\dot{\xi}_2$ and p_2 the velocity amplitude and pressure amplitude respectively of the transmitted wave.

These amplitudes can be complex, i.e. have different phases (see (2-15)).

We can form the following expressions for the particle velocity and acoustic pressure:

For first medium:

$$\left.\begin{array}{l} \dot{\xi}_1 e^{j(\omega t - kx)} + \dot{\xi}_1' e^{j(\omega t + kx)}; \\ p_1^{j(\omega t - kx)} + p_1' e^{j(\omega t + kx)}. \end{array}\right\} \qquad (3\text{-}1)$$

For second medium:

$$\dot{\xi}_2 e^{j(\omega t - kx)} \text{ and } p_2 e^{j(\omega t - kx)}.$$

At the boundary of the two media ($x = 0$) the velocity and pressure must change continuously from one medium to the next, i.e. neither the velocity nor the pressure must experience a discontinuity at the boundary at any instant of time.

The emergence of a discontinuity in velocity would signify the appearance of a discontinuity in the boundary of the media which must be considered impossible. A permanent sudden change in pressure is also physically impossible, since a pressure difference between two infinitely close layers of the two media must balance out instantaneously. A sudden change in pressure could exist if there were a layer of sound sources at the boundary, whilst a sudden change in velocity could occur if there were a layer of dipoles at the boundary. Since there are no grounds to suppose that such sources are present at the boundary we can assume that both pressure and velocity are continuous across the boundary. Thus, at the boundary

$$\dot{\xi}_1 + \dot{\xi}'_1 = \dot{\xi}_2$$

and

$$p_1 + p'_1 = p_2.$$

It is known that between the pressure and particle velocity there exists the relationship $p = \pm \rho c \dot{\xi}$, where the plus sign corresponds to the forward wave, and the minus sign corresponds to the reverse wave. For the first medium $p_1 = \rho_1 c_1 \dot{\xi}_1$, in the incident wave, and in the reflected $p'_1 = -\rho_1 c_1 \dot{\xi}'_1$; and for the second medium $p_2 = \rho_2 c_2 \dot{\xi}_2$.

Two equations are obtained if we substitute these expressions into the boundary conditions for the velocity and pressure:

$$\begin{gathered} \dot{\xi}_1 + \dot{\xi}'_1 = \dot{\xi}_2, \\ \rho_1 c_1 (\dot{\xi}_1 - \dot{\xi}'_1) = \rho_2 c_2 \dot{\xi}_2. \end{gathered} \tag{3-2}$$

The velocity ratios can be found from these equations:

$$\begin{aligned} r_{\dot{\xi}} &= \frac{\dot{\xi}'_1}{\dot{\xi}_1} = \frac{R_1 - R_2}{R_1 + R_2}, \\ t_{\dot{\xi}} &= \frac{\dot{\xi}_2}{\dot{\xi}_1} = \frac{2R_1}{R_1 + R_2}. \end{aligned} \tag{3-3}$$

For the pressure ratio we get:

$$\begin{aligned} r_p &= \frac{p'_1}{p_1} = -\frac{R_1 - R_2}{R_1 + R_2}, \\ t_p &= \frac{p_2}{p_1} = \frac{2R_2}{R_1 + R_2}. \end{aligned} \tag{3-4}$$

If $R_2 > R_1$, i.e. if the second medium is acoustically more "rigid" than the first, then the numerator of the first relationship in (3-3) will be negative. This means that the particle velocity changes in phase by π on reflection, that is, the reflected wave is opposite in phase to the incident wave. The difference in phase between the particle velocities in the incident and transmitted waves (i.e. between $\dot{\xi}_1$ and $\dot{\xi}_2$) is not independent of the relative magnitudes of R_2 and R_1. It is also obvious that whereas the particle velocity changes in phase by π on reflection from a more rigid medium, the phase of the pressure remains constant.

If $R_2 < R_1$, i.e. if the second medium is acoustically more "soft", then the phase of the particle velocity remains unchanged on reflection, whereas that of the pressure changes by π. Finally, if $R_2 = R_1$ no reflected wave will appear, and the propagation of the wave on into the second medium is unimpeded. In this case, it is obvious that

$$\frac{c_1}{c_2} = \frac{\rho_2}{\rho_1},$$

where the ratio $\frac{c_1}{c_2}$ is the *index of refraction*. For incidence at an oblique angle partial refraction occurs on transition from one medium to the other if $R_1 = R_2$ (but $\rho_1 \neq \rho_2$).

The coefficient of energy transmission from one medium into the other is defined as the ratio of the intensity of the transmitted wave to the intensity of the incident wave:

$$\tau = \frac{R_2 \dot{\xi}_2^2}{R_1 \dot{\xi}_1^2} = \frac{4R_1 R_2}{(R_1 + R_2)^2}. \tag{3-5}$$

Since formula (3-5) is symmetric in R_1 and R_2, it follows that the coefficient of energy transmission will be identical independently of whether or not the wave goes from the first medium into the second or from the second into the first. For example, $\tau = 0{\cdot}0011$ on transition from water into air or vice versa, i.e. 0·9989 of the total incident energy is reflected back from the boundary. For water and steel $\tau = 0{\cdot}013$. For water and certain grades of wood $\tau \approx 1$, i.e. practically all the sound penetrates from the water into the wood.

For reflection at the boundary of two layers of air at a temperature difference $\Delta\vartheta$ there is no difficulty in finding that $\tau = 1 - 0{\cdot}83 \times 10^{-6}\Delta\vartheta^2$. If $\Delta\vartheta = 10°$, then $\tau = 1 - 0{\cdot}83 \times 10^{-4}$ and there is almost complete transmission with only $0{\cdot}83 \times 10^{-4}$ of the acoustic energy being reflected. It is also easy to find the energy reflected at the boundary between dry and saturated moist air (at the same temperature). Under normal atmospheric conditions the density of the moist air is about one part in 220 less than that of the dry air, and its sound speed is about one part in 440 greater. The reflected acoustic energy thus is $1{\cdot}3 \times 10^{-6}$ of the incident energy.

It should be noted that even if τ is a very small quantity, as it would be, for example, on transition from air into water, nevertheless, as equation (3-4) shows, the acoustic pressure in the water is practically twice that in the wave incident from the air. The total pressure in either the air or the water at the boundary is almost exactly equal to twice the pressure in the incident wave. If the same *pressure receiver* is used in air and water (e.g. a hydrophone) then an incoming sound from the air will be received just as strongly in the water as in the air despite the fact that only a negligible part of the acoustic energy penetrates into the water. But if use is made of a velocity receiver, we then get only very weak reception in the water in accordance with expression (3-3).

Suppose that the reflection takes place at an absolutely rigid surface so that $R_2 = \infty$. The phase of the particle velocity of the reflected wave is opposite to that of the incident wave, but its amplitude is equal to the amplitude of the incident wave. The resultant particle velocity at the boundary is therefore zero:

$$\dot{\xi}_1 + \dot{\xi}_1' = 0. \tag{3-6}$$

Since the pressure phase is constant, it follows that pressure at the boundary is doubled:

$$p_1 + p_1' = 2p_1.$$

Thus, the reflection results in a standing wave which has a node at the wall, and a pressure amplitude there equal to twice that of the incident wave. This case occurs in practice only if the conditions exist for the formation of a plane reflected wave, namely, when the dimensions of the plane reflecting surface are considerably greater than the wavelength and when diffraction phenomena at the edges do not appreciably alter the general character of the reflection. If on the other hand, the wavelength greatly exceeds the dimensions of the reflecting surface, then owing to diffraction the sound skirts it, no plane reflected wave is produced and the increase in pressure at the boundary which is associated with it does not take place. For this reason a microphone with a relatively rigid diaphragm (condenser type) measures double the pressure in a progressive wave at high frequencies when the diameter of the diaphragm is rather larger than the wavelength, whereas at low frequencies it measures the true acoustic pressure. Corrections for such effects have to be made in acoustic measurements.

Reflection of Plane Waves Incident at an Angle on a Plane Surface

Suppose that a wave is incident at an angle θ (Fig. 5) on an absolutely rigid plane surface and that it is propagated a distance $AO = S$ during a certain period of time.

This distance can be expressed in terms of the coordinates x and y at point A:

$$S = x\cos\theta - y\sin\theta.$$

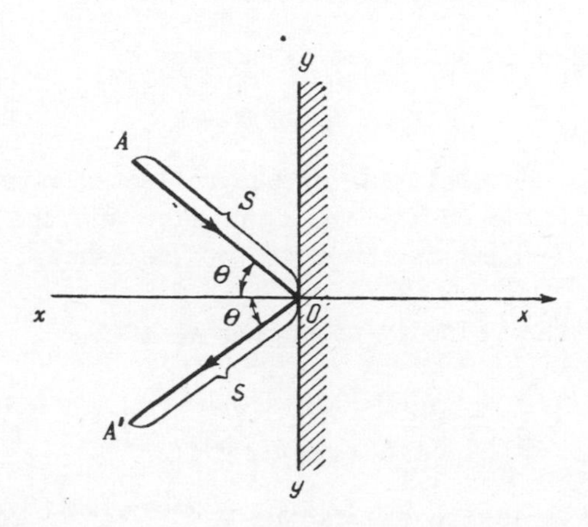

Fig. 5

The quantity S now plays the role of the phase path in the equation of the wave. Previously, for instance in formula (3-1), the role of the phase path was played by the coordinate x. Here, the direction of the wave is taken as the positive direction of S. The velocity potential for the incident wave is:

$$\Phi_1 = A_1 e^{j(\omega t - kS)} = A_1 e^{j(\omega t - kx\cos\theta + ky\sin\theta)}. \quad (3\text{-}7)$$

Likewise, for the reflected wave the distance OA' along the path of the wave equals $S' = -x\cos\theta' - y\sin\theta'$, where θ' is the angle of reflection, and the velocity potential is

$$\Phi_1 = A_1' e^{j(\omega t + kx\cos\theta' + ky\sin\theta')}. \quad (3\text{-}8)$$

The sum $\Phi_1 + \Phi_1'$ of the two solutions (3-7) and (3-8) must satisfy the linear differential equation of the wave, as follows from the principle of superposition. At the boundary ($x = 0$) it is necessary that the normal component of velocity be zero for all y:

$$\frac{d\Phi_1}{dx}+\frac{d\Phi'_1}{dx}=0.$$

This condition is satisfied by taking

$$A'_1=A_1 \text{ and } \theta'=\theta.$$

Consequently, the amplitude of the reflected wave is equal to the amplitude of the incident wave and the angle of reflection is equal to the angle of incidence.

Thus, for the velocity potential we get:

$$\Phi=\Phi_1+\Phi'_1=A_1 e^{j(\omega t+ky\sin\theta)}\left[e^{jxk\cos\theta}+e^{-jkx\cos\theta}\right]= \\ =2A_1\cos(kx\cos\theta)\,e^{j(\omega t+ky\sin\theta)}. \tag{3-9}$$

In this expression the factor $e^{j(\omega t+ky\sin\theta)}$ represents the trace of the wave on the y- axis, which progresses along the y axis in the negative direction (i.e. downwards, see Fig.5). The speed of this wave trace is found from the expression $c'=\frac{\omega}{k\sin\theta}$, since in this case the wave number equals $k\sin\theta$. Consequently,

$$c'=\frac{c}{\sin\theta}. \tag{3-10}$$

It is clear from the formula that the phase velocity of the wave trace is greater than the speed of sound c. The multiplier $\cos(kx\cos\theta)$ in equation (3-9) which depends only on x, shows that the wave amplitude experiences periodic changes along the x axis. Thus, the configuration is that of a wave progressing along the y axis, "modulated" in space according to the law $\cos(kx\cos\theta)$. In planes transverse to the x axis the amplitude has everywhere the same value. Planes of maximum amplitude occur when

$kx\cos\theta = n\pi$. The distance between planes of maximum amplitude,

$$\Delta x = \frac{\pi}{k\cos\theta} = \frac{\lambda/2}{\cos\theta},$$

will be greater than a half-wave length. Thus, interference bands will be formed parallel to the reflecting surface with distances between the antinodes and nodes equal to $\frac{\lambda/2}{\cos\theta}$ (Fig. 6). These bands can be called "pseudo-standing waves". As has been said, a front-modulated wave progresses in parallel with the reflecting surface at a speed $c' = \frac{c}{\sin\theta}$, The flow of energy in this wave is parallel to the y axis, i.e. along the boundary.

If $\theta = 0$ (normal incidence), we then get from (3-9):

$$\Phi = 2A_1 \cos kx \cdot e^{j\omega t} \quad \text{or} \quad \mathrm{Re}\Phi = 2A_1 \cos kx \cdot \cos\omega t.$$

In this case the wave along the surface disappears and we have conventional standing waves with nodal planes $\frac{\lambda}{2}$ apart. (Note that a standing wave is given by an expression containing two factors, one of which is a function only of x, the other only of t). It is important to mention that the speed of the wave trace is infinite if $\theta = 0$ as (3-10) shows, but in this case the energy flow along the wall is zero.

The situation is precisely the same as in reflection at an angle if two plane waves of the same amplitude proceed at an angle to each other. Suppose that waves progress along AA' and BB' at the angle $180° - 2\theta$ (Fig. 7). The particle velocity transverse to the y axis will everywhere be zero, since the x-components of the particle velocities of the two constituent waves will be equal and opposite to each other owing to the symmetry. In the right-hand semi-space, $x > 0$, the wave configuration corresponds to reflection at $x = 0$ of a wave incident along BB'. The reflection from an absolutely rigid surface of the plane wave along AO can in this way be formally represented as a superposition on the incident wave along AA' of its specular reflection in the plane $x = 0$, i.e. the wave along BB'.

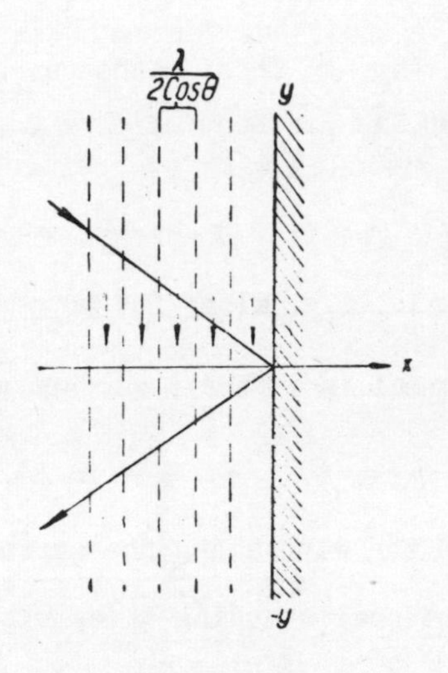

Fig. 6

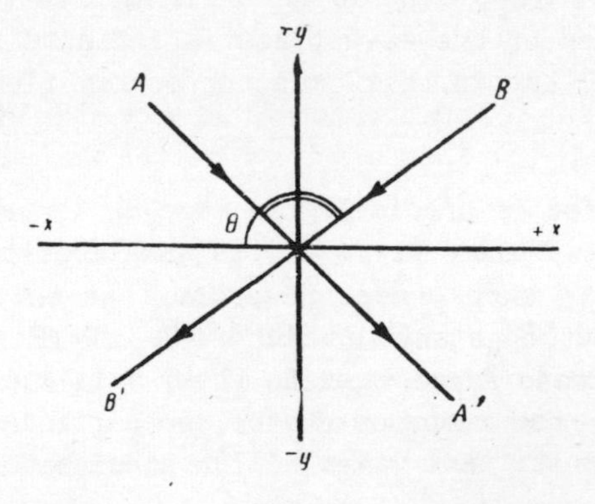

Fig. 7

The Refraction of Plane Waves at a Plane Boundary between Two Media

Suppose that two media are separated by a plane boundary $x=0$ (Fig. 8) and that in the first medium a plane wave is reflected at the angle θ_1. In the second medium there is a refracted wave at the angle θ_2. Suppose we put $R_1=\rho_1 c_1$ for the specific acoustic impedance of the first medium, and $R_2=\rho_2 c_2$ for the second medium. We write the wave equations for each medium separately:

$$c_1^2\left(\frac{\partial^2\Phi_1}{\partial x^2}+\frac{\partial^2\Phi_1}{\partial y^2}\right)=\frac{\partial^2\Phi_1}{\partial t^2} \text{ (first medium)}, \qquad (3\text{-}11)$$

$$c_2^2\left(\frac{\partial^2\Phi_2}{\partial x^2}+\frac{\partial^2\Phi_2}{\partial y^2}\right)=\frac{\partial^2\Phi_2}{\partial t^2} \text{ (second medium)}. \qquad (3\text{-}12)$$

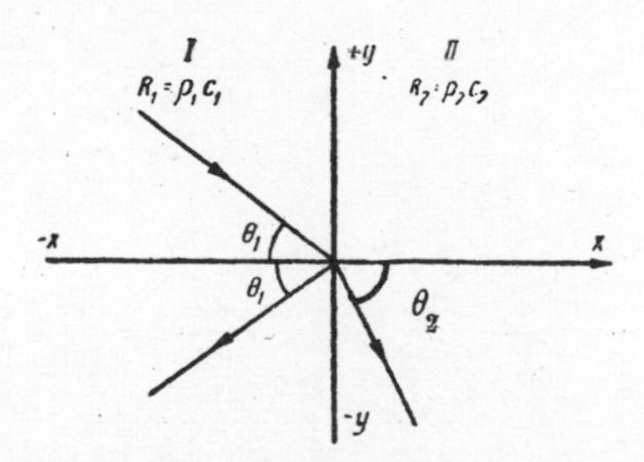

Fig. 8

The pressures and the normal components of the particle velocities at the boundary must be the same on both sides. The boundary conditions can therefore be written:

$$\rho_1\frac{\partial\Phi_1}{\partial t}\bigg|_{x=0}=\rho_2\frac{\partial\Phi_2}{\partial t}\bigg|_{x=0};$$

$$\frac{\partial\Phi_1}{\partial x}\bigg|_{x=0}=\frac{\partial\Phi_2}{\partial x}\bigg|_{x=0}. \qquad (3\text{-}13)$$

The velocity potentials in media I and II can be written in the form:

$$\left.\begin{aligned}\Phi_1 = A_1 e^{j(\omega t - a_1 x + b_1 y)} + A_1' e^{j(\omega t + a_1 x + b_1 y)}\\ \Phi_2 = A_2 e^{j(\omega t - a_2 x + b_2 y)},\end{aligned}\right\} \tag{3-14}$$

where

$$\begin{gathered}a_1 = k_1 \cos\theta_1;\ b_1 = k_1 \sin\theta_1;\ a_2 = k_2 \cos\theta_2;\quad b_2 = k_2 \sin\theta_2;\\ k_1 = \frac{\omega}{c_1};\ \ k_2 = \frac{\omega}{c_2}.\end{gathered} \tag{3-15}$$

It is easy to show that $b_1 = b_2 = b$. The speeds of the wave traces on the y- axis in media I and II are respectively equal to $\frac{\omega}{b_1}$ and $\frac{\omega}{b_2}$. Further, if a pressure maximum or minimum moves along the boundary on the left-hand side, then, by virtue of the continuity of pressure, there must be a pressure maximum or minimum on the right-hand side, equal in magnitude, moving at the same velocity. Thus,

$$\frac{\omega}{b_1} = \frac{\omega}{b_2} \qquad \text{or} \qquad b_1 = b_2,$$

whence

$$\frac{k_1}{k_2} = \frac{c_2}{c_1} = \frac{\sin\theta_2}{\sin\theta_1} \quad \text{or} \quad \frac{c_1}{\sin\theta_1} = \frac{c_2}{\sin\theta_2}. \tag{3-16}$$

This gives us Snell's law, which is valid for any wave process, not only for sound waves. Substituting expressions (3-14) in boundary conditions (3-13), we get:

$$\begin{gathered}\rho_1 (A_1 + A_1') = \rho_2 A_2,\\ a_1 A_1 - a_1 A_1' = a_2 A_2.\end{gathered}$$

The ratio of the amplitudes can be found from this set of equations

$$\begin{aligned}\frac{A_1'}{A_1} &= \frac{\frac{\rho_2}{\rho_1} - \frac{a_2}{a_1}}{\frac{\rho_2}{\rho_1} + \frac{a_2}{a_1}} = \frac{\rho_2 c_2 \cos\theta_1 - \rho_1 c_1 \cos\theta_2}{\rho_2 c_2 \cos\theta_1 + \rho_1 c_1 \cos\theta_2};\\ \frac{A_2}{A_1} &= \frac{2}{\frac{\rho_2}{\rho_1} + \frac{a_2}{a_1}} = \frac{2\rho_1 c_2 \cos\theta_1}{\rho_2 c_2 \cos\theta_1 + \rho_1 c_1 \cos\theta_2}.\end{aligned} \tag{3-17}$$

From these formulae, if the densities of the two media are the same ($\rho_1 = \rho_2$) we find, after certain transformations:

$$\frac{A_1'}{A_1} = \frac{\sin(\theta_2 - \theta_1)}{\sin(\theta_2 + \theta_1)}. \tag{3-18}$$

If the bulk moduli are equal ($\rho_1 c_1^2 = \rho_2 c_2^2$) then

$$\frac{A_1'}{A_1} = \frac{\tan(\theta_1 - \theta_2)}{\tan(\theta_1 + \theta_2)}. \tag{3-19}$$

Formulae (3-18) and (3-19) are identical, respectively, with Fresnel's formulae for the reflection coefficients of light which is polarized either parallel or transverse to the plane of incidence.*

Substituting a_1 and a_2 in equation (3-17) and using the law of refraction, we get:

$$\frac{A_1'}{A_1} = \frac{\frac{\rho_2}{\rho_1} - \frac{\cot\theta_2}{\cot\theta_1}}{\frac{\rho_2}{\rho_1} + \frac{\cot\theta_2}{\cot\theta_1}}; \qquad \frac{A_2}{A_1} = \frac{2}{\frac{\rho_2}{\rho_1} + \frac{\cot\theta_2}{\cot\theta_1}}.$$

For the reflection and transmission coefficients of the pressure wave we find, since $p = j\omega\rho\Phi$:

$$r_p = \frac{p_1'}{p_1} = \frac{A_1'}{A_1} \quad \text{and} \quad t_p = \frac{\rho_2}{\rho_1}\frac{A_2}{A_1}$$

If we bear in mind that by virtue of (3-14) the amplitudes of the velocity potentials are related to the corresponding amplitudes q_i of the particle velocities as follows: $A_1 = \frac{c_1}{\omega} q_1$; $A_1' = \frac{c_1}{\omega} q_1'$ and $A_2 = \frac{c_2}{\omega} q_2$,

---

* A. Schuster and J.M Nicholson. *An Introduction to the Theory of Optics*. London: Edward Arnold 1924 (see pp.48 and 238).

we can find the reflection coefficient r_q and the transmission coefficient t_q for the particle velocity wave:

$$r_q = \frac{q'_1}{q_1} = \frac{A'_1}{A_1} \quad \text{and} \quad t_q = \frac{q_2}{q_1} = \frac{c_1}{c_2}\frac{A_2}{A_1}.$$

It follows from formula (3-17) that there will be no reflected wave provided that

$$\frac{\rho_2}{\rho_1} = \frac{a_2}{a_1} = \frac{\cot\theta_2}{\cot\theta_1}. \qquad (3\text{-}20)$$

Using the law of refraction we get:

$$\cot^2\theta_1 = \frac{\frac{c_1^2}{c_2^2} - 1}{\frac{\rho_2^2}{\rho_1^2} - \frac{c_1^2}{c_2^2}}. \qquad (3\text{-}21)$$

If $\frac{\rho_2}{\rho_1} \lesseqgtr \frac{c_1}{c_2} \lesseqgtr 1$, then $\cot^2\theta_1$ will be positive and a certain angle θ_1 can be found between 0° and 90° at which there will be no reflection of sound at the boundary between the two media. For example, for ethyl alcohol $\rho_1 = 0{\cdot}79$ and $c_1 = 1{\cdot}18 \times 10^5$, and for chloroform $\rho_2 = 1{\cdot}49$ and $c_2 \approx$ $\approx 1{\cdot}00 \times 10^5$. It follows from equation (3-21) that for these media

$$\cot\theta_1 \approx 0{\cdot}43 \text{ and } \theta_1 \approx 67^\circ.$$

If the speed of sound is much less in the second medium than in the first ($c_2 \ll c_1$), then $\sin\theta_2 \approx 0$ and $\theta_2 \approx 0$. Thus, the second medium can transmit waves only along the normal to the boundary. For example, this would be the property of a model material consisting of thin capillaries perpendicular to the boundary (a Rayleigh model). Under these conditions

$$r_D = \frac{A'_1}{A_1} = \frac{\rho_2 c_2 \cos\theta_1 - \rho_1 c_1}{\rho_2 c_2 \cos\theta_1 + \rho_1 c_1} = \frac{R_2 \cos\theta_1 - R_1}{R_2 \cos\theta_1 + R_1}.$$

Generally speaking, in such cases the specific impedance

of the second medium can be complex and characterized by a certain *normal impedance* Z_2 (for example, this is true of many porous sound absorbing materials used in architectural acoustics). If the medium on which the sound is incident can be characterized by a normal impedance Z_2, then the reflection coefficient is

$$r_p = \frac{Z_2 \cos\theta_1 - R_1}{Z_2 \cos\theta_1 + R_1}.$$

Total Internal Reflection of Sound at a Plane Boundary between Two Media

It follows from the law of refraction (3-16) that $\sin\theta_2 = \frac{c_2}{c_1}\sin\theta_1$.

If $c_2 > c_1$ and $\sin\theta_1 > \frac{c_1}{c_2}$, then $\sin\theta_2 > 1$ and $\cos\theta_2 = \sqrt{1-\sin^2\theta_2}$ will be imaginary. The quantity $a_2 = k_2\cos\theta_2$ will also be imaginary and can be represented in the form:

$$a_2 = \pm j\alpha, \text{ where } \alpha = |a_2|. \tag{3-22}$$

It is easy to show that *the angle of refraction is in this case a purely imaginary quantity* $j\theta_2'$, given by the expression $\sinh\theta_2' = \frac{\alpha}{k_2}$.

The relative amplitude of the reflected wave is obtained from equation (3-17):

$$\frac{A_1'}{A_1} = \frac{\frac{\rho_2}{\rho_1} \mp j\frac{\alpha}{a_1}}{\frac{\rho_2}{\rho_1} \pm j\frac{\alpha}{a_1}} = e^{j2\varepsilon},$$

where

$$\tan\varepsilon = \pm\frac{\alpha\rho_1}{a_1\rho_2}.$$

Since the numerator and the denominator are conjugate complex quantities, the modulus of $\frac{A_1'}{A_1}$ is equal to unity, i.e. the amplitude of the reflected wave is equal to the amplitude of the incident wave ($|r_p|=1$) and complete internal reflection of the wave takes place. The multiplier $e^{j2\varepsilon}$ indicates that the reflected wave is shifted in phase by an angle 2ε relative to the incident wave.

In the second medium

$$\frac{A_2}{A_1}=\frac{2}{\frac{\rho_2}{\rho_1}\pm j\frac{\alpha}{a_1}}=\frac{2}{\sqrt{\frac{\rho_2^2}{\rho_1^2}+\frac{\alpha^2}{a_1^2}}}\cdot e^{j\varepsilon}.$$

In accordance with equation (3-14), the total wave in the first medium has the form:

$$\Phi_1=A_1\left[e^{j(\omega t-a_1x+by)}+e^{j(\omega t+a_1x+by+2\varepsilon)}\right].$$

For the wave in the second medium

$$\Phi_2=\frac{2A_1}{\sqrt{\frac{\rho_2^2}{\rho_1^2}+\frac{\alpha^2}{a_1^2}}}e^{\pm\alpha x}\cdot e^{j(\omega t+by+\varepsilon)}. \tag{3-23}$$

In this equation we must take only the negative sign in front of αx, since if the positive sign were taken we would have an unlimited increase in amplitude in the second medium, which is physically unacceptable.

Equation (3-23) represents a wave along the negative y axis, i.e. along the dividing boundary. In this case its amplitude *diminishes along the wavefronts* with increasing distance from the boundary according to the law $e^{-\alpha x}$. Such waves can be called front-modulated waves.

The rate of diminution in wave amplitude depends upon the quantity α, which we find by taking into account the relationship between a_2 and a_1 which follows from the wave equations (3-11) and (3-12). Substituting in them the quantities Φ_1 and Φ_2 of equation (3-14) we get:

$$c_1^2(a_1^2+b_1^2)=\omega^2 \text{ and } c_2^2(a_2^2+b_2^2)=\omega^2.$$

since $b_1=b_2=b$, it therefore follows from these relationships that

$$a_2^2+b^2=\frac{c_1^2}{c_2^2}(a_1^2+b^2).$$

Substituting the values a_1 and b from the relationship (3-15) we find:

$$a_2=k_1\sqrt{\frac{c_1^2}{c_2^2}-\sin^2\theta_1}.$$

whence, if $\sin\theta_1>\frac{c_1}{c_2}$ we get an imaginary value for a_2, the modulus of which is

$$|a_2|=\alpha=k_1\sqrt{\sin^2\theta_1-\frac{c_1^2}{c_2^2}}=\frac{2\pi}{\lambda_1}\sqrt{\sin^2\theta_1-\frac{\lambda_1^2}{\lambda_2^2}}.$$

At the critical angle, i.e. if $\sin\theta_1=\frac{c_1}{c_2}$, $\alpha=0$. Consequently, the amplitude along the wavefront (in the second medium) will not decay, and a plane wave arises travelling parallel to the boundary. If, however, $\sin\theta_1>\frac{c_1}{c_2}$, i.e. if θ_1 is greater than the critical angle of total internal reflection, then $\alpha>0$ and the amplitude along the wavefront will diminish rapidly.

If $\theta_1=\frac{\pi}{2}$ the maximum of α is obtained:

$$\alpha_{max}=k_1\sqrt{1-\frac{c_1^2}{c_2^2}}=\frac{2\pi}{\lambda_1}\sqrt{1-\frac{\lambda_1^2}{\lambda_2^2}}.$$

When $\arcsin\frac{c_1}{c_2}<\theta_1<\frac{\pi}{2}$, the values of α will lie between the limits 0 and α_{max}.

For sound incident from air into water

$$\frac{c_1}{c_2} \approx 0{\cdot}23 \text{ and } \alpha_{max} = \frac{2\pi}{\lambda}(1 - 0{\cdot}027) \approx \frac{2\pi}{\lambda}.$$

At a distance $\frac{\lambda}{2\pi}$ the wave in the second medium is reduced by a factor e. Figure 9 shows a photograph* of ultrasonic waves at the boundary between vaseline oil (on top) and a saturated solution of NaCl (below). The dividing boundary corresponds exactly to the lower edge of the dark horizontal band (meniscus band). In the second medium, since $\theta_1 > 55^\circ$ (the critical angle), the wavefronts are clearly visible parallel with the boundary and gradually weakening as they go deeper into the second medium.

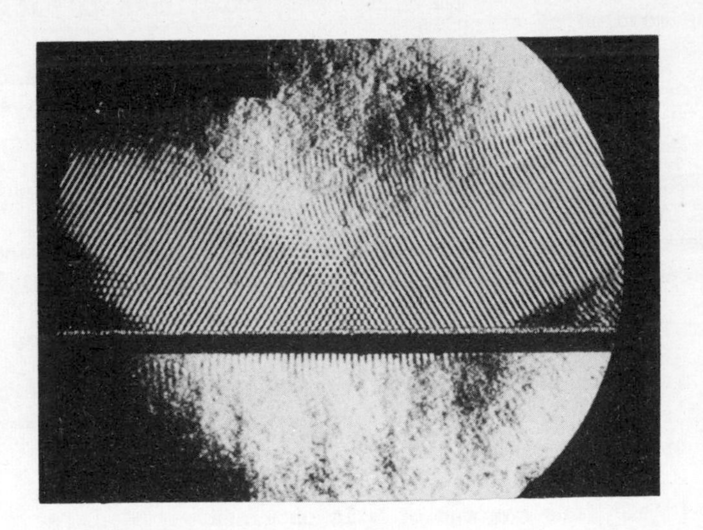

Fig. 9

* S.N. Rschevkin and S.I. Krechmer, *C.R. Acad. Sci. U.S.S.R.* 20, No.1, 1938.

From equation (3-23), the acoustic pressure is

$$p = \rho_2 \frac{\partial \Phi_2}{\partial t} = j\omega\rho_2\Phi_2$$

and the particle velocities along the x and y axes are

$$\dot{\xi} = -\frac{\partial \Phi_2}{\partial x} = \alpha\Phi_2,$$

$$\dot{\eta} = -\frac{\partial \Phi_2}{\partial y} = -jb\Phi_2 = b\Phi_2 e^{-j\frac{\pi}{2}}.$$

Thus, the particle velocities along the x and y axes are not in phase; one is in advance of the other by 90°. This implies that the resultant motion of the particles in the second medium is along an ellipse lying in the plane of incidence of the acoustic beam (the xy plane).

Transmission of Sound through a Plane Layer

If a sound wave in medium I, with constants ρ_1 and c_1, is incident at an angle θ_1 on an intermediate layer of liquid or gas with constants ρ_2 and c_2 and a thickness d (medium II), reflected waves will occur at the first and second boundary (Fig. 10); there will be only one progressive wave, a forward wave.

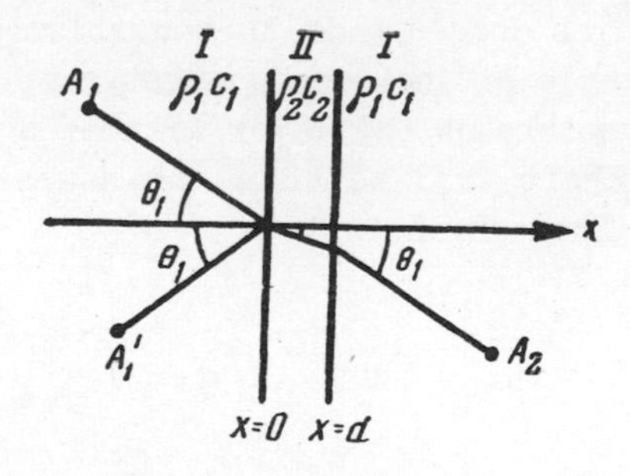

Fig. 10

This problem can be solved as follows. The velocity

potential in the first medium (to the left of the layer.) is the sum of two terms (see the first equation of (3-14)), and that in the second medium is expressed by a similar formula except that a_1 and b_1 are replaced by the quantities $a_2 = k_2 \cos\theta_2$ and $b_2 = k_2 \sin\theta_2$. At the first and second boundaries, ($x = 0$, $x = d$), the conditions of continuity must be satisfied for the acoustic pressure and particle velocity, which gives four equations for the four velocity potential amplitude ratios, that of the reflected wave, $\frac{A_1'}{A_1}$, that of the transmitted wave, $\frac{A_2}{A_1}$, and the two similar ratios for the transmitted and reflected waves in the layer. Solving these equations,* we find the reflection coefficient (r_p) and transmission coefficient (t_p) for the pressure wave (through the layer):

$$r_p = \frac{A_1'}{A_1} = \frac{\delta^{-1} - \delta}{\sqrt{(\delta^{-1} + \delta)^2 + 4\cot^2 a_2 d}}, \tag{3-24}$$

$$t_p = \frac{A_2}{A_1} = \frac{2}{\sqrt{4\cos^2 a_2 d + (\delta^{-1} + \delta)^2 \sin^2 a_2 d}}, \tag{3-25}$$

where

$$\delta = \frac{a_1\rho_2}{a_2\rho_1} = \frac{\rho_2 k_1 \cos\theta_1}{\rho_1 k_2 \cos\theta_2} = \frac{R_2 \cos\theta_1}{R_1 \cos\theta_2} = \frac{\frac{\rho_2}{\cot\theta_2}}{\frac{\rho_1}{\cot\theta_1}}.$$

If $\delta = 1$, which corresponds to condition (3-20), then, at a certain angle of incidence, we get complete transmission of the wave through the layer without any reflection. Furthermore, there will be total transmission provided $\cot a_2 d = \infty$, from which follows:

$$a_2 d = n\pi, \qquad \text{or} \qquad d = n\frac{\frac{\lambda_2}{2}}{\cos\theta_2}.$$

For a layer very thin relative to a wavelength we get,

---

* Lord Rayleigh, *Theory of Sound*, vol. II. London: Constable, 1945 (see Sect. 271).

if $a_2 d \ll 1$ and the value of δ is not too large or small:

$$r_p \approx \frac{a_2 d}{2}(\delta^{-1} - \delta) = \frac{\omega d \cos\theta_2}{2c_2}(\delta^{-1} - \delta).$$

Thus the reflection from a thin layer is directly proportional to the frequency at a given angle of incidence and, consequently, at given θ_2 and b. It will be seen from expression (3-24) that the reflection is not total at a layer, as is the case at the boundary of a half-space, if the angle of incidence θ_1 is greater than critical (a_2 imaginary). The waves in the second medium proceeding parallel with the front boundary of the layer have a finite amplitude at the rear boundary which can be quite large if the thickness of the layer d is quite small or if the angle of incidence is quite close to critical. Thus waves of compression and rarefaction will move along the second (rear) boundary which inevitably causes disturbance in the medium beyond the layer and leads to the emergence of a progressive wave there. There is no difficulty in showing that practically all the energy will pass through a very thin layer even at angles greater than the critical. At angles of incidence close to 90°, waves in the second medium are damped very considerably after penetration to a depth of the order of a wavelength. Hence, transmission is very small, i.e. there is almost complete reflection, if grazing incidence occurs on a layer which is greater in thickness than λ.

For incidence at the angle 0°, formulae (3-24) and (3-25) take the form

$$r_p = \frac{\frac{R_1}{R_2} - \frac{R_2}{R_1}}{\sqrt{\left(\frac{R_1}{R_2} + \frac{R_2}{R_1}\right)^2 + 4\cot^2 k_2 d}} =$$

$$= \frac{\left(\frac{R_1}{R_2} - \frac{R_2}{R_1}\right)\sin k_2 d}{\sqrt{\left(\frac{R_1}{R_2} + \frac{R_2}{R_1}\right)^2 \sin^2 k_2 d + 4\cos^2 k_2 d}}, \qquad (3\text{-}26)$$

$$t_p = \frac{1}{\sqrt{\left(\frac{R_1}{R_2} + \frac{R_2}{R_1}\right)^2 \left(\frac{\sin k_2 d}{2}\right)^2 + \cos^2 k_2 d}}.$$

With a very thin layer or very low frequencies ($k_2d \ll 1$) and a large acoustic resistance in the second medium ($R_2 \gg R_1$)

$$\frac{1}{t_p} \approx \sqrt{1+\frac{1}{4}\left(\frac{R_2}{R_1}\right)^2 \frac{d^2\omega^2}{c_2^2}} = \sqrt{1+\left(\frac{\omega M_2}{2R_1}\right)^2},$$

where $M_2 = \rho_2 d$ is the mass of the layer per cm^2. The ratio of the energy of the incident wave to that of the transmitted wave (the coefficient of sound insulation of the layer) is approximately:

$$\eta = \frac{1}{t_p^2} \approx 1+\left(\frac{\omega M_2}{2R_1}\right)^2 = 1+\left(\frac{\pi M_2}{R_1} f\right)^2. \qquad (3\text{-}27)$$

The following analogy with electricity can be drawn. Suppose that the voltage A_1 is applied to a circuit containing a series-connected inductive reactance ωM_2 and resistance $2R_1$. The current (velocity) in the circuit is $\frac{A_1}{\sqrt{(2R_1)^2+(\omega M_2)^2}}$, and the voltage drop across the resistance $2R_1$ is $A_2 = A_1 \frac{2R_1}{\sqrt{(2R_1)^2+(\omega M_2)^2}}$. The ratio of the total power of the circuit to the power expended across the resistance $2R_1$ (the coefficient of sound insulation) is $\left(\frac{A_1}{A_2}\right)^2$, which leads to formula (3-27).

Given normal incidence, we can apply formulae (3-26) and (3-27) to a solid wall such as a monolithic (single-structure) partition. For the transmission of sound through such a partition in air, we always have $\left(\frac{\omega M_2}{2R_1}\right)^2 \gg 1$ and, therefore

$$\eta \approx \left(\frac{\omega M_2}{2R_1}\right)^2 = \left(\frac{\pi M_2 f}{\rho_1 c_1}\right)^2.$$

For air $\rho_1 c_1 = 41$ we have $\eta \approx \frac{1}{170} M_2^2 f^2$. The sound insulation partition in decibels is then:

$$10 \log_{10} \eta = -22 + 20 \log_{10} f + 20 \log_{10} M_2.$$

This formula is similar to that known in architectural acoustics as "the mass law" of sound insulation. The calculated sound insulation is 64 db for a thin brick wall (d = 10 cm) with a weight 200 kg/m^2 (or 20 g/cm^2) at 1024 c/s. The experimentally-determined sound insulation is 58 dB, i.e. 4 times less.* It should be borne in mind that the stated experiment corresponds to conditions of diffuse incidence (in every possible direction) and not normal incidence. The discrepancy is also explained by the fact that the partition is fixed along a certain contour and behaves as a diaphragm which is capable of bending. Such a diaphragm transmits sounds by means of bending vibrations as well as by the compression and rarefaction waves which are taken into account by formulae (3-26) and (3-27). This has a particularly marked effect at low frequencies.

An interesting case is the transmission of sound from a liquid into a liquid again through a solid body. We consider the transmission through an iron plate, of thickness d = 1 cm, immersed in water, of a sound wave in the water, normally incident on the plate. In this case

$$\frac{R_2}{R_1} = \frac{5 \times 10^5 \times 7{\cdot}8}{1{\cdot}45 \times 10^5} = 26{\cdot}8,$$

$$t_p \approx \frac{1}{\sqrt{\left(\frac{R_2}{R_1}\right)^2 \left(\frac{\sin k_2 d}{2}\right)^2 + \cos^2 k_2 d}}$$

and

$$\eta = \frac{1}{t_p^2} \approx \left(\frac{R_2}{2R_1}\right)^2 \sin^2 k_2 d + \cos^2 k_2 d = 179 \sin^2 (1{\cdot}25 \times 10^{-5} f) + $$
$$+ \cos^2 (1{\cdot}25 \times 10^{-5} f).$$

For frequencies less than 2000 c/s, the first term will

---

* V. Knudsen, *Architectural Acoustics*. New York: John Wiley 1932 (see p.311).

be considerably less than unity so that $\eta \approx 1$, i.e. there is practically no sound insulation; all the energy passes through the iron plate. At the frequency $f \approx 6000$ c/s, $\eta \approx 2$, whilst at the frequency $f \approx 125{,}000$ c/s $\left(k_2 d = \frac{\pi}{2}\right)$ the sound insulation attains its maximum value equal to $\eta \approx 179$ (25·5 db). If $f \approx 250{,}000$ c/s $\left(k_2 d = \pi, \quad d = \frac{\lambda_2}{2}\right)$ the sound insulation is again equal to unity. In general η will be a maximum if $f \approx 125{,}000 \times (2n+1)$ c/s and a minimum equal to unity if $f \approx 125{,}000 \times (2n)$ c/s (Fig. 11).

For a layer with acoustic impedance R_2 considerably less than R_1 - for example, air or sponge rubber ($R_2 \approx 40$), embedded in a liquid or in a solid body - the coefficient of sound insulation from formula (3-26) is

$$\eta = \frac{1}{t^2_p} \approx \left(\frac{R_1}{2R_2}\right)^2 \sin^2 k_2 d + \cos^2 k_2 d.$$

For a layer of air in water $\frac{R_1}{2R_2} = 1{\cdot}83 \times 10^3$. At very low frequencies or with very thin layers, such that $k_2 d \ll \frac{2R_2}{R_1}$, the first term will be small compared with the second, which is close to unity, and so $\eta \approx 1$. With increasing frequency η rapidly increases, reaching the value $(1{\cdot}83 \times 10^3)^2 = 3{\cdot}35 \times 10^6$ (about 65 dB) when $k_2 d = \frac{\pi}{2}$, or $f = \frac{c_2}{4d}$, and then begins to decrease, being equal to unity if $k_2 d = \pi$, $\left(d = \frac{\lambda_2}{2}\right)$. The behaviour of η is similar to that shown in Fig. 11. At low frequencies when $k_2 d \ll 1$, the coefficient of sound insulation can be represented in the form:

$$\eta \approx \left(\frac{\rho_1 c_1}{2\,\frac{\rho_2 c_2^2}{\omega d}}\right)^2 + 1 = \left(\frac{S\rho_1 c_1}{2\,\frac{\rho_2 c_2^2 S^2}{\omega V}}\right)^2 + 1 = \frac{Z_v^2 + \left(\frac{R_s}{2}\right)^2}{Z_v^2}. \quad (3\text{-}28)$$

Again in this case there is a formal analogy with electricity. Consider a capacitor of impedance $Z_v = \frac{\rho_2 c_2^2 S^2}{\omega v}$ ($v = Sd$ is the volume of the layer corresponding to the area S)

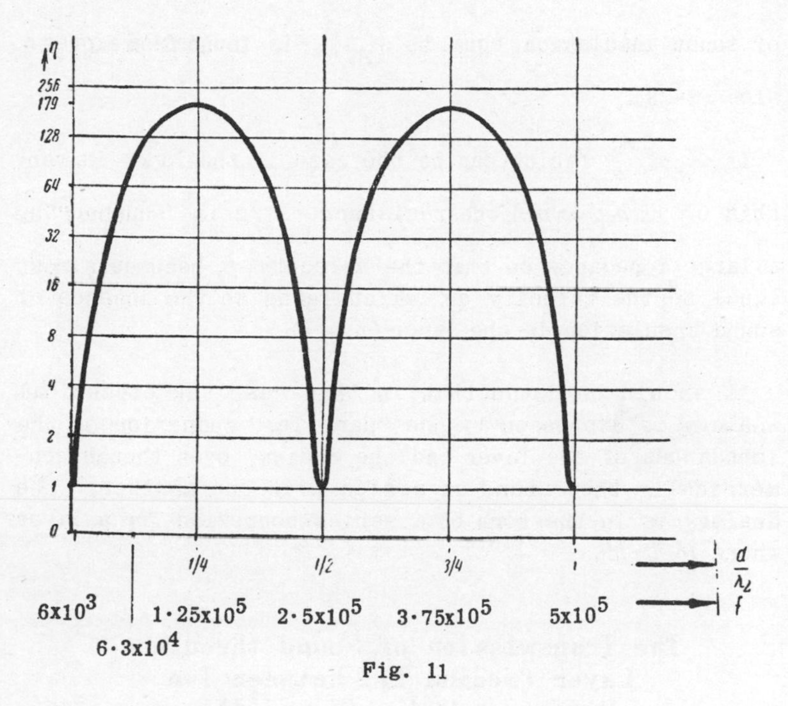

Fig. 11

connected in parallel with a resistance $\frac{R_s}{2}$ ($R_s = R_1 \cdot S$, where R_1 is the acoustic resistance of the medium beyond the intermediate layer). The ratio of the currents (velocities) in the branches will equal $\frac{q_v}{q_2} = \frac{R_s/2}{Z_v}$. The absolute ratio of the total current $|q_1|$, through the parallel connexion $R_s/2$

and Z_v to the current $|q_2|$ is

$$\frac{|q_v+q_2|}{|q_2|}=\frac{\left|\frac{R_s}{2}+Z_v\right|}{|Z_v|}=\frac{\sqrt{\left(\frac{R_s}{2}\right)^2+|Z_v|^2}}{|Z_v|}.$$

The velocity $|q_v+q_2|$ is determined by the pressure at the input which is proportional to the amplitude of the velocity potential (A_1) in the incident wave, whilst the the quantity $|q_2|$ is proportional to the amplitude (A_2) of the wave transmitted beyond the layer. The coefficient of sound insulation, equal to $\left(\frac{A_1}{A_2}\right)^2$, is found from expression (3-28).

If $Z_v \ll \frac{R_s}{2}$ (which can be the case if the layer is very thin or if $k_2d=n\pi$), the resistance $R_s/2$ is "shunted" by a large impedance so that the velocity q_2 becomes almost equal to the velocity q_1, which leads to the absence of sound insulation in the layer $(\eta \approx 1)$.

It should be noted that in this case the electrical analogy is expressed by the "parallel" connexion of the impedances of the layer and the medium, even though geometrically they stand in series with one another; the analogy is in the form of a series connexion for a layer where $R_2 \gg R_1$.

The Transmission of Sound through a Layer (medium II) between Two Different Media (I and III)

The formulae for this case are derived by the method described previously. The coefficient of sound insulation for normal incidence of sound $(\theta_1=0)$ is

$$\eta = \frac{\left(\frac{R_3}{R_1}+1\right)^2 - \left(\frac{R_3^2}{R_2^2}-1\right)\left(\frac{R_2^2}{R_1^2}-1\right)\sin^2 k_2 d}{4\frac{R_3}{R_1}}, \qquad (3\text{-}29)$$

where $R_1 = \rho_1 c_1$, $R_2 = \rho_2 c_2$ and $R_3 = \rho_3 c_3$ are the acoustic impedances of media I, II and III. This formula can also be applied to solid bodies.

When $k_2 d \ll 1$ and $\lambda_2 \gg d$, as well as when $k_2 d \approx n\pi$, i.e. $\sin k_2 d \approx 0$, we get:

$$\eta \approx \frac{\left(\frac{R_3}{R_1}+1\right)^2}{4\frac{R_3}{R_1}} = \frac{(R_1+R_3)^2}{4R_1R_3}.$$

This expression coincides with equation (3-5) for the case of transmission across a boundary between two media. Thus, for very thin layers or very low frequencies, and also for $d_2 \approx n\frac{\lambda_2}{2}$, the sound insulation is independent of the properties of the intermediate layer. If $\sin k_2 d \neq 0$, then the presence of an intermediate layer increases the sound insulation, provided R_2 is intermediate in value between R_1 and R_3; if this is not the case, then the presence of a layer reduces the sound insulation. If $\sin k_2 d = 1$, i.e. $d = \left(n+\frac{1}{2}\right)\frac{\lambda_2}{2}$, then

$$\eta = \left(1+\frac{R_1R_3}{R_2^2}\right)^2 \cdot \frac{R_2^2}{4R_1R_3}. \qquad (3\text{-}30)$$

It will be seen from (3-29) that if R_2 is between R_1 and R_3, then (3-30) is the expression for the minimum sound insulation; if $R_2 = \sqrt{R_1R_3}$, then $\eta = 1$, i.e. there is no sound insulation.

The condition $d = \left(n+\frac{1}{2}\right)\frac{\lambda}{2}$ for the minimum sound insulation, i.e. for the greatest sound transparency, is analogous to the condition used in optics for analysing "translucent" layers. In order to illustrate the use of "translucent" layers in acoustics, we will consider the transmission of sound from water into air, in which case the translucent layer must have $R_2 \approx \sqrt{41 \times 1{\cdot}5 \times 10^5} \approx 2{\cdot}45 \times 10^3$. It is impossible to find natural substances possessing such an acoustic resistance. However, we can artificially create such a material by using aerated rubber. It is easy to see that if a part V_2 of the total volume $(V_1 + V_2)$ is filled with air and the other part V_1 with rubber, then the bulk modulus of the composite material will be

$$\varkappa = \frac{V_1 + V_2}{\frac{V_1}{\varkappa'} + \frac{V_2}{\varkappa''}},$$

where $\varkappa'$ and $\varkappa''$ are the bulk moduli of the rubber and air, respectively (for rubber the modulus is roughly the same as for water, i.e. $\varkappa' \approx 2 \times 10^{10}$; for air $\varkappa'' = 1{\cdot}4 \times 10^6$).

The density of the material, ρ, is equal to $\frac{\rho' V_1}{V_1 + V_2}$, with sufficient accuracy, where $\rho' \approx 1{\cdot}1$ is the density of the rubber. For the square of the acoustic resistance of the layer we get:

$$R_2^2 = (\rho c)^2 = \rho\varkappa = \frac{\rho' V_1}{V_1 + V_2} \cdot \frac{V_1 + V_2}{\frac{V_1}{\varkappa'} + \frac{V_2}{\varkappa''}} = \frac{\rho'}{\frac{1}{\varkappa'} + \frac{V_2}{V_1}\frac{1}{\varkappa''}}.$$

Equating this quantity to the value $R_1 R_2 \approx 6 \times 10^6$, we get $\frac{V_1}{V_2} \approx \frac{1}{2{\cdot}55}$, which corresponds to an air bubble content equal to 27 per cent of the total volume.

CHAPTER IV

SIMPLE SOUND RADIATORS
(pulsating and oscillating sphere)

Pulsating Sphere

The wave equation for the acoustic field of a sphere whose entire surface pulsates uniformly can be obtained from the wave equation written in spherical coordinates on the assumption that derivatives with respect to the polar angle ϑ and the azimuthal angle ψ are equal to zero, i.e. if there is complete symmetry about the centre. However, it is of interest in this case to form the equation for the propagation of the wave independently in order to bring out the essential features of the acoustic field.

We consider the motion of an element of a spherical layer (Fig. 12a) bounded by spheres of radius r and $r+\Delta r$ and a four-sided solid angle with apex at the origin and sides at the angle $\Delta\varphi$ to each other at the apex. The mass of the element will equal $\Omega r^2 \Delta r \rho$, where $\Omega = \Delta\varphi^2$ is the solid angle. The pressure in the medium depends solely on r and time t. Suppose we put p for the acoustic pressure at the central point of the element. It can then be assumed that two pairs of forces, each force being of magnitude $(r\Delta\varphi\Delta r)p$ and at an angle $\Delta\varphi$ to its partner, are exerted on the sides by the surrounding medium (Fig. 12b). The resultant force of each pair Δp is of magnitude $\Delta p = (r\Delta\varphi\Delta r)p \cdot 2\tan\frac{\Delta\varphi}{2} \approx r\Delta\varphi^2 \Delta r p = \Omega r \Delta r p$ and is directed along the radius through the centre of the element (Fig. 12c). The magnitude of the resultant force due to these two pairs is

$$2\Delta p = +2\Omega rp\Delta r.$$

The force on the internal spherical surface of the element is also radial and is equal to

$$+\left(\Omega r^2 p - \frac{1}{2}\frac{\partial(\Omega r^2 p)}{\partial r}\Delta r\right),$$

and that on the external surface is

$$-\left(\Omega r^2 p + \frac{1}{2}\frac{\partial(\Omega r^2 p)}{\partial r}\Delta r\right).$$

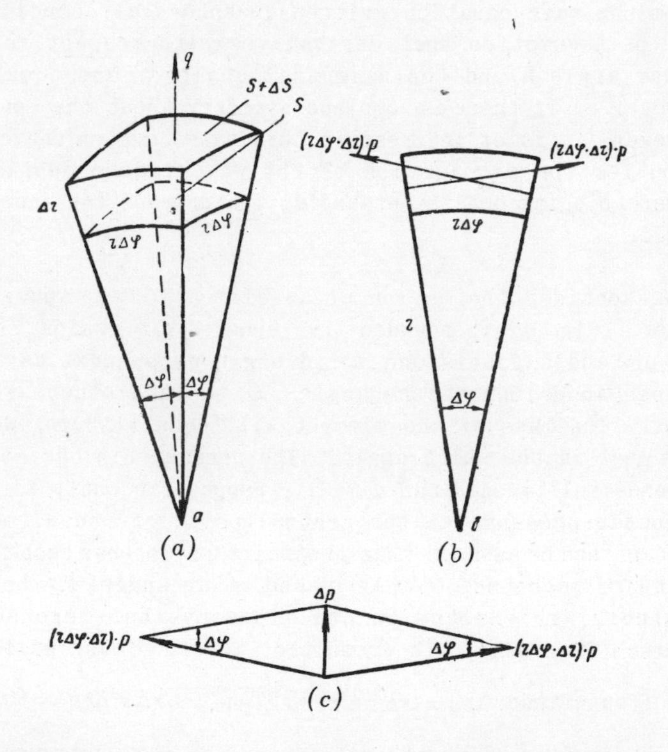

Fig. 12

The radial resultant of these two forces is:

$$-\frac{\partial(\Omega r^2 p)}{\partial r}\Delta r = -\Omega\frac{\partial(r^2 p)}{\partial r}\Delta r = -2\Omega rp\,\Delta r - \Omega r^2\frac{\partial p}{\partial r}\Delta r.$$

The resultant of all the forces on the element again is directed along the radius and is equal to:

$$-\Omega r^2\frac{\partial p}{\partial r}\Delta r.$$

Suppose we put q for the radial velocity of the element as a whole. The acceleration is then

$$\frac{dq}{dt} = \frac{\partial q}{\partial t} + \frac{\partial q}{\partial r}\frac{dr}{dt} = \frac{\partial q}{\partial t} + \frac{\partial q}{\partial r}q,$$

and in view of the smallness of q, we may retain only the first term, i.e, neglect the convective acceleration $\frac{\partial q}{\partial r}q$ relative to the local acceleration.

The equation of motion of the element can be written in the form:

$$\Omega r^2\rho\frac{\partial q}{\partial t}\Delta r = -\Omega r^2\frac{\partial p}{\partial r}\Delta r.$$

Cancelling $\Omega r^2\Delta r$, we find:

$$\rho\frac{\partial q}{\partial t} = -\frac{\partial p}{\partial r}, \tag{4-1}$$

i.e. the equation of motion has the same form as for a plane wave.

The equation of continuity may be written in the form:

$$\Omega r^2\rho q - \left[\Omega r^2\rho q + \frac{\partial(\Omega r^2\rho q)}{\partial r}\Delta r\right] = \Omega r^2\Delta r\frac{\partial\rho}{\partial t}.$$

Since the density $\rho=\rho_0+\delta\rho$ changes insignificantly over the length Δr we can assume that

$$\frac{\partial(\Omega r^2\rho q)}{\partial r}\approx\rho\Omega\frac{\partial(r^2 q)}{\partial r};$$

Then

$$-\Omega\rho\frac{\partial(r^2 q)}{\partial r}\Delta r=\Omega r^2\frac{\partial\rho}{\partial t}\Delta r.$$

Differentiating and cancelling $\Omega\Delta r$, we get:

$$\frac{1}{\rho}\frac{\partial\rho}{\partial t}=-\frac{2q}{r}-\frac{\partial q}{\partial r}.$$

In accordance with Hooke's law $p=\varkappa\frac{\delta\rho}{\rho}$. Moreover, we have

$$\frac{1}{\rho}\frac{\partial\rho}{\partial t}=\frac{\partial\left(\frac{\delta\rho}{\rho}\right)}{\partial t}=\frac{1}{\varkappa}\frac{\partial p}{\partial t}.$$

The equation of continuity then takes the form

$$\frac{1}{\varkappa}\frac{\partial p}{\partial t}=-\frac{2q}{r}-\frac{\partial q}{\partial r}. \tag{4-2}$$

Introducing the function $\Pi=pr$ and using $\frac{\partial p}{\partial r}=-\frac{\Pi}{r^2}+\frac{1}{r}\frac{\partial\Pi}{\partial r}$, we reduce (4-1) and (4-2) to the following set of equations:

$$\rho\frac{\partial q}{\partial t}=\frac{\Pi}{r^2}-\frac{1}{r}\frac{\partial\Pi}{\partial r}\text{ and }\frac{1}{\varkappa}\frac{\partial\Pi}{\partial t}=-2q-r\frac{\partial q}{\partial r}.$$

Differentiating the first equation with respect to r and the second equation with respect to t enables us to eliminate q and thus we get:

$$\frac{\partial^2\Pi}{\partial t^2}=\frac{\varkappa}{\rho}\frac{\partial^2\Pi}{\partial r^2}.$$

This equation has the known D'Alembert solution (see Chapter II), and hence:

$$p=\frac{\Pi}{r}=\frac{1}{r}\Phi_1(ct-r)+\frac{1}{r}\Phi_2(ct+r), \qquad (4\text{-}3)$$

where $c=\sqrt{\frac{\varkappa}{\rho}}$, and Φ_1 and Φ_2 are arbitrary functions with arguments $(ct-r)$ and $(ct+r)$; They represent, respectively, pressure waves with a phase velocity c diverging from the centre, and converging on the centre.

It is easy to see that a more complicated differential equation is obtained for the function $Q = qr$:

$$\frac{\partial^2 Q}{\partial t^2}=c^2\frac{\partial^2 Q}{\partial r^2}-\frac{2c^2}{r^2}Q.$$

In the special case of a harmonic process we get for waves diverging from the centre, using equation (4-3):

$$p=\frac{a}{r}e^{jk\,(ct-r)}=\frac{a}{r}e^{j\,(\omega t-kr)}=p_m e^{j(\omega t-kr)}, \qquad (4\text{-}4)$$

where $k=\frac{\omega}{c}$ is the wave number and $p_m=\frac{a}{r}$. The phase velocity for spherical pressure waves is equal to the phase velocity for plane waves.

Expression (4-4) gives the pressure wave created by a point source at the origin $(r=0)$. We require to find the law governing the variation of the particle velocity in a field created by such a source.

Integrating equation (4-1) we find:

$$q=-\int_0^t\frac{1}{\rho}\frac{\partial p}{\partial r}dt\approx-\frac{1}{\rho_0}\frac{\partial}{\partial r}\int_0^t pdt=$$

$$=-\frac{1}{\rho_0}\frac{\frac{\partial p}{\partial r}}{j\omega}=-\frac{a\,e^{j\omega t}}{j\omega\rho}\frac{\partial}{\partial r}\left(\frac{e^{-jkr}}{r}\right)$$

In the integration it is assumed $\rho\approx\rho_0$).

Differentiating, we can represent q in the form:

$$q=\frac{p}{\rho ckr}(kr-j)=\frac{p}{\rho c}\frac{\sqrt{1+k^2r^2}}{kr}\left(\frac{kr}{\sqrt{1+k^2r^2}}-j\frac{1}{\sqrt{1+k^2r^2}}\right)= \\ =\frac{pe^{-j\varphi}}{\rho c\cos\varphi}=\frac{a}{r\rho c\cos\varphi}e^{j(\omega t-kr-\varphi)}, \tag{4-5}$$

where

$$\cos\varphi=\frac{kr}{\sqrt{1+k^2r^2}};\ \sin\varphi=\frac{1}{\sqrt{1+k^2r^2}};\ \tan\varphi=\frac{1}{kr}.$$

Equation (4-5) shows that the relationship between the pressure and particle velocity in a spherical wave is more complicated than in a plane wave, where $q=\frac{p}{\rho c}$. The particle velocity lags the pressure in phase by the angle φ, which is a function of r; the modulus of the particle velocity amplitude is $|q_m|=\frac{|p_m|}{\rho c\cos\varphi}$, i.e. it is always greater than $\frac{|p_m|}{\rho c}$. In the *distant field* $(kr\gg 1)$ $\cos\varphi\rightarrow 1$ and $\sin\varphi\rightarrow 0$. Thus at large distances the spherical wave resembles a plane wave in that $q=\frac{p}{\rho c}$. But the pressure and particle velocity vary in inverse proportion to r. In the *near field*

$$(kr\ll 1),\ \cos\varphi\rightarrow kr,\ \sin\varphi\rightarrow 1 \text{ and } \varphi\rightarrow\frac{\pi}{2}.$$

In this case $q=\frac{pe^{-j\frac{\pi}{2}}}{\rho ckr}$ and the particle velocity wave lags in phase 90° behind the pressure wave. The amplitude of the particle velocity in the near field diminishes with distance in inverse proportion to r^2, whereas p_m varies in inverse proportion to r.

It follows from (4-5) that the particle velocity can be

expressed in terms of the acoustic pressure by the formula:

$$q = \frac{pe^{-j\varphi}}{\rho c \cos \varphi}. \qquad (4\text{-}6)$$

The particle velocity can be represented in the form of a parallel connexion of two velocities:

$$q = \frac{p}{\rho c} - j \frac{p}{\rho ckr} = \frac{p}{\rho c} + \frac{p}{j\omega \rho r} = q_r + q_i,$$

where q_r is the active component of the particle velocity, coinciding in phase with the pressure, whilst q_i, which lags in phase by $\frac{\pi}{2}$, is the reactive component of the particle velocity.

Expression (4-6) must be used when measuring acoustic pressure in a spherical wave by the Rayleigh disc method. It is known that in a steady or fluctuating flow of a liquid (or gas) a light disc tends to turn so that its plane becomes transverse to the flow. If a circular disc of radius R is suspended on a thread with a torsional constant D and its plane forms an angle θ with the direction of the acoustic wave, then the angle of deflection α of the disc due to the wave can be calculated from the formula:

$$\alpha = \frac{1}{D} \cdot \frac{2\rho R^3}{3} \sin 2\theta \cdot q_m^2.$$

The disc will be most sensitive if $\theta = \frac{\pi}{4}$, i.e. $\sin 2\theta = 1$.

Measurement by a Rayleigh disc enables us to find q_m^2, but formula (4-6) shows that is is also necessary to know $\cos \varphi$ in order to calculate the pressure p_m. The value of $\cos \varphi$ near the source can be considerably less than unity and it cannot be assumed that p_m and q_m are related by the expression $p_m = \rho c q_m$, as is the case with a plane wave.

For the particle velocity phase, given in equation (4-5), to be constant we must have

$$\frac{\partial}{\partial t}(\omega t - kr - \varphi)\frac{dt}{dr} + \frac{\partial}{\partial r}(\omega t - kr - \varphi) = 0,$$

Hence the phase velocity of the particle velocity wave is

$$c' = \frac{dr}{dt} = -\frac{\frac{\partial(\omega t - kr - \varphi)}{\partial t}}{\frac{\partial(\omega t - kr - \varphi)}{\partial r}} = c\left(1 + \frac{1}{k^2r^2}\right) = \frac{c}{\cos^2\varphi}.$$

It will be seen from this expression that $c' > c$; in the near zone c' may be considerably greater than c.

We will now consider the physical meaning of the constant term a in equation (4-4). The amplitude of the volume velocity A_0 through an infinitesimal sphere surrounding a point source is

$$A_0 = (4\pi r^2 q_m)_{r\to 0} = \frac{4\pi r^2 e^{-jkr}\cdot e^{-j\varphi}}{\rho c r \cos\varphi} a \underset{r\to 0}{\rightarrow} \frac{4\pi a}{j\omega\rho}.$$

Then

$$a = j\omega\rho\frac{A_0}{4\pi}. \qquad (4\text{-}7)$$

Since the acoustic pressure and the velocity potential Φ are related by the expression $p = \rho\frac{\partial\Phi}{\partial t} = j\omega\rho\Phi$, we see that the quantity $\frac{a}{j\omega\rho r} = \frac{A_0}{4\pi r}$ is the amplitude of the velocity potential and so for a point source we can write:

$$\Phi = \frac{A_0}{4\pi r} e^{j(\omega t - kr)}.$$

The quantity 4π appears because the point source radiates into free space, i.e. into the solid angle 4π. If the radiation of a source of volume velocity A_0 takes place within the limits of a cone of solid angle Ω, having rigid walls, then

$$a = j\omega\rho \frac{A_0}{\Omega}.$$

The magnitude of the volume velocity A_0 across the infinitesimal sphere (or infinitesimal cone of solid angle Ω), surrounding the source is called the *strength of the source.*

If a spherical surface of finite radius r_0 pulsates according to the law $q_0 e^{j\omega t}$, then the boundary condition $q(r_0,t) = q_0 e^{j\omega t}$, must be satisfied on the surface of the sphere, whence on the basis of (4-4) and (4-5)

$$a = \frac{r_0 \rho c \cos \varphi_0}{e^{-jkr_0} \cdot e^{-j\varphi_0}} q_0 = \omega\rho r_0^2 \sin \varphi_0 \cdot e^{jkr_0} \cdot e^{j\varphi_0} \cdot q_0 = = j\omega\rho \frac{Q_0}{4\pi} \cdot \left[\sin \varphi_0 \cdot e^{j\left(kr_0 + \varphi_0 - \frac{\pi}{2} \right)} \right], \tag{4-8}$$

where $Q_0 = 4\pi r_0^2 q_0$ is the amplitude of the volume velocity across the surface of the sphere, and φ_0 is the value of the angle φ at $r = r_0$. Equation (4-8) shows that a spherical radiator of finite radius r_0 having a volume velocity Q_0 will be equivalent to a point source of strength A_0, given by

$$A_0 = Q_0 \sin \varphi_0 = \frac{Q_0}{\sqrt{1 + k^2 r_0^2}};$$

It is obvious that A_0 is always less than Q_0.

Using the expression for a in terms of Q_0 we can write the acoustic pressure in the following form:

$$p = j\omega\rho \frac{Q_0}{4\pi r \sqrt{1 + k^2 r_0^2}} e^{j\left[\omega t - k(r - r_0) + \varphi_0 - \frac{\pi}{2}\right]}.$$

This, the pressure due to a finite source (of volume velocity Q_0), differs from that due to a point source of the same strength only by the presence of the factor $\frac{e^{j\left(\varphi_0-\frac{\pi}{2}\right)}}{\sqrt{1+k^2r_0^2}}$ and by the shift of reference point for the phase path from the origin to the surface of the sphere, i.e. using the effective radius $(r-r_0)$ in place of r.

The Radiation Impedance of a Pulsating Sphere

The total radial force exerted on the surface S of the sphere by the acoustic field surrounding it must be equal in magnitude to the force causing this surface to oscillate. The ratio of this force to the radial velocity of the surface is called the *mechanical impedance* or the *radiation impedance* (Z). Using equations (4-4) and (4-5), we get:

$$\begin{aligned} Z=\frac{Sp(r_0)}{q(r_0)}&=S\rho c\cos\varphi_0\cdot e^{j\varphi_0}= \\ &=S\rho c(\cos^2\varphi_0+j\cdot\sin\varphi_0\cdot\cos\varphi_0)= \\ &=S\rho c\left[\frac{k^2r_0^2}{1+k^2r_0^2}+j\frac{kr_0}{1+k^2r_0^2}\right]=R_0+jY_0= \\ &=S\rho c[R_0'+jY_0']. \end{aligned} \tag{4-9}$$

where R_0 and Y_0 respectively denote the *mechanical resistance and mechanical reactance* and R_0' and Y_0' denote *dimensionless resistance and reactance*. These quantities can be written in the form:

$$R_0=S\rho c R_0'=S\rho c\frac{k^2r_0^2}{1+k^2r_0^2}=\frac{\rho\omega^2S^2}{4\pi c}\cdot\frac{1}{1+k^2r_0^2}, \tag{4-10}$$

$$Y_0=S\rho c Y_0'=S\rho c\frac{kr_0}{1+k^2r_0^2}=\omega\frac{Sr_0\rho}{1+k^2r_0^2}=\omega\frac{3\left(\frac{4}{3}\pi r_0^3\rho\right)}{1+k^2r_0^2}=\omega M_0,$$

where $M_0=\frac{3M}{1+k^2r_0^2}$ and $M=\frac{4}{3}\pi r_0^3\rho$ is the mass of the medium displaced by the sphere.

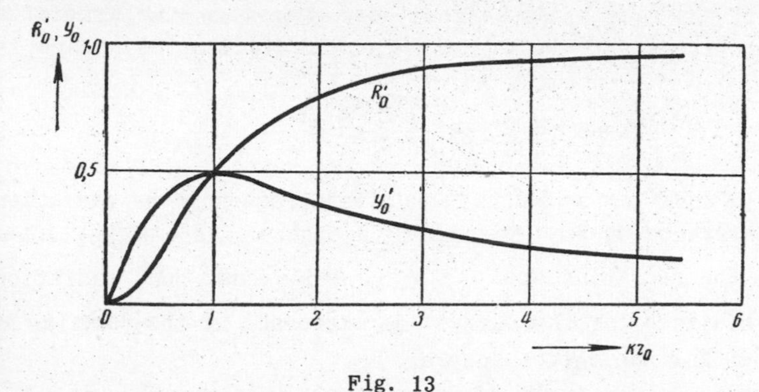

Fig. 13

The reactive component of the impedance has the effect of inertia and is analogous to the inductive reactance in an electrical circuit. For long waves ($\lambda \gg 2\pi r_0$ or $kr_0 \ll 1$)

$$R_0 \Big|_{kr \ll 1} \approx \frac{\rho\omega^2 S^2}{4\pi c} \text{ and } Y_0 \approx \omega 3\, M.$$

Figure 13 shows R'_0 and Y'_0 as a funtion of $kr_0 = \frac{2\pi r_0}{\lambda}$. At low frequencies (long waves) R_0 increases in proportion to ω^2 and S^2, whilst Y_0 increases in proportion to ω and r_0^3. Consequently, if $kr_0 \ll 1$, a spherical radiator will not be at all effective. As the frequency is increased R'_0 tends to unity, whilst $R_0 \to S\rho c$. If $kr_0 \gg 1$, a spherical pulsating surface radiates the same energy per unit area as a plane surface which vibrates in phase.

The conductance of a spherical radiator is equal to the reciprocal of the impedance. From expression (4-9) we get:

$$\frac{1}{Z} = \frac{1}{S\rho c}\,\frac{e^{-j\varphi_0}}{\cos\varphi_0} = \frac{1}{S\rho c} - j\,\frac{1}{S\rho c k r_0} = \frac{1}{S\rho c} + \frac{1}{j\omega M_0}.$$

It follows from this expression that a spherical pulsating radiator can be represented as having an active resistance $S\rho c$, which is connected in parallel with an inertance $j\omega M_0 = jkr_0 S\rho c$.

If the base of a spherical cone of area $S = \Omega r_0^2$ radiates into the solid angle Ω, then the radiation resistance is

$$(R_0)\text{segm} = \Omega r_0^2 \rho c \frac{k^2 r_0^2}{1 + k^2 r_0^2} = \frac{\rho \omega^2 S^2}{\Omega c} \cdot \frac{1}{1 + k^2 r_0^2}.$$

This equation shows that at a given frequency the radiation resistance of any segment of a sphere is proportional to the radiating area Ωr_0^2, and thus the radiation resistance for the segment is expressed by the same law as that for the entire sphere.

The reactive component will equal:

$$(Y_0)\text{segm} = \omega\, 3\left(\frac{S r_0 \rho}{3}\right) \cdot \frac{1}{1 + k^2 r_0^2} = \omega\, 3\left(\frac{\Omega r_0^3 \rho}{3}\right) \frac{1}{1 + k^2 r_0^2}.$$

Since $\frac{\Omega r_0^3 \rho}{3}$ is the mass of the medium displaced by the cone with base area $S = \Omega r_0^2$ on the sphere, it follows that the reactive component of impedance for the radiating cone of base area S is expressed by the same law as that for the entire sphere.

The Attached or Virtual Mass of a Pulsating Sphere

We will now consider the physical meaning of the quantity Y_0. Suppose we have an actual spherical shell of mass M', frictional resistance R' and stiffness E'. All these quantities will be regarded as the parameters of a mechanical oscillatory system of one degree of freedom; this degree of freedom is the displacement, a, of the shell normal to its surface.

With forced vibrations of the spherical shell under the force $\psi_0 e^{j\omega t}$ an acoustic field is formed in the surrounding medium which exerts a reaction on the surface equal to $-Sp(r_0)$. With this reaction included, the equation of motion of the shell is

$$M'\ddot{a}+R'\dot{a}+E'a=\psi_0 e^{j\omega t}-Sp(r_0).$$

From (4-9) and (4-10)

$$Sp(r_0)=(R_0+j\omega M_0)\cdot q(r_0).$$

Since for simple harmonic motion $\ddot{a}=j\omega\dot{a}$, and by virtue of the boundary condition $q(r_0)=\dot{a}$, we can replace $Sp(r_0)$ by $(R_0+j\omega M_0)\dot{a}$ and write the equation of motion thus:

$$(M'+M_0)\ddot{a}+(R'+R_0)\dot{a}+E'a=\psi_0 e^{j\omega t}. \qquad (4\text{-}11)$$

Thus as a result of the reaction of the acoustic field, there is apparently an additional mass M_0 added to the mass of the shell, and an additional resistance R_0 added to the frictional resistance.

The effective mass $M + M_0$ may be called the *effective mass;* the quantity M_0 we shall call the *attached mass*. The appearance of this additional mass due to the reaction of the radiation field is very important. Of course there is no new substance added to the shell itself. The additional mass represents the inertia of that portion of the surrounding medium which tends to be accelerated along with the shell. It appears only in accelerated motion; in uniform motion when $\ddot{a}=0$, it is absent.

Radiated Power

The energy crossing a spherical surface of radius r can be analysed in a more illuminating way if use is made of triogonometric functions of the wave argument $(\omega t-kr)$, in place of the complex expressions for p and q. The work done by the pressure on the surface of the sphere after an infinitesimal period of time dt is

$$pq\,dt=\frac{a}{r}\cos(\omega t-kr)\cdot\frac{u}{r\rho c\cos\varphi}\cos(\omega t-kr-\varphi)\,dt=$$

$$= \frac{a^2}{2r^2\rho c \cos\varphi}\Big[\cos(\omega t - kr)\cos(\omega t - kr)\cos\varphi +$$

$$+ \cos(\omega t - kr)\sin(\omega t - kr)\sin\varphi\Big]dt = \Big[\frac{a^2}{2r^2\rho c} +$$

$$\frac{a^2}{2r^2\rho c}\cos 2(\omega t - kr) + \frac{a^2\tan\varphi}{2r^2\rho c}\sin 2(\omega t - kr)\Big]dt.$$

The first two terms express the expenditure of power on the radiation of sound; the pressure and the active component of velocity in this case contain the same factor $\cos(\omega t - kr)$, i.e. they coincide in phase. The radiated power pulsates from zero to its maximum value $a^2/r^2\rho c$ at the double frequency 2ω. The third term (which gives a zero mean value per unit time) corresponds to the reactive power; the reactive component of the velocity contains the factor $\sin(\omega t - kr)$ and differs in phase from the pressure by $\pi/2$.

Using expression (4-5), we find the mean value of the work per unit area per unit time, i.e. the power crossing 1 cm^2, or the intensity of the sound:

$$J = \overline{pq} = \frac{a^2}{2r^2\rho c} = \frac{p^2_m}{2\rho c} = \rho c\cos^2\varphi\frac{q^2_m}{2} = \rho c\frac{k^2r^2}{1 + k^2r^2}\frac{q^2_m}{2}. \quad (4\text{-}12)$$

Thus, in a spherical wave, the intensity has the same dependence on the acoustic pressure amplitude p_m as in a plane wave, but has a more complicated dependence on the particle velocity amplitude q_m.

The expression for J can also be written in the form

$$J = \frac{1}{2}p_m q_m \cos\varphi,$$

which is similar to the expression for the power in an electrical circuit carrying alternating current.

The total power radiated by a sphere of radius r_0 is

$$\Pi = 4\pi r_0^2 J = \frac{4\pi a^2}{2\rho c} = S\rho c \frac{k^2 r_0^2}{1+k^2 r_0^2} \frac{q_m^2}{2} = R_0 \frac{q_m^2}{2} = R_0 q_e^2,$$

where R_0 is the mechanical (or radiation) resistance defined in (4-9). In this context it is clear that the quantity R_0 should be regarded as the *radiation resistance*. It should also be mentioned that the quantity J can be calculated from the complex expressions for p and q by using the formula:

$$J = \frac{1}{2} \operatorname{Re}(pq^*).$$

The third term in the expression for pq give zero when averaged over a period. However, the mean power per unit area crossing the surface of a sphere of radius r_0 during the quarter-period from

$$(\omega t - kr_0) = \frac{\pi}{2} \text{ to } (\omega t - kr_0) = 0 \text{ (or } t = \frac{r_0}{c} - \frac{T}{4} \text{ to } t = \frac{r_0}{c})$$

due to the third term, is seen to be

$$J' = \frac{a^2 \tan\varphi}{2r_0^2 \rho c} \cdot \frac{2}{\pi} = \frac{a^2}{\pi r_0^3 \rho\omega}.$$

The corresponding work done by the radiator on the medium during this time is

$$W_i = S J \frac{T}{4} = \frac{a^2}{\pi r_0^3 \rho\omega} 4\pi r_0^2 \frac{T}{4} = [3 \frac{4}{3} \pi r_0^3 \rho \sin^2\varphi_0] \frac{q_0^2}{2} = \frac{1}{2} M_0 q_0^2.$$

This quantity is the kinetic energy of a mass M_0 (attached mass) having the same velocity amplitude q_0 as the surface of the sphere. Thus, the reactive work performed by the radiator in the first quarter period is expended on creating the kinetic energy $\frac{1}{2} M_0 q_0^2$. During the next quarter period $r_0/c = 0$ to $t = r_0/c + T/4$ the corresponding power pq will still be the same, but opposite in sign. This implies that the kinetic energy stored by the attached mass during the first quarter period is given back to the radiator during the next quarter period.

From this it is clear that the power associated with the component of velocity which lags 90° behind the pressure is the reactive power analogous to the power consumed by an inductance in an a.c. circuit.

The kinetic energy associated with the reactive velocity component can be regarded as the sum of the reactive kinetic energies of all the elements of the medium surrounding the radiator, i.e. the kinetic energies associated with the reactive components of the velocities of the elements, which diminish with increasing distance from the surface of the radiator (see Chapter VIII).

A pulsating sphere is a good approximation for calculating the acoustic field of any source of pulsating type provided that the wavelength is considerably greater than the dimensions of the source. In this case the diffraction phenomena lead to uniform distribution of the radiation on all sides, no matter what the shape of the pulsating source. For example, the radiation of a telephone receiver diaphragm, one side of which is enclosed and unable to radiate sound, is of a pulsating type. Another example is the siren, where air is intermittently expelled through a number of holes. Whenever $kD \ll 1$ (D is a typical linear dimension of the radiating element), we can calculate the radiation on the assumption that $A_0 \approx Q_0$, where Q_0 is the volume velocity of the pulsating source. The vibration of a telephone diaphragm is non-uniform since its amplitude increases from the edge to the centre. In such a case

$Q_0 = \int\limits_S q(r)dS$, where the integration is performed over the entire surface of the membrane. For sirens Q_0 will be the total volume flow through all the holes, i.e. the volume of air discharged per second. In all these cases the radiated power can be estimated by the formula:

$$\Pi = \frac{\rho\omega^2}{4\pi c} \cdot \frac{Q_0^2}{2}.$$

Acoustic Dipole and Oscillating Sphere

Suppose that two point sources of identical strength but opposite in phase lie on the z axis at a distance apart δz, which is very small compared with the wavelength. The first is situated at the origin and the second a distance δz away (Fig. 14). The acoustic pressure created by the first source at the point P, which is a distance r away and at a polar angle ϑ, is denoted by p_1; the pressure created by the second source at the same point will be equal and opposite in sign to the pressure created by the first at the point P' which lies a distance δz above P, i.e.

$$p_2 = -\left(p_1 + \frac{\partial p_1}{\partial z}\delta z\right).$$

The total pressure at the point P is then:

$$p = p_1 + p_2 = -\frac{\partial p_1}{\partial z}\delta z = -\frac{\partial p_1}{\partial r}\delta z \cdot \cos\vartheta.$$

Defining p_1 in the form $p_1 = \frac{a}{r} e^{-jkr} \cdot e^{j\omega t}$, we get:

$$p = \frac{a\delta z}{r^2}(1 + jkr)\cos\vartheta \cdot e^{j(\omega t - kr)}. \qquad (4\text{-}13)$$

A source of this type is called a *dipole source* and the quantity $a\delta z = b$ is called the *dipole moment*.

In the *near field*, where $kr \ll 1$.

$$p \approx \frac{b \cos \vartheta}{r^2} e^{j\omega t},$$

Hence, it will be seen that the pressure is in phase at all points and the progressive wave character of the field disappears. It is important to point out that the motion in the near field is similar to motion in an incompressible fluid. In fact, for an incompressible fluid $\varkappa = \infty$ and $c = \infty$, and, consequently $k = \frac{\omega}{c} = 0$. Since $c = \infty$, it follows that all fluctuations take place simultaneously throughout space and that there can be no waves. Consequently, the character of the oscillations in the near field can be studied on the assumption that the medium is incompressible.

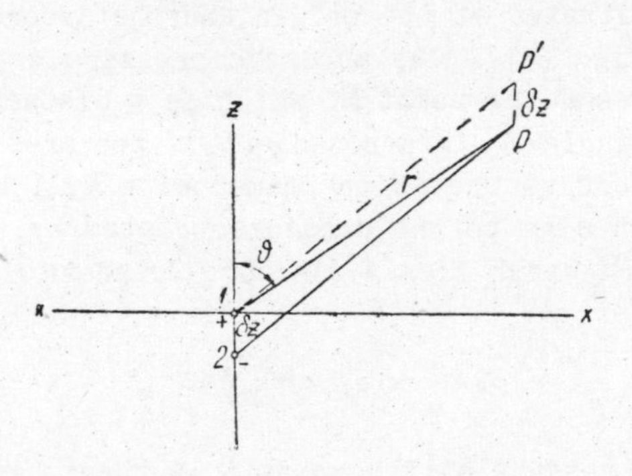

Fig. 14

In the near field of the dipole the radial and tangential particle velocities q_r and q_ϑ are, respectively:

$$q_r = -\frac{1}{j\omega\rho} \cdot \frac{\partial p}{\partial r} = 2b \frac{\cos \vartheta}{j\omega\rho r^3} e^{j\omega t} = \frac{dr}{dt},$$

$$q_\vartheta = -\frac{1}{j\omega\rho} \frac{\partial p}{r \partial \vartheta} = b \frac{\sin \vartheta}{j\omega\rho r^3} e^{j\omega t} = \frac{r d\vartheta}{dt}.$$

The particle velocity diminishes inversely as r^3, i.e.

considerably more quickly than the pressure. Dividing q_r by q_ϑ and multiplying by $d\vartheta$, we get the differential equation of the stream lines:

$$\frac{dr}{r} = 2\frac{\cos\vartheta}{\sin\vartheta}d\vartheta = 2\frac{d(\sin\vartheta)}{\sin\vartheta}.$$

The solution of this equation has the form $\ln r = \ln(\sin^2\vartheta) + \ln C$ or

$$r = C\sin^2\vartheta, \qquad (4\text{-}14)$$

where C is an arbitrary constant which is the parameter of the family of streamline curves. Figure 15 shows these curves for various values of C. The oscillation of a particle at a particular point in space takes place along the tangent to the streamline through that point.

At great distances from the radiator the acoustic pressure is

$$p \approx jk\frac{b}{r}\cos\vartheta\, e^{j(\omega t - kr)},$$

and the radial particle velocity is

$$q_r = -\frac{\frac{\partial p}{\partial r}}{j\omega\rho} = \frac{b\cos\vartheta}{\rho c r^2}(1 + jkr)e^{j(\omega t - kr)} \approx jk\frac{b\cos\vartheta}{\rho c r}e^{j(\omega t - kr)}. \qquad (4\text{-}15)$$

Consequently, in the distant field (or radiation field) p and q_r diminish inversely as r and are in the same phase. The directivity characteristic of the dipole (the ratio $p(\vartheta)/p(0)$ at the same distance r) is just the function $\cos\vartheta$ and has the shape of a figure eight (Fig. 16). Intensity is greatest along the axis of the dipole (the z axis); no radiation occurs in the direction transverse to the axis (in the equatorial plane), since

$$p\left(\frac{\pi}{2}\right) = q_r\left(\frac{\pi}{2}\right) = 0.$$

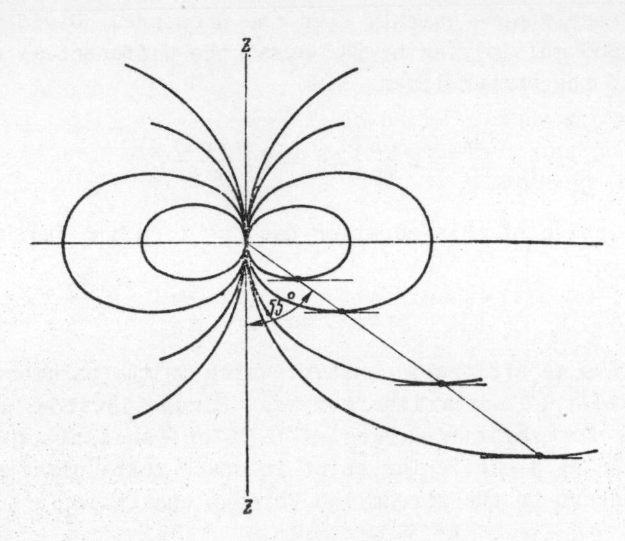

Fig. 15

We can show that a sphere of radius r_0 which oscillates along the z axis at a velocity $q_0 e^{j\omega t}$, creates an acoustic field identical to the radiation field of the dipole (4-13). This must be true if the radial component of the velocity in the dipole acoustic field is equal, at $r = r_0$, to the given radial velocity $q_0 \cos\vartheta \cdot e^{j\omega t}$:

$$q_0 \cos\vartheta = -\frac{\left.\frac{\partial p}{\partial r}\right|_{r=r_0}}{j\omega\rho} = \frac{be^{-jkr_0}}{j\omega\rho r_0^3}\left[(2 - k^2r_0^2) + j2kr_0\right]\cos\vartheta .$$

This boundary condition enables us to find b:

$$b = \frac{j\omega\rho e^{jkr_0}\cdot r_0^3}{(2-k^2r_0^2)+j2kr_0}\cdot q_0 = \frac{\omega\rho r_0^3}{\sqrt{4+k^4r_0^4}}\, q_0 e^{j\left(kr_0 - \varphi_1 + \frac{\pi}{2}\right)},$$

$$\text{where } \tan\varphi_1 = \frac{2kr_0}{2 - k^2r_0^2}$$

Thus, the field of a dipole with this moment b gives the same distribution of radial velocity on the surface of a sphere of radius r_0 as does the oscillatory motion of the whole sphere at a velocity $q_0 e^{j\omega t}$. There is no need to require equality between the tangential component of velocity $q_0 \sin\vartheta \cdot e^{j\omega t}$ and the tangential component of the field on the surface, because we have an ideal medium without friction.

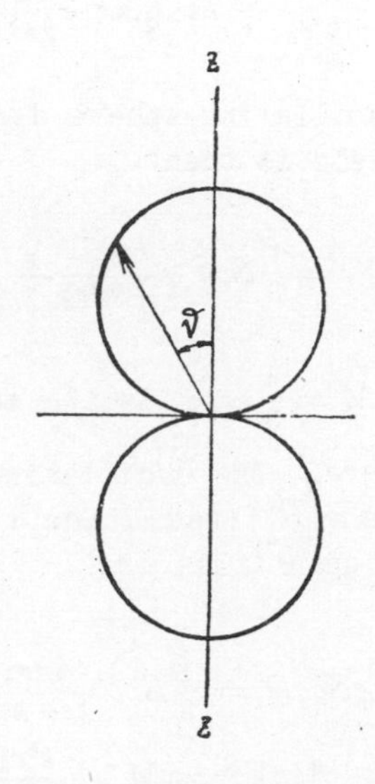

Fig. 16

Substituting the value b in formula (4-13) and assuming that $r=r_0$, we get for the pressure on the surface of the sphere

$$p(r_0)=\rho c \cdot kr_0 \frac{k^3 r_0^3 + j(2+k^2 r_0^2)}{4+k^4 r_0^4} q_0 \cos\vartheta \cdot e^{j\omega t}.$$

The Impedance of an Oscillating Sphere

The force on the whole sphere is obtained from the expression

$$F=\int_0^\pi p(r_0)\cos\vartheta\cdot 2\pi r_0^2\sin\vartheta\cdot d\vartheta=$$

$$=2\pi r_0^2\rho c k r_0\frac{k^3r_0^3+j(2+k^2r_0^2)}{4+k^4r_0^4}q_0\int_0^\pi\cos^2\vartheta d(\cos\vartheta)=$$

$$=\left[\frac{1}{3}4\pi r_0^2\rho c\frac{k^4r_0^4}{4+k^4r_0^4}+j\omega\left(\frac{4}{3}\pi r_0^3\rho\right)\frac{2+k^2r_0^2}{4+k^4r_0^4}\right]\cdot q_0.$$

The impedance of an oscillating sphere due to the reaction of the surrounding field is then:

$$Z_1=\frac{F}{q_0}=R_1+jY_1=\frac{1}{3}S\rho c\frac{k^4r_0^4}{4+k^4r_0^4}+j\omega M\frac{2+k^2r_0^2}{4+k^4r_0^4},$$

where $S=4\pi r_0^2$ and $M=\frac{4}{3}\pi r_0^3\rho$ is the mass of the medium displaced by the sphere. The oscillating sphere will experience a resistance R_1 (radiation resistance) and a reactance Y_1. These quantities are:

$$\left.\begin{aligned}R_1&=\frac{1}{3}S\rho cR_1'=\frac{1}{3}S\rho c\frac{k^4r_0^4}{4+k^4r_0^4},\\ Y_1&=\frac{1}{3}S\rho cY_1'=\omega M\frac{2+k^2r_0^2}{4+k^2r_0^4}.\end{aligned}\right\}\qquad(4\text{-}16)$$

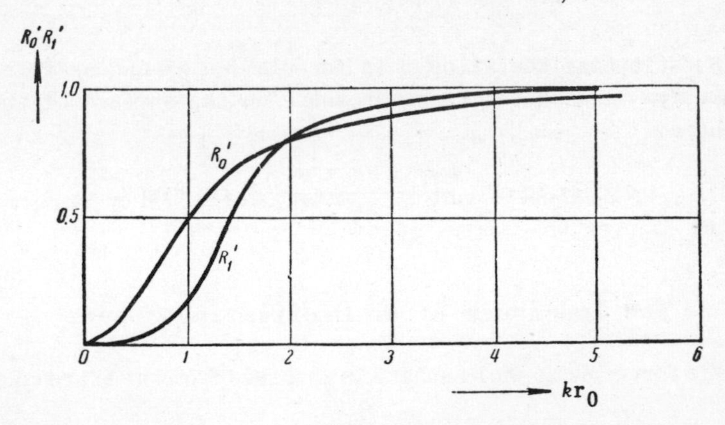

Fig. 17

The reactance can be ascribed to the effect of the additional attached mass:

$$M_1 = M\frac{2+k^2r_0^2}{4+k^4r_0^4}. \tag{4-16a}$$

For long waves ($kr_0 \ll 1$)

$$R_1 = \frac{1}{3}S\rho c\cdot\frac{k^4r_0^4}{4} = \frac{\rho\omega^4S^3}{192\pi^2c^3},$$

$$Y_1 = \omega\frac{M}{2} = \omega\frac{2}{3}\pi r_0^3\rho.$$

In the region of long waves the radiation resistance of an oscillating sphere increases in proportion to ω^4 and S^3 (for a pulsating sphere in proportion to ω^2 and S^2), whilst the attached mass is $M/2$ (instead of $3M$ for a pulsating sphere).

In the region of short waves, ($kr_0 \gg 1$) $R_1 \to \frac{1}{3}S\rho c$, and $M_1 \approx \frac{1}{k^2r_0^2} \to 0$. The radiation resistances R_0' and R_1' are compared in Fig. 17.

Sound Intensity in the Field of an Oscillating Sphere

The sound intensity in the radial direction is:

$$J_1 = \overline{pq_r} = \frac{1}{2}\operatorname{Re}(pq_r^*) = \frac{1}{2}\frac{|b|^2k^2\cos^2\vartheta}{\rho cr^2} = \\ = \frac{1}{2}\rho c\left(\frac{r_0}{r}\right)^2\frac{k^4r_0^4}{4+k^4r_0^4}\cos^2\vartheta . q_0^2. \tag{4-17}$$

The total (global) radiated power is obtained by integrating J_1 over the entire sphere:

$$\Pi_1 = \int_0^\pi 2\pi r^2\sin\vartheta\cdot J_1 d\vartheta = \frac{1}{3}S\rho c\frac{k^4r_0^4}{4+k^4r_0^4}q_0^2 = \\ = \frac{1}{2}R_1q_0^2 = R_1q_e^2. \tag{4-17a}$$

Thus it is seen that the resistance R_1 is due to the energy loss by radiation.

The radial component of the particle velocity q_r is found by differentiating the quantity $\frac{p}{j\omega\rho}$ with respect to r:

$$q_r = -\frac{\frac{dp}{dr}}{j\omega\rho} = -j\frac{b\cos\vartheta}{\omega\rho r^3}\left[(2-k^2r^2)+j2kr\right]e^{j(\omega t-kr)} = \\ = -j\frac{b\cos\vartheta}{\omega\rho r^3}\sqrt{4+k^4r^4}\cdot e^{j\varphi_1}\cdot e^{j(\omega t-kr)}, \tag{4-18}$$

where $\tan\varphi_1 = \frac{2kr}{2-k^2r^2}$.

The tangential component of the particle velocity is

$$q_\vartheta = -\frac{\frac{dp}{rd\vartheta}}{j\omega\rho} = -j\frac{b\sin\vartheta}{\omega\rho r^3}(1+jkr)\sin\vartheta e^{j(\omega t-kr)} = \\ = -j\frac{b\sin\vartheta}{\omega\rho r^3}\sqrt{1+k^2r^2}\cdot e^{j\varphi_2}\cdot e^{j(\omega t-kr)}, \tag{4-19}$$

where $\tan\varphi_2 = kr$.

It is seen, by comparing this expression with (4-13), that q_ϑ is 90° behind p in phase. Consequently, the energy flow in the tangential direction, $J_\vartheta = \frac{1}{2}\mathrm{Re}(pq_\vartheta^*)$, is zero.

The intensity $J = \frac{1}{2}\frac{p_m^2}{\rho c}$ for a spherical wave from a uniformly pulsating sphere is of the same form as for a plane wave. The intensity created by an oscillating sphere cannot be expressed so simply. In fact, using expressions (4-13) and (4-17), we get:

$$J_1 = \frac{1}{2}\frac{|p_m|^2}{\rho c}\frac{k^2r^2}{1+k^2r^2}.$$

Only if $kr \gg 1$ (in the distant field) is the sound intensity given by $J_1 \approx \frac{1}{2} \frac{|p_m|^2}{\rho c}$. The expression for the intensity of a uniformly pulsating sphere as a function of the velocity amplitude q_m (see formula (4-12)), is identical with the similar expression for a plane wave if $kr \gg 1$. There is no difficulty in showing that for an oscillating sphere

$$J_1 = \frac{1}{2} \rho c \frac{k^4 r_0^4}{4 + k^4 r_0^4} \left| q_m \right|^2. \tag{4-20}$$

If $kr \gg 1$ then $J_1 \approx \frac{1}{2} \rho c \left| q_m \right|^2$.

Special Features of the Acoustic Field of an Oscillating Sphere

The acoustic field of an oscillating sphere (dipole) contains a tangential component of particle velocity, shifted in phase relative to the radial component (see formulae (4-18) and (4-19)), which causes the particles to move along elliptical trajectories and not along straight lines. Only in the direction of the axis ($\vartheta = 0, \pi$) and in the equatorial direction $\left(\vartheta = \frac{\pi}{2}\right)$ are the trajectories always straight lines parallel to the axis of the dipole; at intermediate values of ϑ the trajectories are elliptical. Figure 18 shows the form of the trajectories of the particles at various angles ϑ to the axis of the dipole and for various values of kr, namely, $kr \ll 1$, $kr = 2$ and $kr \gg 1$. The scale of amplitudes (for each value of kr) has been selected so that if $\vartheta = 0$ identical values of velocity amplitude are obtained for all values of kr; thus, a decrease in amplitude with increase in r is not taken into account on the diagram. If $kr \ll 1$ and $kr \gg 1$ the trajectories become rectilinear at all angles ϑ, but in the first case the direction of the oscillations does not coincide with the radial direction (except at the angle $\vartheta=0$), whilst in the second case there is coincidence at all angles. For values of kr of the order of unity, the trajectories acquire a distinct elliptical shape at angles ϑ between 20° and 70°, and can become circles. It follows from formulae (4-18) and (4-19) that the ratio of amplitudes of the radial and tangential velocities is:

$$\frac{|q_r|}{|q_\vartheta|}=\frac{\sqrt{4+k^4r^4}}{\sqrt{1+k^2r^2}}\cot\vartheta,$$

whilst the tangent of the phase angle between them is

$$\tan(\varphi_1-\varphi_2)=\frac{k^3r^3}{2+k^2r^2}.$$

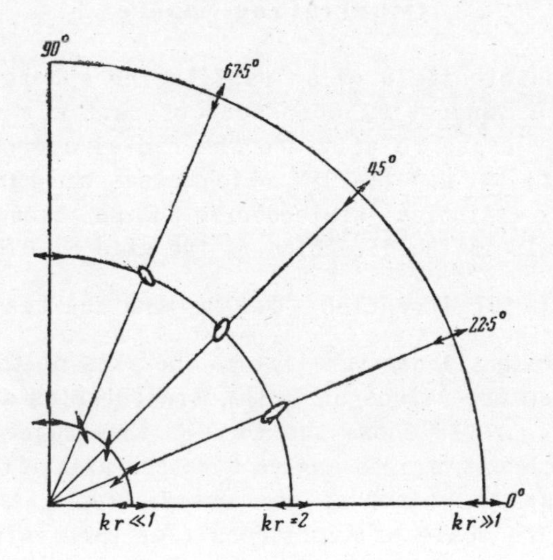

Fig. 18

This circumstance is important from the point of view of acoustic measurements. If a measurement is taken in the near field, the use of a receiver which reacts to the particle velocity, such as a Rayleigh disc or a ribbon microphone, cannot give correct results in general, since the tip of the particle velocity vector does not maintain a constant direction during a period, but describes a certain ellipse. Measurements at $\vartheta = 0$ or π are possible, but the intensity must be calculated from the measured velocity by the exact formula (4-20). If the measurement is taken at $\vartheta = \frac{\pi}{2}$, then by putting $\sin\vartheta = 1$, we can calculate $|b|$ by formula (4-19) and hence find the intensity of sound in any direction by formula (4-17).

The acoustic field of an oscillating sphere can be used as an approximation in studying the acoustic properties of various radiators of a similar type such as plates, bars, etc., oscillating in free space. It is typical of such systems that the velocity along the normal on one side of the body is opposite to the velocity on the other. This leads to a short circuit of the streamlines and greatly decreases the efficiency of the radiator when the dimensions of the body are small compared with the wavelength. Thus, at low frequencies all radiators of the oscillation type are ineffective. In order to increase the output of diaphragm-type loudspeakers, a large screen, or baffle, is provided which reduces the short circuiting of the streamlines; the baffle in effect increases the parameter kr_0.

The directivity characteristic curve of oscillating-type radiators in free-field is always a figure eight.

CHAPTER V

PROPAGATION OF SOUND IN A STRAIGHT TUBE OF CONSTANT CROSS-SECTION

The Propagation of Sound in a Tube

Straight tubes of constant cross-section are components of nearly all sound conductors in practical use. The laws governing sound propagation in such systems are therefore very important in the solution of many experimental problems in acoustics. We will assume that the side walls of our tube are absolutely rigid and non-heat-conducting. The assumption of walls having elasticity and thermal conductivity considerably complicates the solution of the problem. These factors result in additional attenuation of the sound through transfer of oscillatory energy to the wall and cause distortion of the plane wavefront. A simplified analysis of the effects of internal friction in a gas (or fluid) filling the tube can be made on the assumption that the particle velocity $\dot{\xi}$ is the same over the entire cross-section (i.e. assuming a plane wave) and that the friction is proportional to this velocity. In fact, if the viscosity is slight, the velocity is almost constant over the entire cross-section, decreasing rapidly only in the narrow boundary layer near the wall. Finally, it is assumed that the diameter of the tube is considerably less than the wavelength. When these conditions are satisfied non-uniformity of velocity over the section of the tube, even if it arises, is rapidly balanced out and the wave becomes plane (see Chapter VI).

In a tube of section S we consider a small element of volume $S\Delta x = \Delta v$ bounded by two planes with coordinates x_1 and $x_2 = x_1 + \Delta x$, which are transverse to the axis of the tube, it being assumed that $\Delta x \ll \lambda$. Upon being traversed by a sound wave, the layer of particles with the coordinate x_1 is shifted by a quantity ξ, and that with the coordinate x_2 by $\xi + \frac{\partial \xi}{\partial x}\Delta x$. The volume of the element which contains all the particles which were found earlier between x_1 and x_2, is:

$$S\left(x_2 + \xi + \frac{\partial \xi}{\partial x}\Delta x\right) - S\left(x_1 + \xi\right) = S\Delta x + S\frac{\partial \xi}{\partial x}\Delta x =$$
$$= S\left(1 + \frac{\partial \xi}{\partial x}\right)\Delta x = \Delta v + \delta v = \Delta v\left(1 + \frac{\delta v}{\Delta v}\right).$$

The relative change in volume (strain) is

$$\frac{\delta v}{\Delta v} = \frac{\partial \xi}{\partial x} = -\frac{\delta \rho}{\rho_0}.$$

This expression is equivalent to the equation of continuity (see Chapter I).

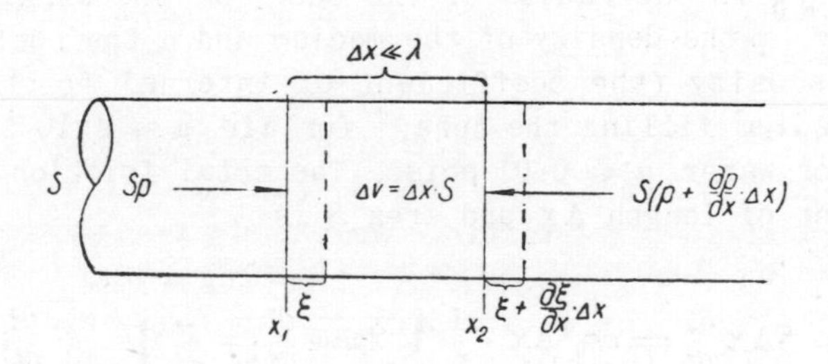

Fig. 19

Suppose we form the equation of motion of the element Δv. As in the derivation of the fundamental equations of acoustics, instead of the total acceleration $\frac{d\dot{\xi}}{dt}$, we only take the local acceleration $\frac{\partial \dot{\xi}}{\partial t} = \ddot{\xi}$, on the assumption that the particle velocity and its gradient are small. The reaction arising due to the inertia of the element is then

$$\rho\Delta x S\frac{\partial\dot{\xi}}{\partial t}=\rho S\Delta x\frac{\partial^2\xi}{\partial t^2}.$$

The friction is assumed to be proportional to the velocity $\frac{\partial\xi}{\partial t}$:

$$r_1 S\Delta x\frac{\partial\xi}{\partial t}.$$

The quantity r_1 is the coefficient of friction calculated per unit area and per unit length of the tube. For tubes with a diameter which is slightly less than the wavelength, but all the same not too small (in practice not less than 0·5-1 cm), we get on the basis of the investigations of Stokes and Helmholtz

$$r_1=\frac{1}{r_0}\sqrt{2\rho\mu\omega}, \tag{5-1}$$

where r_0 is the radius of the tube, ω the angular frequency, ρ the density of the medium and μ the coefficient of viscosity (the coefficient of internal friction) of the medium filling the tube; for air $\mu\approx 2\times10^{-4}$ poise, and for water $\mu\approx 0{\cdot}01$ poise. The total friction for the element of length Δx and area S is

$$r_1\ S\Delta x\frac{\partial\xi}{\partial t}=\pi r_0^2\Delta x\cdot\frac{1}{r_0}\sqrt{2\rho\mu\omega}\frac{\partial\xi}{\partial t}=\bar{S}\sqrt{\frac{\rho\mu\omega}{2}}\frac{\partial\xi}{\partial t}, \tag{5-2}$$

i.e. it is proportional to the "curved" surface of the element

$$\bar{S}=2\pi r_0\,\Delta x.$$

For capillary tubes the relationship (5-1) is no longer valid and the coefficient of friction is determined in accordance with Poiseuille's law

$$r_1 = \frac{8\mu}{r_0^2}. \tag{5-3}$$

Thus, for capillary tubes the value of the total coefficient of friction, which is equal to $R = \pi r_0^2 \Delta x r_1 = 8\pi\mu\Delta x$, is independent of the radius of the tube r_0 and the frequency ω; the derivation of formulae (5-1) and (5-3) is given in chapter VII on acoustic waveguides.

If the walls of the tube are good heat conductors, then an effective coefficient of viscosity μ' can be used, which is larger than μ owing to the energy loss on heat transfer,

$$\sqrt{\mu'} = \sqrt{\mu}\left[1 + (\gamma - 1)\left(\frac{\nu}{\mu c_p}\right)^{1/2}\right],$$

where $\gamma = \frac{c_p}{c_v}$, and ν is the coefficient of thermal conductivity of the gas in the tube.

The external force acting on the element Δv, is the resultant of the pressure forces on the bases of the cylinder of area S and length Δx; the side pressures are mutually compensated. The total external fluctuating force on the element Δv is

$$Sp - S\left(p + \frac{\partial p}{\partial x}\Delta x\right) = -S\frac{\partial p}{\partial x}\Delta x.$$

By virtue of our assumptions (including that of small amplitudes) it can be assumed that the disturbance in the tube is an adiabatic process so that the following relationship is satisfied

$$p = -\varkappa\frac{\delta v}{\Delta v} = -\varkappa\frac{\partial \xi}{\partial x}. \tag{5-4}$$

For a gas the bulk modulus is $\varkappa = \gamma P_0$, where P_0 is the static pressure.

Thus, the total force due to the pressures on the element ΔV is

$$S\varkappa \frac{\partial^2 \xi}{\partial x^2} \Delta x.$$

Taking into account both frictional and pressure forces, we get the equation of motion

$$\rho S \Delta x \frac{\partial^2 \xi}{\partial t^2} + r_1 S \Delta x \frac{\partial \xi}{\partial t} = \varkappa S \Delta x \frac{\partial^2 \xi}{\partial x^2}$$

or, cancelling $S\Delta x$,

$$\rho \frac{\partial^2 \xi}{\partial t^2} + r_1 \frac{\partial \xi}{\partial t} = \varkappa \frac{\partial^2 \xi}{\partial x^2}. \quad (5\text{-}5)$$

Differentiating equation (5-5) with respect to t, we multiply by S under the differentiation sign and then multiply the whole equation by S. If we put $S\dot{\xi} = \dot{X}$, for the volume velocity (current), we get the equation of motion in the form:

$$M_1 \frac{\partial^2 \dot{X}}{\partial t^2} + R_1 \frac{\partial \dot{X}}{\partial t} - K_1 \frac{\partial^2 \dot{X}}{\partial x^2} = 0, \quad (5\text{-}6)$$

where

$$M_1 = \rho S, \quad R_1 = r_1 S \text{ and } K_1 = \varkappa S.$$

The quantity K_1 is the coefficient of elasticity, M_1 the mass, and R_1 the coefficient of friction. All of these quantities are calculated per unit length of the tube. Equation (5-6) is similar to the equation of propagation of waves in an electric line, the telegraph equation:

$$L_1 \frac{\partial^2 i}{\partial t^2} + R_1 \frac{\partial i}{\partial t} - \frac{1}{C_1} \frac{\partial^2 i}{\partial x^2} = 0 . \quad (5\text{-}7)$$

The volume velocity $\dot{X}$ in equation (5-6) is analogous to the current i in equation (5-7), the mass M_1 is analogous to the inductance per unit length of the line L_1, the coefficient of friction R_1 is analogous to the resistance R_1 per unit length of the line, and the coefficient of elasticity K_1 is analogous to the reciprocal of the capacitance per unit length of the line $\frac{1}{C_1}$. Consider a solution of equation (5-5) in the form of a progressive sinusoidal wave:

$$\frac{\partial \xi}{\partial t} = \dot{\xi} = \dot{\xi}_0 e^{j\omega\left(t \mp \frac{x}{c_1}\right)}, \tag{5-8}$$

where c_1 is a certain, as yet, unknown quantity which represents the phase velocity. Since $\ddot{\xi} = j\dot{\xi}\omega$ and $\xi = \frac{\dot{\xi}}{j\omega}$, it follows that by substituting (5-8) in formula (5-5) we get, after cancelling $\dot{\xi}_0 e^{j\omega\left(t \mp \frac{x}{c_1}\right)}$:

$$j\omega\rho + r_1 = j\frac{\varkappa\omega}{c_1^2}, \tag{5-8a}$$

or

$$\frac{1}{c_1^2} = \frac{\rho}{\varkappa} - j\frac{r_1}{\omega\varkappa} = \frac{\rho}{\varkappa}\left(1 - j\frac{r_1}{\omega\rho}\right) = \frac{1}{c^2}(1 - j2\varphi),$$

where c is the speed of sound in the medium, and

$$2\varphi = \frac{r_1}{\omega\rho}.$$

Rough calculations show that in the region of audio frequencies $\varphi \ll 1$ for tubes with diameters greater than 1 cm. For tubes filled with air, $\varphi \approx \frac{0{\cdot}12}{r_0\sqrt{f}}$, whence if $f = 100$ c/s and $r_0 = 1$ cm $\varphi \approx 0{\cdot}012$. The quantity c_1 which is found from the above equation has a complex value. Suppose

$$j\frac{\omega}{c_1} = j\frac{\omega}{c}\sqrt{1 - j2\varphi} = \beta + j\alpha = \gamma. \tag{5-8b}$$

After squaring we have

$$\frac{\omega^2}{c^2}(1-j2\varphi)=\alpha^2-\beta^2-j2\alpha\beta.$$

By equating real and imaginary parts it is found that

$$\alpha=k\left|\frac{\sqrt{1+\sqrt{1+4\varphi^2}}}{\sqrt{2}}\right| \text{ and } \beta=k\varphi\left|\frac{\sqrt{2}}{\sqrt{1+\sqrt{1+4\varphi^2}}}\right|.$$

The formula for the wave (5-8) takes the form:

$$\dot{\xi}=\dot{\xi}_0 e^{j\omega t}e^{\mp\gamma x}=\dot{\xi}_0 e^{j(\omega t\mp\alpha x)}\cdot e^{\mp\beta x}. \qquad (5\text{-}9)$$

The quantity $\gamma=\beta+j\alpha$ is known as the *propagation constant*. The real part β of this constant characterizes the attenuation of the wave amplitude per unit path length and is known as the *damping factor*. It follows from formula (5-9) that the wave is damped by a factor of $e^{\beta x}$ on a section of length x. In the theory of electrical lines damping is conventionally expressed in a natural logarithmic unit which is called a *neper*. It is said that the damping amounts to βx neper or β neper per unit length. Since $e^{\beta x}=10^{0\cdot 43\beta x}$, it follows that the damping can be given in common logarithmic units. The amplitude damping on the section x is $0\cdot 43\,\beta x$ logarithmic units or $20\times 0\cdot 43\beta x=8\cdot 6\beta x$ dB, i.e. the attenuation in decibels is obtained by multiplying the attenuation in nepers by 8·6.

The imaginary part (α) of the propagation constant is known in line theory as the *phase constant*. It can be seen from formula (5-9) that this quantity is analogous to the wave number, but corresponds to a speed of propagation c_1 rather than c. In wide tubes r_1 (and likewise α) depends on the frequency. Thus, dispersion will occur and an acoustic pulse will change shape on propagation. A similar situation is produced if the medium filling the tube possesses great viscosity.

If the quantity $\varphi = \frac{r_1}{2\omega\rho} \ll 1$, then

$$\alpha \approx k\left|\frac{\sqrt{1+(1+2\varphi^2)}}{\sqrt{2}}\right| = k\sqrt{1+\varphi^2} \approx \frac{\omega}{c\left(1-\frac{\varphi^2}{2}\right)} \approx k.$$

If damping is present, the phase velocity is

$$c' = \frac{\omega}{\alpha} \approx c\left(1-\frac{\varphi^2}{2}\right),$$

i.e. it is near to c but slightly smaller.

If $\varphi \ll 1$, the damping factor is approximately

$$\beta \approx \frac{k\varphi}{1+\frac{\varphi^2}{2}} \approx k\varphi = \frac{r_1}{2\rho c}. \tag{5-10}$$

The damping per wavelength is:

$$\beta' = k\varphi\lambda \approx 2\pi\varphi = \frac{\pi r_1}{\omega\rho} = \frac{r_1}{2\rho f}.$$

Unlike damping in a free medium, where, according to Stokes, $\beta = \frac{2\mu f^2}{3\rho c^3}$, it is found in tubes of large diameter for which $r_1 \sim \sqrt{f}$, that there is an additional damping $\beta \sim \sqrt{f}$. The total damping will therefore be greater than Stokes' value. However, β is independent of frequency in capillary tubes where $r_1 = \frac{8\mu}{r_0^2}$.

Using equation (5-5) in which the right-hand side in accordance with formula (5-4) is replaced by $-\frac{\partial p}{\partial x}$, we get the pressure $p(x,t)$:

$$p(x,t) = -\int \rho \frac{\partial \dot{\xi}}{\partial t} dx - r_1 \int \dot{\xi} dx + C(t) =$$

$$= -\bar{\rho} \int \frac{\partial \dot{\xi}}{\partial t} dx - r_1 \int \dot{\xi} dx + C(t),$$

where $C(t)$ is an arbitrary function of time, and the average density $\bar{\rho}$ can be assumed equal to the static density ρ at small amplitudes. Substituting (for a forward wave)

$$\dot{\xi}=\dot{\xi}_0 e^{-\gamma x}\cdot e^{j\omega t} \text{ and } \frac{\partial\dot{\xi}}{\partial t}=j\omega\dot{\xi}_0 e^{-\gamma x}\cdot e^{j\omega t}$$

and integrating with respect to x, we find

$$p(x,t)=\dot{\xi}_0\frac{e^{-\gamma x}\cdot e^{j\omega t}}{\gamma}(r_1+j\omega\rho)+C(t).$$

If $\omega=0$ there is no acoustic wave and p and $\dot{\xi}$ are zero. Consequently, $C(t)$ is zero.

If losses are negligible ($\varphi\ll 1$), then by using (5-8a) and (5-8b) we get:

$$p(x,t)=\dot{\xi}\,\frac{j\omega x}{c_1^2}\cdot\frac{c_1}{j\omega}=\dot{\xi}\,\frac{x}{c_1}=\dot{\xi}\,\rho c\sqrt{1-j2\varphi}\approx\rho c\dot{\xi}e^{-j\varphi}, \quad (5\text{-}11)$$

whence it can be seen that the pressure lags behind the particle velocity in phase by the angle φ. In accordance with equation (5-10) this phase difference is related to the damping factor per cm (β) by the expression $\varphi\approx\frac{\beta}{k}=\frac{\beta}{2\pi}\lambda$, and to the damping factor per wavelength (β') by the expression $\varphi=\frac{\beta'}{2\pi}$.

If there is negligible attenuation there is no appreciable error in assuming that

$$\begin{aligned} p&=\rho c\dot{\xi} \text{ for a forward wave,} \\ p&=-\rho c\dot{\xi} \text{ for a reverse wave,} \end{aligned} \quad (5\text{-}12)$$

as in a frictionless medium. The attenuation is taken into account by the real part in the expression for γ.

In order to calculate the energy flow, it is necessary to know the phase difference between p and $\dot{\xi}$, since the expression for intensity has the form

$$J = \frac{1}{2}\,\mathrm{Re}\,(p\dot{\xi}^*) = \frac{1}{2}\,p_0\dot{\xi}_0 \cos\varphi \cdot e^{-2\beta x},$$

where p_0 and $\dot{\xi}_0$ are the amplitudes of the acoustic pressure and the particle velocity of the medium at the point $x = 0$.*

Propagation of Sound in a Tube of Finite Length

If we have a piston of impedance Z_0 at the entry of the tube, driven by the force $\psi_0 e^{j\omega t}$, and if the tube is closed part way down at the point l by another piston with impedance Z_l (Fig. 20), then at the two ends of the tube we have:

	$x=0$	$x=l$
Impedance of piston	Z_0	Z_l
External force	$\psi = \psi_0 e^{j\omega t}$	0
Velocity	$\dot{\xi}_0 e^{j\omega t}$	$\dot{\xi}_l e^{j\omega t}$
Pressure	$p_0 e^{j\omega t}$	$p_l e^{j\omega t}$
Boundary condition	$Z_0\dot{\xi}_0 + Sp_0 = \psi_0$	$Z_l\dot{\xi}_l = Sp_l$

Here, and throughout, $\dot{\xi}_0$ denotes the quantity $|\dot{\xi}(0)|$ and, consequently, it differs from the notation in formula (5-8) where $\dot{\xi}_0$ is the amplitude of the progressive wave at $x = 0$ at the moment $t = 0$.

---

* In deriving the formulae in this section no account has been taken of the lag in phase (φ') of the deformation relative to the pressure due to relaxation in the medium. If this phase shift is included it leads to the ratio $p/\dot{\xi}$ (i.e. the complex wave impedance) being equal to $w_1 = \rho c \exp[j(\varphi' - \varphi)]$; in gas at acoustic frequencies $(\varphi' - \varphi)$ is a small quantity and $w_1 \approx \rho c$.

Formulae which are to be derived later can be used for any medium if the complex wave impedance w_1 is substituted for ρc.

The wave which is excited by the vibrations of the piston Z_0 is propagated to the end of the tube and is reflected back and forth between the impedances Z_l and Z_0.

As a result, there will be an infinite number of positive and negative waves which are superimposed on one another. All the positive waves have the same frequency and the resulting wave will also have the same frequency. The resulting wave is obtained by the addition of all the elementary waves, each of which can be expressed by a vector which characterizes its amplitude and phase; if we add the vector amplitudes of the elemental waves a_1, a_2, a_3,... (Fig. 21), the total amplitude a is then obtained for the forward wave. The total amplitude of the backward wave b is found similarly as the vector sum of the waves with amplitudes b_1, b_2, b_3 ...

In its general form the particle velocity at a certain point with the coordinate x, including both forward and backward waves, can be written

$$\dot{\xi}(x, t) = \dot{\xi}_+(x) + \dot{\xi}_-(x) = (ae^{-\gamma x} + be^{\gamma x})\, e^{j\omega t}, \quad (5\text{-}13)$$

where the sign (+) refers to the forward wave, and the sign (-) refers to the backward wave.

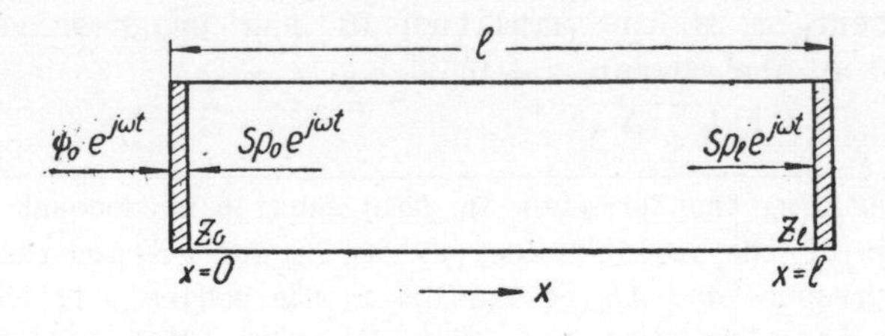

Fig. 20

Using expression (5-12), we get for the acoustic pressure in the tube

$$p(x,t) = \rho c(ae^{-\gamma x} - be^{\gamma x}) \cdot e^{j\omega t}. \quad (5\text{-}14)$$

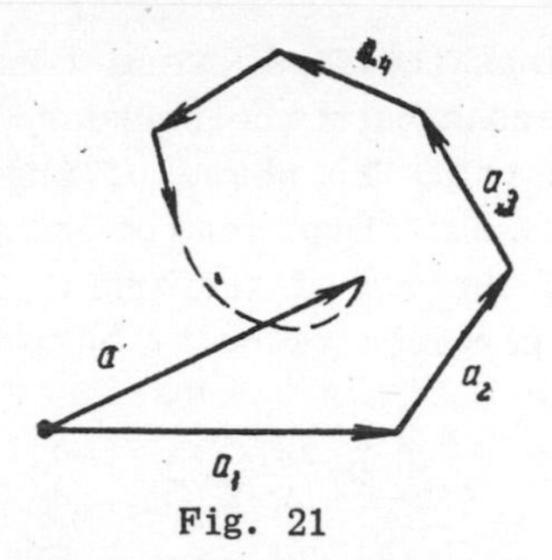

Fig. 21

The quantities a and b can be found from the boundary conditions. Substituting the values of $p(x, t)$ at $x = 0$ and $x = l$ in the boundary conditions and cancelling $e^{j\omega t}$, we get:

$$\left.\begin{array}{l}(Z_0 + S\rho c)\, a + (Z_0 - S\rho c)\, b = \psi_0 \\ (Z_l - S\rho c)\, a e^{-\gamma l} + (Z_l + S\rho c)\, b e^{\gamma l} = 0.\end{array}\right\} \quad (5\text{-}15)$$

We have a linear set of two equations with two unknowns a and b. The determinant of the set is denoted by

$$\Delta = \begin{vmatrix} Z_0 + S\rho c, & Z_0 - S\rho c \\ (Z_l - S\rho c)\, e^{-\gamma l}, & (Z_l + S\rho c) e^{\gamma l} \end{vmatrix} =$$

$$= 2(Z_0 Z_l + S^2\rho^2 c^2)\sinh\gamma l + 2S\rho c\,(Z_0 + Z_l)\cosh\gamma l.$$

From equations (5-15):

$$a = \frac{Z_l + S\rho c}{\Delta} e^{\gamma l} \cdot \psi_0; \; b = -\frac{Z_l - S\rho c}{\Delta} e^{-\gamma l} \cdot \psi_0.$$

Substituting a and b in equations (5-13) and (5-14), we find

$$\dot{\xi} = \left[(Z_l + S\rho c) e^{\gamma(l-x)} - (Z_l - S\rho c) e^{-\gamma(l-x)}\right] \frac{\psi_0 e^{j\omega t}}{\Delta}, \quad (5\text{-}16)$$

$$p = \rho c \left[(Z_l + S\rho c) e^{\gamma(l-x)} + (Z_l - S\rho c) e^{-\gamma(l-x)}\right] \frac{\psi_0 e^{j\omega t}}{\Delta}. \quad (5\text{-}17)$$

In these expressions the first term denotes the forward wave, and the second term the backward wave. It should be borne in mind that the phase of the forward and the backward waves are both functions of the quantity $(l-x)$, the distance from the end of the tube. The amplitudes of the pressure and particle velocity at $x = l$ are:

$$p_l = \frac{2Z_l}{\Delta}\rho c\psi_o,$$

$$\dot{\xi}_l = \frac{2S\rho c}{\Delta}\psi_o.$$

We have to find the amplitude of the velocity $\dot{\xi}_0$ and the pressure p_0 at the beginning of the tube from (5-16) and (5-17):

$$p_o = \rho c\left[(Z_l + S\rho c)e^{\gamma l} + (Z_l - S\rho c)e^{-\gamma l}\right]\frac{\psi_o}{\Delta} =$$

$$= \rho c\left[2Z_l\cosh\gamma l + 2S\rho c\sinh\gamma l\right]\frac{\psi_o}{\Delta} = \cosh\gamma l\cdot p_l + \rho c\sinh\gamma l\cdot\dot{\xi}_l;$$

$$\dot{\xi}_o = \left[(Z_l + S\rho c)e^{\gamma l} - (Z_l - S\rho c)e^{-\gamma l}\right]\frac{\psi_o}{\Delta} = \frac{\sinh\gamma l}{\rho c}p_l + \cosh\gamma l\cdot\dot{\xi}_l. \tag{5-18}$$

Introducing the amplitudes of the forces affecting the area S, $F_0 = Sp_0$ and $F_l = Sp_l$, we get:

$$F_0 = \cosh\gamma l\cdot F_l + S\rho c\sinh\gamma l\cdot\dot{\xi}_l,$$

$$\dot{\xi}_0 = \frac{\sinh\gamma l}{S\rho c}F_l + \cosh\gamma l\cdot\dot{\xi}_l. \tag{5-18a}$$

Similar expressions which link the amplitudes of the wave process at the input to the system with the amplitudes at the output are well known in electrical and radio engineering systems and are known as *fourpoles*.

A Tube as a Fourpole

In the general theory of passive electrical fourpoles, the following relationships are well known between the voltage and current at the input (V_0, I_0) on the one hand and the voltage and current at the output (V_l,I_l): on the other:

$$V_0 = AV_l + BI_l, \quad I_0 = CV_l + DI_l. \tag{5-19}$$

The quantities A,B,C and D are known as coefficients of the fourpole. For a section of a tube with a cross-section S and length l, the coefficients of the fourpole are, in accordance with equations (5-18a),

$$A = D = \cosh\gamma l;\ B = S\rho c \sinh\gamma l;\ C = \frac{\sinh\gamma l}{S\rho c}.$$

It follows from these equations:

$$AD - BC = A^2 - BC = \cosh^2\gamma l - \sinh^2\gamma l = 1.$$

The expressions $A=D$ and $AD-BC=1$ define what is known as a symmetrical fourpole.

Defining V_l and I_l from (5-19) in terms of V_0 and I_0, we find:

$$V_l = \frac{DV_0 - BI_0}{AD - BC} \text{ and } I_l = \frac{-(CV_0 - AI_0)}{AD - BC}.$$

If $AD-BC=1$ and $A=D$, as is the case for a tube, then

$$V_l = AV_0 - BI_0 \text{ and } I_l = -CV_0 + AI_0.$$

If on inversion of the fourpole (when its end is taken as the origin, and its origin as the end) the originally negative direction of the current (velocity) is assumed to be positive and we put $I_0' = -I_0$ and $I_l' = -I_l$, then

$$V_l = AV_0 + BI_0,$$
$$I_l = CV_0 + AI_0. \tag{5-20}$$

Consequently, in the fourpole or tube there are identical relationships (5-19) or (5-20) between the voltage and current at the input and the voltage and current at the output independently of whichever side of the fourpole is taken as the origin. This implies that such a fourpole is reversible or symmetrical.

A tube which is closed at one end is analogous to an electrical line which is open at one end, i.e. under no load $(I_l = 0;\ \dot{\xi}_l = 0)$. The mechanical impedance at the input is

$$Z_k = \frac{F_0}{\dot{\xi}_0}\bigg|_{\dot{\xi}_l = 0} = \frac{A}{C} = S\rho c\ \coth \gamma l \approx -jS\rho c \cot kl.$$

A tube which is open is analogous to a short-circuited electrical line $(V_l = 0;\ p_l = 0)$. Its impedance is

$$Z_s = \frac{F_0}{\dot{\xi}_0}\bigg|_{F_l = 0} = \frac{B}{D} = S\rho c \tanh \gamma \approx jS\rho c \tan kl.$$

The impedance at the input to a symmetrical fourpole is

$$Z = \frac{V_0}{I_0} = \frac{AV_l + BI_l}{CV_l + DI_l} = \frac{A\frac{V_l}{I_l} + B}{C\frac{V_l}{I_l} + A}.$$

But what impedance Z_0 should be connected at the output in order that the impedance at the input should also equal Z_0? By putting $\frac{V_l}{I_l} = \frac{V_0}{I_0} = Z_0$, it is easily found that

$$Z_0 = \sqrt{\frac{B}{C}}.$$

This impedance is known as the *wave impedance* or the *characteristic impedance* of the fourpole. For a tube

$$B = S\rho c \sinh \gamma l;\ C = \frac{\sinh \gamma l}{S\rho c} \text{ and } Z_0 = S\rho c.$$

Reflection of Sound at the End of a Tube

We will now return to expressions (5-16) and (5-17) for the velocity and pressure at any point in a tube. The term in square brackets in which x appears in the exponent with the plus sign, represents the reverse (reflected) wave, and the term in which x has the minus sign represents the forward wave.

The ratio of the amplitudes of the reverse and forward waves at $x = l$ is known as the *reflection coefficient for pressure waves:*

$$r_p = \frac{p_-(l)}{p_+(l)} = \frac{Z_l - S\rho c}{Z_l + S\rho c} = \frac{\frac{Z_l}{S\rho c} - 1}{\frac{Z_l}{S\rho c} + 1} = \frac{Z_1 - 1}{Z_1 + 1},$$

where $\frac{Z_l}{S}$ represents the impedance per unit area of tube cross section *(the specific impedance)*, and $Z_1 = \frac{Z_l}{S\rho c}$ is the specific impedance expressed in units ρc, known as the *dimensionless impedance*.

Using equation (5-16) the reflection coefficient for particle velocity waves is:

$$r_{\xi} = \frac{\dot{\xi}_-(l)}{\dot{\xi}_+(l)} = -\frac{Z_l - S\rho c}{Z_l + S\rho c} = -\frac{Z_1 - 1}{Z_1 + 1} = -r_p,$$

It will be seen from these expressions that if $Z_l = \infty$ (which corresponds to a rigid wall at the end of the tube) there will be total reflection of the velocity with a change of phase ($r_{\xi} = -1$), and of the pressure without a change of phase ($r_p = +1$).

In the case of reflection from an open end, the impedance of a tube without a flange at low frequencies* is

* L. Ya. Gutin, *J. Tech. Phys. (U.S.S.R.)* 7, 1096, 1957 (see especially equations 11 ff.).

$$Z_l \approx \frac{\rho\omega^2 S^2}{4\pi c} + j\omega(2\rho r_0^3),$$

and that of a tube with a flange (according to Rayleigh, see Chapter XI, eq. (11-19)) is

$$Z_l \approx \frac{\rho\omega^2 S^2}{2\pi c} + j\omega\left(\frac{8}{3}\rho r_0^3\right).$$

At very low frequencies $Z_l \to 0$ and we get:

$$r_\xi = +1 \quad \text{and} \quad r_p = -1.$$

When $Z_l = S\rho c$, i.e. the impedance Z_l is purely active (resistive) and equal to the radiation resistance of a plane wave (on the area S), we get:

$$r_p = r_\xi = 0,$$

indicating total absence of reflection, or, in other words, complete transmission of the sound through the output impedance Z_l, which can be regarded as total "absorption" of sound at the section $x = l$.

The case $Z_l = S\rho c$ can be realized by connecting an infinite tube of the same section to the original tube. This is a trivial solution of the problem of total absorption. Besides, other systems are possible for which this condition is satisfied and which possess the property of total absorption of the incident acoustic wave. For example, such a property can be possessed by a resonance system with a particular degree of attenuation and by specially designed absorbers composed of thick layers of porous material (see Chapter VII, p.253 ff.).

At very high frequencies the impedance of a piston diaphragm tends to the quantity $S\rho c$ in which case it creates a pencil of directional waves like a projector. Consequently, sounds of very high frequency (ultrasonic) will experience no reflection at the end of the tube, but will pass out into open space in the form of a pencil of waves.

A tube which is closed by a rigid wall is analogous to an open electrical line. An open tube is analogous to a short-circuited line. In the first case a maximum of pressure (voltage) is formed at the end, and in the second case a maximum of velocity (current). If $Z_l \neq S\rho c$, then part of the acoustic energy is reflected, and part passes into the impedance Z_l, i.e. is absorbed by it.

Suppose we write expression (5-17) for the pressure $p(x,t)$ in a slightly different form, ignoring the attenuation β in the tube and introducing the notation

$$r_p = \frac{Z_l - S\rho c}{Z_l + S\rho c} = re^{j2\delta}, \tag{5-21}$$

where r is the absolute value of the reflection coefficient r_p, and 2δ its phase. We then get

$$p(x,t) = \rho c \frac{\psi_0 e^{j\omega t}}{\Delta}(Z_l + S\rho c)e^{jkl}[e^{-jkx} + re^{j(kx + 2\delta - 2kl)}] =$$

$$= A\sqrt{1 + r^2 + 2r\cos 2[k(x-l)+\delta]} \cdot e^{j\varphi} \cdot e^{j\omega t}. \tag{5-22}$$

Here

$$A = \psi_0 \rho c \frac{Z_l + S\rho c}{\Delta} e^{jkl}$$

and

$$\tan\varphi = \frac{r\sin[k(x-2l)+2\delta] - \sin kx}{r\cos[k(x-2l)+2\delta] + \cos kx}.$$

We add and subtract re^{-jkx} in the bracket in expression (5-22); transforming, we get:

$$p(x,t) = A[e^{-jkx} - re^{-jkx} + re^{-jkx} + re^{j(kx-kl+\delta)} \cdot e^{j(\delta-kl)}]e^{j\omega t} =$$

$$= A(1-r)e^{j(\omega t - kx)} + 2rAe^{j(\omega t+\delta-kl)} \cdot \cos[k(x-l)+\delta]. \tag{5-23}$$

It will be seen from this expression that the wave process in the tube can be regarded as the sum of a progressive forward wave with pressure amplitude $A(1-r)$ and a standing wave with pressure amplitude $2Ar$.

Suppose we now take values of x which satisfy the condition $k(x-l)+\delta=m\pi$, where $m=\pm 0, 1, 2, \ldots$, i.e. we consider points at distances from the end of the tube

$$d=l-x=\frac{\delta}{k}-m\frac{\pi}{k}=\frac{\delta}{k}-m\frac{\lambda}{2}=\left(\frac{\delta}{\pi}-m\right)\frac{\lambda}{2}. \quad (5\text{-}24)$$

At these points are the pressure maxima of the standing wave. In the case of a rigid termination the first maximum of pressure is at the end of the tube ($x = l$) and $d = 0$. This is possible if $2\delta=m\times 2\pi$. Obviously, the reflection coefficient r_p is then a real quantity.

The maximum of pressure nearest to the end of the tube is obtained if $m = 0$, i.e. if

$$l-x=\frac{\delta}{k},$$

or

$$x=l-\frac{\delta}{k}.$$

It will be shown below that δ can vary between $-\pi<2\delta<\pi$. Thus, the impedance Z_l at the end of the tube can provide a shift of the first maximum both towards the inside ($\delta>0$), and towards the outside of the end of the tube ($\delta<0$). In the latter case the first maximum inside the tube occurs when $m=-1$ and its position will be:

$$x'=l-\frac{\delta}{k}-\frac{\lambda}{2}.$$

At values $k(x-l)+\delta=\left(m+\frac{1}{2}\right)\pi$ or

$$d=l-x=\frac{\delta}{k}-\left(m+\frac{1}{2}\right)\frac{\lambda}{2}=\left[\frac{\delta}{\pi}+\left(m+\frac{1}{2}\right)\right]\frac{\lambda}{2}, \quad (5\text{-}25)$$

pressure *minima* of the standing wave occur as can be seen from formula (5-22). The total acoustic pressure at the minima is obtained from (5-23) and (5-25):

$$p_{\min}=A(1-r)\,e^{j(\delta-kl)}\cdot e^{j\omega t}\cdot e^{-j\left(m+\frac{1}{2}\right)\pi}=$$
$$=|p_{\min}|\cdot e^{j\left(\delta-\kappa l-m\pi-\frac{\pi}{2}\right)}\cdot e^{j\omega t},$$

where $|p_{\min}|=A(1-r)$ is the amplitude of pressure in the progressive part of the wave. In accordance with (5-24) and since $\cos m\pi=e^{-jm\pi}$ we get at the maxima:

$$p_{\max}=A(1-r)\,e^{j\omega t}\cdot e^{j(\delta-kl)}\cdot e^{-jm\pi}+$$
$$+2A\cdot r\cdot e^{j\omega t}\cdot e^{j(\delta-kl)}\cdot e^{-jm\pi}=|p_{\max}|\cdot e^{j\omega t}\cdot e^{j(\delta-kl-m\pi)},$$

where

$$|p_{\max}|=A(1+r).$$

The amplitude of the pressure at the maxima is $A(1+r)$; the phase shift between $p_{\max}$ and $p_{\min}$ is $\frac{\pi}{2}$.

The ratio of the amplitude of the acoustic pressure at the maximum to that at the minimum is known as the *standing wave ratio*, which is equal to:

$$N=\frac{|p_{\max}|}{|p_{\min}|}=\frac{1+r}{1-r}, \quad (5\text{-}26)$$

whence

$$r=\frac{N-1}{N+1}. \quad (5\text{-}27)$$

The Sound Absorption Coefficient as a Function of the Impedance Z_l at the the End of the Tube

We will consider expression (5-21) in somewhat greater detail:

$$r_p = \frac{Z_l - S\rho c}{Z_l + S\rho c} = re^{j2\delta}.$$

The impedance Z_l is generally speaking a complex quantity; suppose we put R_l for the resistance and Y_l for the reactance. Then

$$Z_l = R_l + jY_l = S\rho c\,(R_1 + jY_1), \tag{5-28}$$

where

$$R_1 = \frac{R_l}{S\rho c} \text{ and } Y_1 = \frac{Y_l}{S\rho c} \tag{5-29}$$

are the *dimensionless resistance and reactance per unit area of the piston at the end of the tube.* Considering expressions (5-28) and (5-29), we can write formula (5-21) in the form

$$r_p = \frac{R_1 - 1 + jY_1}{R_1 + 1 + jY_1} = re^{j2\delta}.$$

The quantities r and δ can be expressed in terms of R_1 and Y_1

$$r = \frac{|\sqrt{(R_1^2 + Y_1^2 - 1)^2 + 4Y_1^2}|}{(R_1 + 1)^2 + Y_1^2} = \left|\sqrt{\frac{(R_1 - 1)^2 + Y_1^2}{(R_1 + 1)^2 + Y_1^2}}\right|; \tag{5-30}$$

$$\left.\begin{aligned} \tan 2\delta &= \frac{2Y_1}{R_1^2 + Y_1^2 - 1}; \\ \cos 2\delta &= \frac{R_1^2 + Y_1^2 - 1}{(R_1 + 1)^2 + Y_1^2} \cdot \frac{1}{r} = \frac{R_1^2 + Y_1^2 - 1}{|\sqrt{(R_1^2 + Y_1^2 - 1)^2 + 4Y_1^2}|}, \\ \sin 2\delta &= \frac{2Y_1}{(R_1 + 1)^2 + Y_1^2} \cdot \frac{1}{r} = \frac{2Y_1}{|\sqrt{(R_1^2 + Y_1^2 - 1)^2 + 4Y_1^2}|}. \end{aligned}\right\} \tag{5-31}$$

If $Y_1 = 0$, then

$$\cos 2\delta = \frac{R_1^2 - 1}{|R_1^2 - 1|} = \pm 1; \quad \sin 2\delta = 0.$$

Since $0 < R_1 < \infty$, it follows that the phase 2δ can be equal (if $Y_1 = 0$) to ± 0 or $\pm \pi$. It is obvious that if $Y_1 \neq 0$ $\cos 2\delta$ and $\sin 2\delta$ can assume all values between -1 and +1, passing through zero. Consequently:

$$-\pi < 2\delta < \pi. \tag{5-32}$$

The quantity r can be represented in the form

$$r = e^{-2\varepsilon} = \frac{N-1}{N+1}, \tag{5-33}$$

where always $\varepsilon > 0$; there is no difficulty in showing that

$$\coth\varepsilon = N; \sinh^2\varepsilon = \frac{1}{N^2 - 1}; \cosh^2\varepsilon = \frac{N}{N^2 - 1}. \tag{5-33a}$$

If r changes from 1 to 0, then the quantity ε changes from 0 to ∞.

Table 3 shows some values of r and ε for various values of N.

TABLE 3

20 log N	0	0·2	2	6	20	∞
ε	∞	1·87	0·82	0·52	0·11	0
r	0	0·024	0·205	0·33	0·82	1

Using expression (5-33), we get

$$r_p = \frac{Z_1 - 1}{Z_1 + 1} = e^{-2(\varepsilon - j\delta)} = e^{-2\psi}, \tag{5-34}$$

where

$$\psi = \varepsilon - j\delta.$$

Then from formula (5-34) it follows that

$$Z_1 = \frac{Z_l}{S\rho c} = R_1 + jY_1 = \frac{e^{\psi} + e^{-\psi}}{e^{\psi} - e^{-\psi}} = \coth\psi = \coth(\varepsilon - j\delta). \quad (5\text{-}35)$$

We now expand $\coth\psi$ into its real and imaginary parts and take into account that $\cosh j2\delta = \cos 2\delta$ and $\sinh j2\delta = j\sin 2\delta$, and hence find without difficulty

$$R_1 = \frac{\sinh 2\varepsilon}{\cosh 2\varepsilon - \cos 2\delta}; \quad Y_1 = \frac{\sin 2\delta}{\cosh 2\varepsilon - \cos 2\delta}. \quad (5\text{-}36)$$

Alternatively, considering equations (5-26) and (5-33a) and the expressions for $\cosh 2\varepsilon$ and $\sinh 2\varepsilon$ in terms of N, we get:

$$R_1 = \frac{2N}{(N^2+1) - (N^2-1)\cos 2\delta}; \quad Y_1 = \frac{(N^2-1)\sin 2\delta}{(N^2+1) - (N^2-1)\cos 2\delta}. \quad (5\text{-}36a)$$

Using this formula we can calculate R_1 and Y_1 from the experimentally measured quantities N and δ. The geometric interpretation of transformation (5-35) or its inverse transformation (5-30) and (5-31) will be given below. A transformation of this type is very often used in the theory of electrical lines.

If the value of N has been found experimentally, then the reflection coefficient is found from formula (5-27), $r = \frac{N-1}{N+1}$. This ratio can be used to find the reflection coefficient from measurements of standing waves in a tube (the method of an acoustic interferometer).

For practical purposes it is usual to calculate the ratio of the absorbed acoustic energy to the energy of the incident sound. Since the intensity of sound is proportional to the square of the amplitude of the acoustic pressure, it follows that the ratio of the intensity of the reflected sound J_r to the intensity of the incident sound J_i is equal to r^2, whilst

$$\alpha = 1 - r^2 = \frac{4}{2 + N + \frac{1}{N}} = 1 - \frac{J_r}{J_i} = \frac{J_i - J_r}{J_i}$$

represents the ratio of the absorbed energy to the incident energy, i.e. the coefficient of sound energy absorption. The quantity α is known as the *sound absorption coefficient*. It should be borne in mind that the coordinate x in (5-23) is contained in the second term only in the argument $[k(x-l)+\delta]$. This implies that the distance $(x-l)$ between the maxima and minima and the end of the tube for the value of k in question depends solely on the value of δ, which is solely a function of Z_l, and independent of Z_0.

The value of δ can easily be measured experimentally so that Z_l can also be determined.

The transformation expressed by formulae (5-30) and (5-31), or the inverse transformation (5-35), $\coth \psi = R_1 + jY_1$, are conformal transformations which can easily be represented graphically on the plane of the complex variable. Suppose we mark off the quantity R_1 along the abscissa, and the quantity Y_1 along the ordinate. Any impedance $Z_l = R_l + jY_l = S\rho c(R_1 + jY_1)$ is represented by a certain point on the plane of the complex variable Z_1.

It is necessary to find those curves on the plane Z_1 on which the sound absorption coefficient α (or the quantities r and ε) will be constant in value. Using equation (5-30)

$$\alpha = 1 - r^2 = \frac{4R_1}{(R_1 + 1)^2 + Y_1^2}.$$

This expression can be transformed into

$$\left(R_1-\frac{2-\alpha}{\alpha}\right)^2+Y_1^2=\left(\frac{2\sqrt{1-\alpha}}{\alpha}\right)^2, \quad (5\text{-}37)$$

$$\text{or } \left(R_1-\frac{1}{\tanh 2\varepsilon}\right)^2+Y_1^2=\left(\frac{1}{\sinh 2\varepsilon}\right)^2$$

Likewise, from equation (5-31) we can obtain without difficulty the equation of the curves on which $\delta=\text{const}$:

$$R_1^2+\left(Y_1-\frac{1}{\tan 2\delta}\right)^2=\left(\frac{1}{\sin 2\delta}\right)^2. \quad (5\text{-}38)$$

Regarding R_1 and Y_1 in (5-37) and (5-38) as unknown variables, and α and δ as parameters, we come to the conclusion that the curves of constant α as expressed by equation (5-37) are a family of circles with their centres on the R_1 axis at a distance from the origin equal to

$$R_{10}=\frac{2-\alpha}{\alpha}, \text{ and with radii } \rho_0=\frac{2\sqrt{1-\alpha}}{\alpha}.$$

The circle corresponding to $\alpha=0$ $(r=1,\ \ 2\varepsilon=0)$, is of infinitely large radius and its centre is at the point $R_1=\infty$, $Y_1=0$. If α tends to 1 $(r\to 0,\ 2\varepsilon\to\infty)$ the radius of the circle is reduced and it tends to zero, whilst its centre tends to the point $R_1=1$ and $Y_1=0$.

The curves of constant δ (or of constant $\tan 2\delta$) can similarly be represented by equation (5-38) as a family of circles with centres on the Y_1 axis at a distance from the origin

$$Y_{10}=\frac{1}{\tan 2\delta},$$

and with radii equal to $\rho_0'=\frac{1}{\sin 2\delta}$.

All these circles pass through the point $R_1=1$, $Y_1=0$,

corresponding to $\alpha = 1$.

The families of curves of constant α and δ are shown in Fig. 22, which we will refer to as an *impedance diagram.* A complete impedance diagram suitable for practical calculations is shown in Fig. 23 on a reduced scale.

In order to find the phase, it is not advantageous to determine the position of the pressure maximum since the maximum is not very sharp. It is better to find the position of the first minium d_1 experimentally and then find δ from formula (5-25).

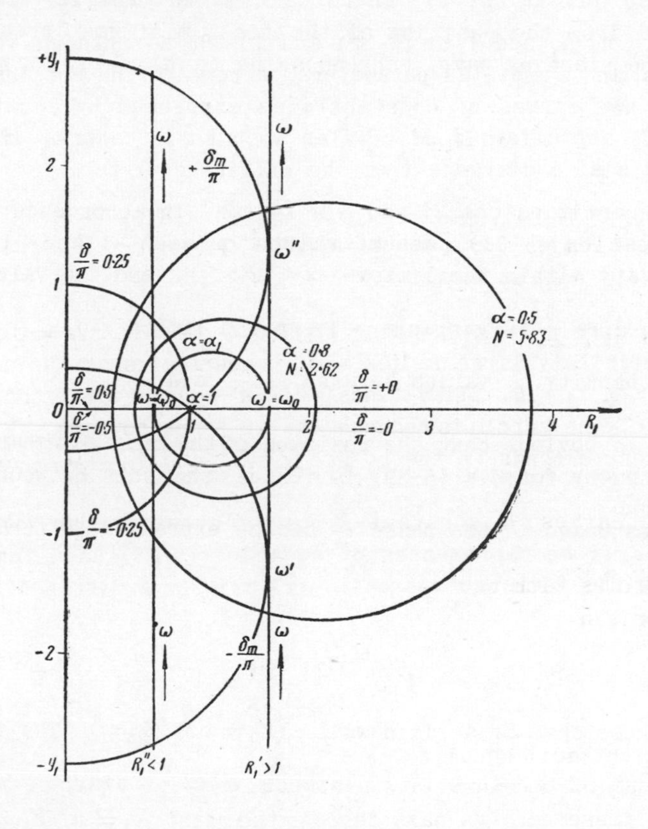

Fig. 22

The phase circle with its centre at the origin (Fig. 24) and a radius equal to one, refers to the value $\frac{\delta}{\pi}=0\cdot25$ $\left(2\delta=\frac{\pi}{2}\right)$. The section of the R_1 axis from the origin to $R_1=1$ corresponds to the phase circle $\frac{\delta}{\pi}=0\cdot5$, whilst the section from $R_1=1$ to $R_1=\infty$ corresponds to the circle $\frac{\delta}{\pi}=0$.

The quantity N can be found by the method of standing waves, and 2ε (or r) can be calculated from it; 2δ is found from the position of the first minimum of pressure in the standing wave, corresponding to $m=-1$, for which

$$d_1=\frac{\delta}{k}+\frac{\lambda}{4}=\frac{\delta}{\pi}\cdot\frac{\lambda}{2}+\frac{\lambda}{4}. \tag{5-39}$$

The quantities cos 2δ and sin 2δ can, in accordance with expression (5-31), assume values between -1 and $+1$; 2δ can vary within the limits $-\pi<2\delta<\pi$, and the value of the phase $\frac{\delta}{\pi}$ is variable between the limits $-\frac{1}{2}<\frac{\delta}{\pi}<\frac{1}{2}$; the quantity $\frac{\delta}{k}$ varies between $-\frac{\lambda}{4}$ and $+\frac{\lambda}{4}$.

It is obvious that the position of the first minimum calculated by formula (5-39) is inside the tube between the limits 0 and $\frac{\lambda}{2}$; the phase $\frac{\delta}{\pi}$ can be expressed in terms of d_1 by the formula

$$\frac{\delta}{\pi}=\frac{d_1}{\lambda/2}-\frac{1}{2}. \tag{5-39a}$$

In the case of a rigid wall $(Y_1=\infty)$ $2\delta=0$. The first minimum of pressure is a distance $d_1=\frac{\lambda}{4}$ away.

In the case of an inertance $(Y_1>0)$ it is always the

case that $\sin 2\delta > 0$ and $-1 < \cos 2\delta < 1$ (see formula (5-31)). This implies that $0 < 2\delta < \pi$, and that the position of the first minimum is between the limits $\frac{\lambda}{4} < d_1 < \frac{\lambda}{2}$ (Fig. 24). If the inertance is very small and the resistance $R_1 < 1$, then $\cos 2\delta$ is approximately

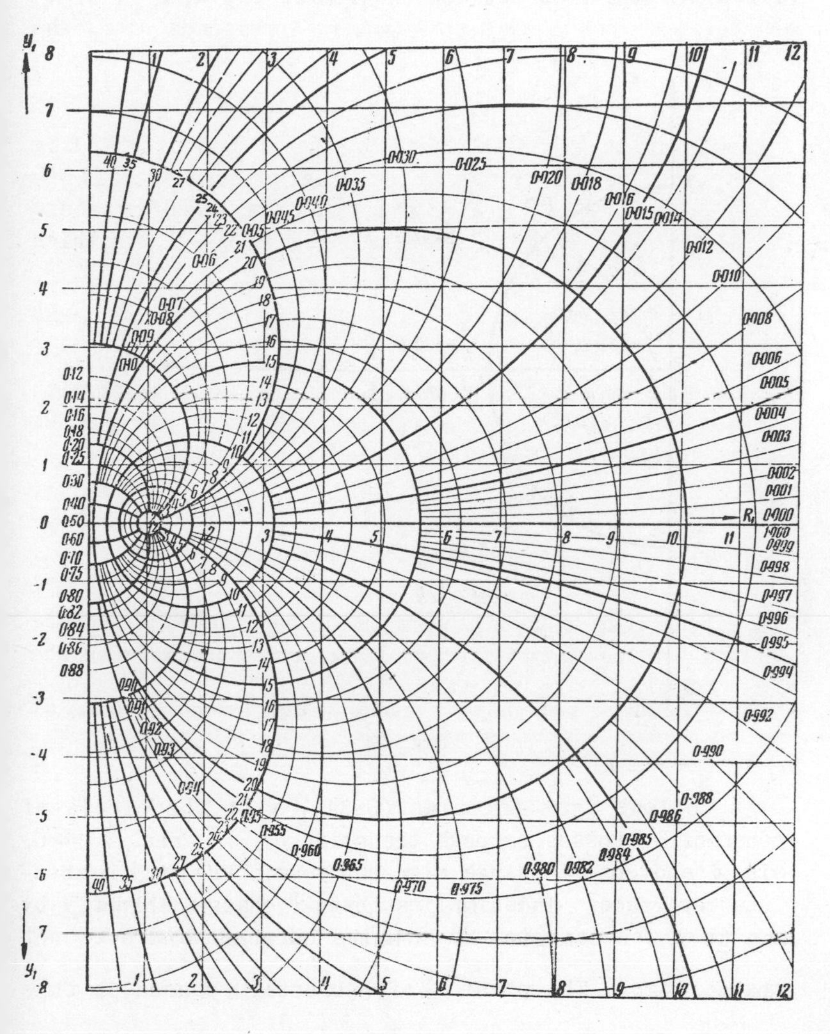

Fig. 23

-1, and sin 2δ is approximately zero; consequently, $\frac{\delta}{\pi}$ is approximately $\frac{1}{2}$, and d_1 approximately $\frac{\lambda}{2}$.

For an elastic impedance $(Y_1 < 0)$, $-\pi < 2\delta < 0$; the first minimum lies between the limits $0 < d_1 < \frac{\lambda}{4}$.

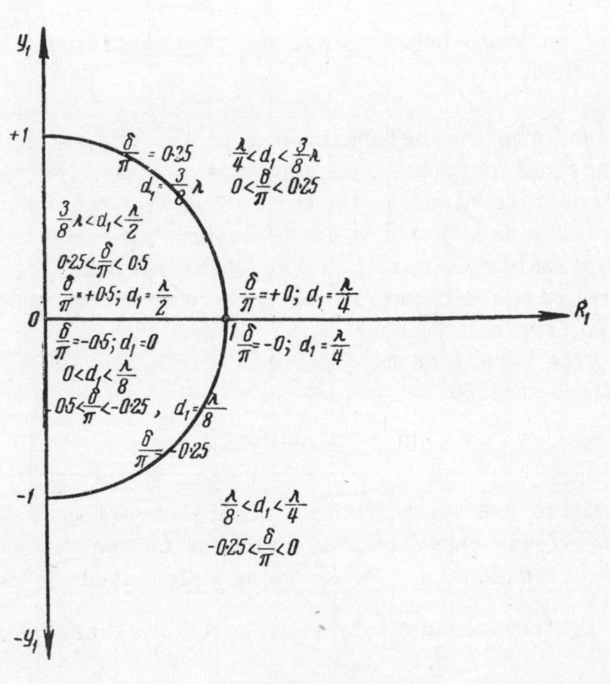

Fig. 24

As follows from formulae (5-31), when the circle of constant δ crosses through the point $R_1 = 1$ and $Y_1 = 0$, sin 2δ and cos 2δ change sign but remain the same in absolute magnitude. This implies that 2δ changes abruptly by π, in which case tan 2δ remains constant and does not change sign. The phase $\frac{\delta}{\pi}$ is abruptly reduced in this case by $0{\cdot}5$. Thus, if on the upper part of the circle the phase retains a certain constant value $\frac{\delta}{\pi}$, then on its lower part the phase will be $\frac{\delta}{\pi}-\frac{1}{2}$. The values $\frac{\delta}{\pi}$ on the line of constant R_1 differ only in sign at values $+Y_1$ and $-Y_1$. On the impedance diagram (Fig. 23) the numbers on the circles of equal phase in the upper half-plane $(Y_1>0)$ denote $\frac{\delta}{\pi}$, and in the lower half-plane $(Y_1<0)$, in order to avoid negative values, the quantities $\left(1+\frac{\delta}{\pi}\right)$. are recorded.

The conformal transformation $\coth(\varepsilon-j\delta)=R_1+jY_1$ for practical purposes can conveniently be represented on two separate diagrams for the region of small absorption coefficients and that for large absorption coefficients. It is advisable to mark off the quantities 20 log N (in decibels) on the diagram, since these quantities are found directly from experiments. The value of α is found from 2ε (or vice versa) by the formula;

$$\varepsilon=\frac{1}{2}\ln\frac{1}{r}=0{\cdot}575\log_{10}\frac{1}{1-\alpha}.$$

The acoustic pressures at the minima and maxima (p_{min} and p_{max}) are found experimentally along with the position of the first minimum d_1. Then, having calculated 20 log N, $\frac{\varepsilon}{\pi}$ and $\frac{\delta}{\pi}$, from the above formulae, the values R_1 and Y_1 are found from the impedance diagram.

On passing through resonance (as the frequency changes) the sign of the reactive part is changed and the point on the diagram always crosses the R_1 axis. In accordance with formulae (5-31), the sign of $\sin 2\delta$ is reversed on passage of Y_1 through 0, but $\cos 2\delta$ remains unchanged. If $R_1<1$, then the phase $\frac{\delta}{\pi}$ will abruptly change from the value -0·5 to the value +0·5 and d_1 = 0 or $\lambda/2$. Conversely, if $R_1 > 1$, then on passage across the base, the phase $\frac{\delta}{\pi}$ varies continuously, passing through zero and $d_1 = \lambda/4$. If Z_{1l} is the dimensionless impedance of a simple resonance system

$$Z_{1l} = R_1 + j\left(\omega M_1 - \frac{E_1}{\omega}\right), \tag{5-40}$$

then at resonance when $\omega M_1 = \frac{E_1}{\omega}$, the impedance will be a pure resistance ($Z_{1l} = R_1$). Formula (5-40) is represented on the impedance diagram by a straight line parallel to the Y_1 axis passing through the point $R_1 = \frac{R_l}{S\rho c}$, $Y_1 = 0$. This straight line is tangential at resonance to a certain circle of constant absorption ($\alpha = \alpha_1$, see Fig. 22). It will be seen from the diagram that at frequencies other than the resonant frequency, i.e. when $Y_1 \neq 0$, it is inevitable that $\alpha < \alpha_1$, i.e. α will have a maximum at resonance. Consideration should however be paid to the fact that with the same parameters M_1 and E_1, but with a smaller R_1, the same circle $\alpha = \alpha_1$ is tangential to a second straight line parallel to the Y_1 axis. The first straight line corresponds to $R_1' > 1$, and the second line to $R_1'' < 1$; the resonant frequency in both cases is the same, $\omega_0 = \sqrt{\frac{E_1}{M_1}}$. It is easy to see that $R_1' R_1''$ is always equal to unity. The first case corresponds to resonance in a system with great attenuation, and the second to slight attenuation. For both systems at resonance

$$\alpha_{\max} = \frac{4R_1'}{(R_1' + 1)^2} = \frac{4R_1''}{(R_1'' + 1)^2},$$

but the first system will have a more gently sloping resonance curve and the second will have a steeper curve.

It can be seen from Fig. 22 that the phase $\frac{\delta}{\pi}$ for a resonator with a large resistance $(R'_1 > 1)$ will change continuously on passing through resonance from low frequencies to high frequencies and through zero from negative values to positive values. Figure 25 illustrates the variation of $\frac{\delta}{\pi}$ and d_1 as a function of the frequency ω (here the two cases $R'_1 > 1$ and $R''_1 < 1$ are taken into account separately).

If $R''_1 < 1$, the resonator at $\omega < \omega_0$ has a negative reactance; with a gradual increase in frequency the phase $\frac{\delta}{\pi}$ decreases from zero to -0·5 and d_1 diminishes from $\lambda/4$ to zero (at resonance). On passing through resonance, the phase abruptly changes from the value -0·5 to +0·5, and the position of the minimum d_1 abruptly changes from zero to $\lambda/2$ (the dotted line). With a further increase in $\omega (\omega > \omega_0)$ the phase decreases from 0·5 to zero, and d_1 is shifted from $\lambda/2$ to $\lambda/4$ (if $\omega \rightarrow \infty$).

If $R'_1 > 1$, the change in phase and position of the first minimum can usually be traced from Fig. 22 or Fig. 25. With an increase in ω (beginning from 0) the point which represents the impedance is moved along a straight line $R_1 = R'_1$ from $-\infty$ upwards, whilst the phase diminishes from zero to a certain minimum (negative) quantity $\frac{\delta_m}{\pi}$, which is attained at the frequency ω' and is defined by the condition that the straight line $R_1 = R'_1$ is tangential to a certain phase circle $\frac{\delta_m}{\pi}$ in the lower half-plane. Under these conditions the radius of this phase circle $\rho'_0 = \frac{1}{|\sin(-2\delta_m)|} = \frac{1}{\sin 2\delta_m}$ must equal R'_1. The phase then begins to increase and at resonance,

$(Y_1=0)$ reaches zero. With a further increase in ω, the phase becomes positive and the point passes into the upper half-plane. At the frequency ω'' the straight line is tangential to a second phase circle of the same radius $+\frac{\delta_m}{\pi}$ as the first, which corresponds to the condition $R_1' = \frac{1}{|\sin 2\delta_m|}$. At this point the phase attains its maximum value and then with ω increasing to infinity it decreases to zero.

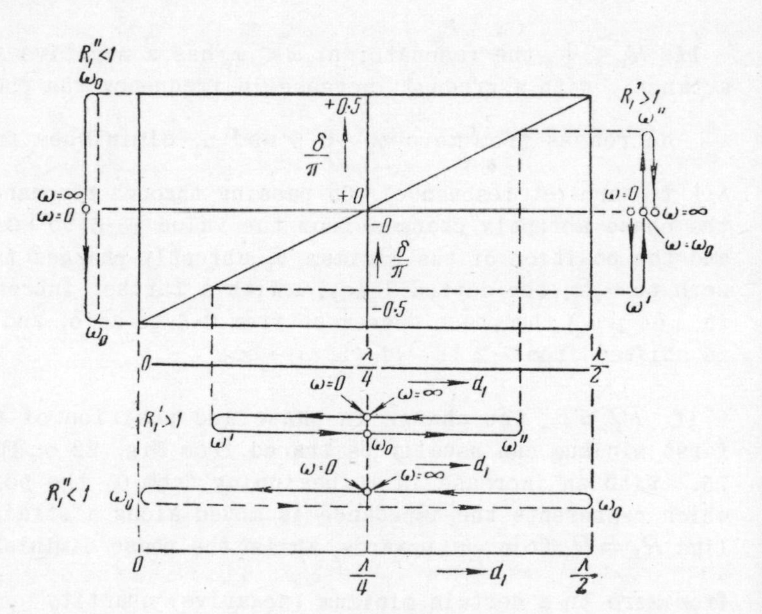

Fig. 25

The frequencies ω' and ω'' at which the phase path changes direction are found from equation (5-38). The tangency conditions have the form:

$$Y_1 - \frac{1}{\tan 2\delta_m} = \left(M_1\omega - \frac{E_1}{\omega}\right) - \frac{1}{\tan 2\delta_m} = 0.$$

Since

$$\frac{1}{\tan 2\delta_m} = \sqrt{\frac{1}{(\sin 2\delta_m)^2} - 1} = \sqrt{(R_1')^2 - 1},$$

we get the quadratic equation

$$M_1\omega^2 - \sqrt{R_1'^2 - 1}\cdot\omega - E_1 = 0,$$

from which we find the two values of the frequency ω' and ω''. It is easy to see, in accordance with equation (5-39), that d_1 first falls from $\lambda/4$ to $\lambda/4 - \delta_m\cdot\lambda/2\pi$ (at $\omega = \omega'$), with increasing ω, and that it then begins to increase continuously to $\lambda/4 + \delta_m\cdot\lambda/2\pi$ (at $\omega = \omega''$), but that it again diminishes to $\lambda/4$.

Impedance at the Driving Point and the Transfer Impedance

From formula (5-16) an expression can be found for the impedance at the point of application of a force ($x = 0$) to a tube with an impedance Z_l at the end:

$$Z_{00} = \frac{\psi_0 e^{i\omega t}}{\dot{\xi}(0)} = \frac{(Z_0 + S\rho c)(Z_l + S\rho c)e^{\gamma l} - (Z_0 - S\rho c)(Z_l - S\rho c)e^{-\gamma l}}{(Z_l + S\rho c)e^{\gamma l} - (Z_l - S\rho c)e^{-\gamma l}} =$$

$$= \frac{(Z_0 Z_l + S^2\rho^2c^2)\sinh\gamma l + S\rho c(Z_0 + Z_l)\cosh\gamma l}{Z_l\sinh\gamma l + S\rho c\cosh\gamma l} = \qquad (5\text{-}41)$$

$$= Z_0 + S\rho c\,\frac{S\rho c\sinh\gamma l + Z_l\cosh\gamma l}{Z_l\sinh\gamma l + S\rho c\cosh\gamma l}.$$

The *transfer impedance* is defined as the ratio of the force acting to the velocity at the point $x = l$, where the impedance is Z_l,

$$Z_{0l} = \frac{\psi_0 e^{j\omega t}}{\dot{\xi}(l)} = \frac{(Z_0 + S\rho c)(Z_l + S\rho c)e^{\gamma l} - (Z_0 - S\rho c)(Z_l - S\rho c)e^{-\gamma l}}{(Z_l + S\rho c) - (Z_l - S\rho c)} =$$

$$= \frac{Z_0 Z_l + S^2\rho^2c^2}{S\rho c}\sinh\gamma l + (Z_0 + Z_l)\cosh\gamma l.$$

Since with small attenuation $\gamma = jk + \beta \approx jk$, it follows that

$$Z_{00} = Z_0 + S\rho c\,\frac{jS\rho c\sin kl + Z_l\cos kl}{jZ_l\sin kl + S\rho c\cos kl};$$

$$Z_{0l} = \frac{Z_0 Z_l + S^2\rho^2c^2}{S\rho c} j \sin kl + (Z_0 + Z_l) \cos kl. \quad (5.42)$$

If $Z_0 = 0$, i.e. if there is no impedance at the entry of the tube (for example, the inertance due to the mass of the piston is small), then

$$Z_{00} = S\rho c \frac{S\rho c \sinh \gamma l + Z_l \cosh \gamma l}{Z_l \sinh \gamma l + S\rho c \cosh \gamma l}.$$

If $\gamma \approx jk$

$$Z_{00} = S\rho c \frac{jS\rho c \sin kl + Z_l \cos kl}{jZ_l \sin kl + S\rho c \cos kl} =$$

$$= S\rho c \frac{jS\rho c \tan kl + Z_l}{jZ_l \tan kl + S\rho c}. \quad (5\text{-}43)$$

This formula defines only that impedance which is added to Z_0 in consequence of the fact that a tube with a finite impedance Z_l is affixed to Z_0.

If $Z_0 = 0$ and $\gamma \approx jk$

$$Z_{0l} \approx jS\rho c \sin kl + Z_l \cos kl. \quad (5\text{-}44)$$

The quantity Z_{0l} obviously depends on the impedance at the end of the tube and on the length of the tube.

Provided $kl = n\pi$

$$Z_{00} = \pm Z_l.$$

This implies that a tube of length $l = \frac{n\pi}{k} = n\frac{\lambda}{2}$, completely transfers the impedance Z_l to the entry of the tube, or in other words, a tube of length $n\frac{\lambda}{2}$ acts like an absolutely rigid bar. If this condition is satisfied, tubes which are filled with fluid can transmit very large variable forces.

We will now consider the special case of a tube with a closed end. Since $Z_l = \infty$, it then follows that if $Z_0 = 0$

$$Z_{00} = S\rho c \coth \gamma l \approx \frac{S\rho c \cos kl}{j \sin kl} = -jS\rho c \cot kl. \quad (5\text{-}45)$$

At low frequencies ($kl \ll 1$) we get:

$$Z_{00} \approx \frac{S\rho c}{jkl} = \frac{\rho c^2 S^2}{j\omega(Sl)} = \frac{\rho c^2 S^2}{j\omega V} = \frac{E}{j\omega}.$$

The quantity $E = \frac{\rho c^2 S^2}{V}$, where V is the volume of the tube, represents the bulk modulus of the air, with the force of pressure being uniform over the entire area S. In fact, in the static case, in accordance with Hooke's law,

$$p = -\varkappa \frac{\delta V}{V}, \text{ whilst } \varkappa = \rho c^2 \text{ and } \delta V = S\xi.$$

Introducing the total force $\psi = Sp$, we get:

$$\psi = Sp = -\frac{\rho c^2 S^2}{V}\xi = -E\xi.$$

Thus, the quantity

$$E = \frac{\rho c^2 S^2}{V} = \frac{\gamma P_0 S^2}{V}$$

$\left(\gamma = \frac{c_p}{c_v}\right.$, and P_0 is the static pressure) is the bulk modulus of the closed volume V.

The quantity Z_{00}, according to (5-45), will be negative and imaginary from $kl = 0$ to $kl = \frac{\pi}{2}$ ($l = \lambda/4$). Thus, between zero frequency and $f = \frac{c}{4l}$ the reactance is negative and the tube element acts like a spring.

In the interval from $kl = \frac{\pi}{2}$ to $kl = \pi$ $\left(\text{i.e. } \frac{\lambda}{4} < l < \frac{\lambda}{2}\right)$, the sign of Z_{00} changes to positive and the tube element acts like an inertance.

If $kl = \pi$, i.e. $l = \lambda/2$, then $Z_{00} = \infty$. The same result will be obtained if $l=n\frac{\lambda}{2}$, where n is a whole number. Consequently, a closed (at $x=l$) tube of length $l=n\frac{\lambda}{2}$ is, as it were, an absolutely rigid incompressible body. This conclusion is of course an idealization, obtained on the assumption that there is no attenuation of sound in the tube ($\beta=0$).

If $\beta\neq 0$ then if $Z_0=0$ and $Z_l=\infty$ it is found from formula (5-45) after simple transformations that

$$Z_{00}=S\rho c\coth\gamma l=S\rho c\coth(jk+\beta)l= \tag{5-46}$$
$$=S\rho c\frac{\cos kl\cosh\beta l+j\sin kl\sinh\beta l}{j\sin kl\cosh\beta l+\cos kl\sinh\beta l}.$$

If

$$kl=\left(n+\frac{1}{2}\right)\pi,\ \text{i. e.}\ l=\left(n+\frac{1}{2}\right)\frac{\lambda}{2},\quad Z_{00}=S\rho c\tanh\beta l,\ \text{but if}$$
$$kl=n\pi,\ \text{i. e.}\ l=n\frac{\lambda}{2},\ Z_{00}=S\rho c\coth\beta l.$$

If βl is small, then in the first case $Z_{00}\approx S\rho c\beta l$ (instead of zero as obtained from formula (5-45)); in the second case $Z_{00}\approx S\rho c/\beta l$. Provided $l=\left(n+\frac{1}{2}\right)\frac{\lambda}{2}$ (resonance), a closed tube has a very slight resistance if βl is small and it can serve better as an acoustic "short circuit" than an open aperture which has a resistance and reactance.

If the degree of attenuation in the tube is large, for example, when it is filled with a porous material (at large values of l), $Z_{00}\approx S\rho c$, since $\coth\beta l$ tends to unity if l is large. This conclusion is not quite correct since it was assumed that β was small in deriving formula (5-41).

In a tube with an open end it is necessary to assume that Z_l is equal to the impedance of a piston of area S which radiates into open space. At low frequencies $Z_l\to 0$ and from expression (5-43) we get:

$$Z_{00} = S\rho c \tanh \gamma l \approx jS\rho c \tan kl. \qquad (5\text{-}47)$$

In a short tube ($kl \ll 1$)

$$Z_{00} \approx jS\rho ckl = j\omega(Sl\rho) = j\omega M, \qquad (5\text{-}48)$$

where $M = Sl\rho$.

Consequently, a short open tube (short compared with the wavelength) gives an impedance with the effect of inertia, which corresponds to a moving mass $M = Sl\rho$, equal to the mass of the medium in the tube. At higher frequencies Z_{00} increases and becomes equal to infinity when $kl = \frac{\pi}{2}, \left(l = \frac{\lambda}{4}\right)$, and then becomes negative (elastic reactance) within the limits from $kl = \frac{\pi}{2}, \left(l = \frac{\lambda}{4}\right)$ to $kl = \pi$, $\left(l = \frac{\lambda}{2}\right)$. If $l = n\frac{\lambda}{2}, Z_{00} = 0$, i.e. an open tube of length $l = n\frac{\lambda}{2}$ does not in practice produce resistance to sound (in this case it is assumed that $\beta = 0$ and $Z_l \approx 0$, which is possible if $\lambda \gg \sqrt{S}$).

In order to refine expression (5-48) for a short tube, it is necessary to take into account the attached mass (M') at its end and use the concept of total effective mass. For a tube of radius r_0 with a flange (as per Rayleigh) $M' = \frac{8}{3}\rho r_0^3$, and for a tube without a flange (as per Gutin) $M' = 2\rho r_0^3$. (see Chapter XI). If the attached mass at the open end of the tube is included, we then get for the impedance of a tube with a flange (if $kr_0 \ll 1$)

$$Z_{00} \approx j\omega S\rho\left(l + \frac{8}{3\pi} r_0\right) = j\omega S\rho\,(l + 0{\cdot}85 r_0),$$

and for a tube without a flange:

$$Z_{00} \approx j\omega S\rho\left(l + \frac{2}{\pi}r_0\right) = j\omega S\rho\,(l + 0{\cdot}64r_0).$$

Thus, an open tube without a flange becomes as it were longer by an amount $0{\cdot}64\ r_0$. This effect has to be taken into account when tuning an organ pipe to a definite pitch.

Method of the Impedance Diagram

Expression (5-43) for the input impedance of a tube is used in a large number of applied problems. After simple transformations it is easy to see that equation (5-43) can be simplified by putting $Z_l = S\rho c \coth \psi_l$ and $Z_0 = 0$ in (5-41):

$$Z_{00} = S\rho c \frac{\sinh\psi_l \sinh\gamma l + \cosh\psi_l \cosh\gamma l}{\cosh\psi_l \sinh\gamma l + \sinh\psi_l \cosh\gamma l} = S\rho c \coth(\psi_l + \gamma l) = \quad (5\text{-}49)$$
$$= S\rho c \coth\,[(\varepsilon_l + \beta l) - j(\delta_l - \alpha l)].$$

If $l = 0$, i.e. if the force acts directly on the impedance Z_l, then $Z_{00} = S\rho c\ \coth(\varepsilon_l - j\delta_l) = Z_l$, which corresponds to formula (5-35).

Formula (5-49) provides a very convenient graphical method of finding the impedance Z_{00} at the beginning of a tube given the impedance Z_l at the end of the tube, if the damping βl is small. The use of this method in acoustics was first suggested by Morse* in 1936. This method had however been used previously in the theory of electrical lines.

Having determined the quantities ε_l and δ_l, from the impedance Z_l it is necessary in accordance with (5-49)

* P.M. Morse, *Vibration and Sound*. New York: McGraw-Hill, 1936 (see pp.191 ff.).

to subtract the quantity $\alpha l = \pi l / \frac{\lambda}{2}$ (definable by the length of the tube and frequency of the sound) from δ_l without changing ε_l, i.e. on the diagram it is necessary to move from the point with the coordinates R_{1l} and Y_{1l} (corresponding to the impedance Z_l) along the circle of constant ε_l (i.e, the circle of constant N and α) through a distance $\frac{\delta}{\pi} = \frac{l}{\lambda/2}$ (equal to the number of half-waves in the section l) in the clockwise direction so that δ decreases in value. At this point those values R_{10} and Y_{10} are found from the diagram which correspond to the impedance Z_{00}. An increase in the length of the tube by $\Delta l = n\frac{\lambda}{2}$ $(k\Delta l = n\pi)$ corresponds to a decrease in phase $\frac{\delta}{\pi}$ by n, or to a movement along the circle of constant ε (or α) by n whole revolutions in the clockwise direction. An increase in length of the tube by $\lambda/4$ reduces the phase $\frac{\delta}{\pi}$ by ½. Owing to the different phase scales on the circles of constant absorption, this will not correspond to a half-revolution, but it will always correspond to a move from the lower part to the upper part of the same circle or vice versa.

In order to illustrate the use of impedance diagrams, we will determine the impedance of a closed tube of length l with a layer of cloth having the resistance $R_1 = \frac{R}{S\rho c}$. at its entry. The impedance Z_{1l} at the closed end of the tube corresponds to $Y_{1l} = -\infty$ and $R_{1l} = 0$ (no losses). The point which represents this impedance lies on the circle $\alpha = 0$, $(\varepsilon = 0,\ N = \infty)$, which has an infinitely large radius and coincides with the Y_1 axis; the centre of the circle lies on the R_1 axis at minus infinity. The angle δ_l is zero because $r_p = re^{j2\delta}$ (and $r_p = +1$).

In order to find the impedance at the entry of the tube, it is necessary to move the point a distance kl/π along the circle $\varepsilon = 0$ in the clockwise direction, i.e. along the Y_1 axis from $-\infty$. If $kl = n\pi$ $\left(\delta/\pi = n,\ l = n\frac{\lambda}{2}\right)$ the quantity $\frac{\delta}{\pi}$ varies a whole number of units. Having made a number of complete revolutions, we again come to the same point on the diagram, i.e. we again get $Y_1 = -\infty$ and $R_1 = 0$. Thus, if $l = n\frac{\lambda}{2}$ the impedance of the solid wall $Z_l = \infty$ is transferred without variation to the beginning of the tube as shown previously. In this case the resistance of the cloth adds nothing to the impedance of the tube. If $kl = \left(n + \frac{1}{2}\right)\pi$, or $l = \left(n + \frac{1}{2}\right)\frac{\lambda}{2}$, then the phase $\frac{\delta}{\pi}$ changes by $(n + 1/2)$ and the point is moved along the circle $\varepsilon = 0$ (the Y_1 axis) a whole number of revolutions plus one half revolution and it comes to the origin $\left(\frac{\delta}{\pi} = 0{\cdot}5\right)$. The impedance of the tube will be zero ($R_1 = 0$ and $Y_1 = 0$). This implies that a closed tube of length $n\frac{\lambda}{2} + \lambda/4$ has zero resistance and reactance (this result was also obtained previously).

In order to find the impedance of a tube of length $\left(n + \frac{1}{2}\right)\frac{\lambda}{2}$, which is closed at the end and has a layer of cloth (R_1) at the entry, it is necessary to add the impedance of the layer to the resistance and reactance of the tube. Since the impedance of the layer is a pure resistance, this only means moving the point from the position (0,0) to the position $(R_1, 0)$. If $R_1 = 1$, we then come to the point (1,0), where $\varepsilon = \infty$, i.e. $\alpha = 1$. Consequently a tube of length $l = n\frac{\lambda}{2} + \frac{\lambda}{4}$ with a layer of cloth having a specific resistance $R_1 = 1$, $(R = S\rho c)$ at the entry gives $\alpha = 1$, or total sound absorption; of course $\alpha = 1$, only at discrete frequencies $f_n = \frac{\left(n + \frac{1}{2}\right)c}{2l}$, and not over the entire frequency band.

If $kl = n\pi + \frac{\pi}{4}$, or $l = n\frac{\lambda}{2} + \frac{\lambda}{8}$, we obtain the point (0, -1) on the diagram and, having added R_1, we obtain the impedance $(R_1 - j)$. The tube will behave like a resistance and elastic impedance which are connected in series. At no value of R_1 is it possible in this case to be at the point (1, 0) and obtain $\alpha = 1$.

If $kl = n\pi + \frac{3}{4}\pi$, or $l = n\frac{\lambda}{2} + \frac{3}{8}\lambda$, the point $(R_1 + j)$ is reached on the diagram by adding R_1. The tube will act like a resistance and inertance connected in series. In this case it is also impossible to obtain $\alpha = 1$.

The method of impedance diagrams can naturally be generalized for a layer with any impedance Z_1, or for a number of such layers with impedances Z_i, separated by elements of tube of lengths l_i. The way to find the total impedance at the input to such a system is quite straightforward: after moving along the circle of constant ε_l from the point $\left(\frac{R_l}{S\rho c}, \frac{Y_l}{S\rho c}\right)$ over the phase segment $\frac{kl_1}{\pi}$ in the clockwise direction and thus finding the impedance at the input to the first section of the tube, it is necessary to add the impedance of the first layer Z_{11} to the previously obtained impedance by a vector addition, and the point then moves to a new circle of constant ε_1. Using that we again move over a segment $\frac{kl_2}{\pi}$ in the clockwise direction and find the impedance at the input to the second section of the tube.

We then add the impedance of the second layer Z_{12}, moving to a circle of constant ε_2, and so on, until we come to the last layer. Having found Z_1 at the input, we can thus find the sound absorption coefficient α for the whole system from the impedance diagram. This method has been successfully used by Maliuzhinets* for calculating the sound absorption of complex laminar systems.

If attenuation of sound in the tube is included, then on moving from a certain point of the tube with the coordinate x to a neighbouring point $(x - \Delta x)$, it is necessary to move along the circle of constant ε over the segment $\frac{\alpha \Delta x}{\pi}$ in the clockwise direction and transfer to a different circle $\frac{\varepsilon + \beta \Delta x}{\pi}$, which will always be smaller in radius. With gradual progression along the tube (in the direction of the negative x axis) the point which represents the impedance on the complex plane will move along a gradually contracting spiral. If the length of tube is sufficient, the spiral will finally coil up at the point (1,0) which corresponds to $\varepsilon = \infty$, $(\alpha = 1)$. Thus, if the tube is long enough and filled with a medium which absorbs sound, then all the sound which enters the tube will be absorbed.

The same result can be obtained by analysing expression (5-49). For a rigid wall at the end, the parameters ε_l and δ_l are equal to zero and

$$Z_{00} = S\rho c \coth(\beta l + j\alpha l).$$

It is easy to see that $Z_{00} \to S\rho c$ if $l \to \infty$ and, consequently, $\alpha \to 1$.

---

* G.D. Maliuzhinets, *Inf-tekh. byull. stroit. Dvortsa Sovetov*, Moscow, 1941.

Natural Oscillations in a Tube Terminated by Impedances Z_0 and Z_l

If natural oscillations occur in a system which consists of a tube terminated by impedances Z_0 and Z_l, the phase of a wave which travels down the tube and back must change by exactly $2\pi n$. By taking into account the phase shifts equal to $2\delta_0$ and $2\delta_l$ at the end impedances, and the phase lead over the double length of tube, this condition can be written in the form:

$$2\delta_l - 2kl + 2\delta_0 = 2\pi n,$$

whence

$$\left.\begin{aligned} \sin 2kl &= \sin(2\delta_0 + 2\delta_l), \\ \cos 2kl &= \cos(2\delta_0 + 2\delta_l), \end{aligned}\right\} \qquad (5\text{-}50)$$

where the cosines and sines of the phase angles $2\delta_0$ and $2\delta_l$ are defined by formulae (5-31) and are functions of the frequency ω. Using equation (5-50) it is possible to find the frequencies of the natural oscillations ω_n of the system. The general solution of these equations is quite complicated. The simplest method of approach is a graphical solution in which the left and right sides of the equations are plotted as functions of ω in order to determine the points of intersection of the respective curves.

In certain special cases the solution can be obtained analytically.

I. Suppose, for example, that a tube is open at the entry but closed at the end by a pure reactance Y_{1l}. Then $Y_{10} = 0$, $R_{10} = 0$ and $2\delta_0 = \pi$. From formulae (5-50) and (5-31)

$$\sin 2kl = \sin(2\delta_l + \pi) = -\frac{2Y_{1l}}{Y_{1l}^2+1};\ \cos 2kl = \cos(2\delta_l + \pi) = -\frac{Y_{1l}^2-1}{Y_{1l}^2+1};$$

$$\tan 2kl = -\frac{2\tan kl}{\tan^2 kl - 1} = \frac{2\cot kl}{\cot^2 kl - 1} = \tan(2\delta_l + \pi) = \frac{2Y_{1l}}{Y_{1l}^2 - 1}. \quad (5\text{-}51)$$

These equations have two solutions

$$\left.\begin{aligned} \tan kl &= -Y_{1l}, \\ \cot kl &= Y_{1l}. \end{aligned}\right\} \quad (5\text{-}52)$$

The second solution does not satisfy the equations for $\cos 2kl$ and $\sin 2kl$ and is a superflous solution of the equation in (5-51) which contains $\cot kl$.

(a) Using the equation $\tan kl = -Y_{1l}$, if $Y_{1l} = 0$ (open end) we get: $kl = n\pi$ and $l = n\frac{\lambda}{2}$, which is the known result for a tube open at both ends.

(b) If $Y_{1l} = \infty$ (a tube which is closed at the end) $kl = \left(n + \frac{1}{2}\right)\pi$ and $l = \left(n + \frac{1}{2}\right)\frac{\lambda}{2}$; this also is a well-known result.

II. If $Y_{1l} = \infty$ and $R_{1l} = 0$ (a rigid wall) and if an impedance Y_{10} is connected at the entry, then $\sin 2\delta_l = 0$ and $\cos 2\delta_l = 1$; consequently, $2\delta_l = 0$. Using expressions (5-50) and (5-31) we get:

$$\sin 2kl = \sin 2\delta_0 = \frac{2Y_{10}}{Y_{10}^2+1};\ \cos 2kl = \cos 2\delta_0 = \frac{Y_{10}^2-1}{Y_{10}^2+1};$$

$$\tan 2kl = \tan 2\delta_0 = \frac{-2\tan kl}{\tan^2 kl - 1} = \frac{2\cot kl}{\cot^2 kl - 1} = \frac{2Y_{10}}{Y_{10}^2 - 1}.$$

As in the case of an open tube, from the last equation we

find:

$$\left.\begin{aligned}\tan kl &= -Y_{10},\\ \cot kl &= Y_{10},\end{aligned}\right\} \quad (5\text{-}53)$$

but only the second solution is suitable.

The condition of resonance will have the form:

$$\cot kl = Y_{10}.$$

III. If the tube is open at the entry but connected to a cavity of volume V at the end (Fig. 26) and provided the size of the cavity is small compared with the length of the tube l and the wavelength λ, it can be assumed that $Y_{1l} = -\frac{1}{S\rho c} \cdot \frac{\rho c^2 S^2}{\omega V}$ and the first of the equations in (5-52) for the natural frequencies takes the form:

$$\tan kl = \frac{cS}{\omega V} = \frac{Sl}{(kl)V}. \quad (5\text{-}54)$$

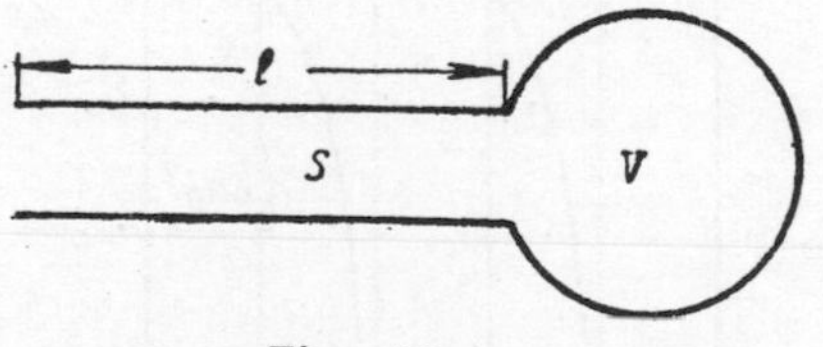

Fig. 26

In order to find the roots of this equation, it is necessary to plot a family of tangent curves and the hyperbola $\frac{Sl}{V} \cdot \frac{1}{kl}$ as functions of kl (Fig. 27). The points of intersection of the hyperbola with the tangent curves will correspond to the roots of the equation for the natural frequencies. When the length of the tube is small, the first root will be considerably less than the others and as an approximation it can be assumed that

$$\tan kl \approx kl = \frac{Sl}{V} \cdot \frac{1}{kl},$$

whence

$$kl = \sqrt{\frac{Sl}{V}} \quad \text{or} \quad \omega = c\sqrt{\frac{S/l}{V}} = c\sqrt{\frac{K}{V}}, \qquad \text{(5-54a)}$$

where $K = \frac{S}{l}$ is a quantity known as the *conductance*. This is the well-known formula for the natural frequency of a resonator.

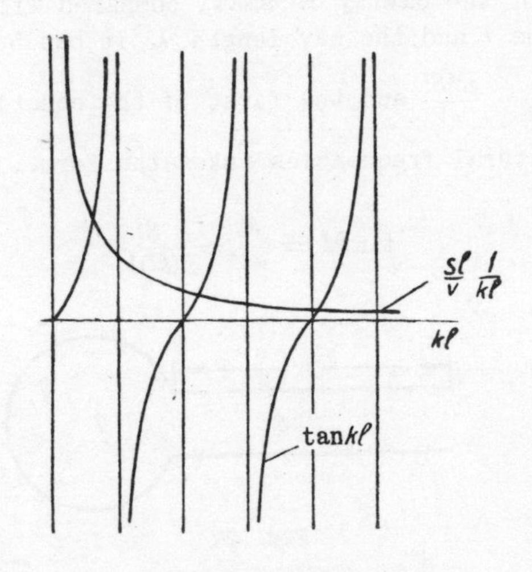

Fig. 27

IV. We will now consider the natural frequency of a tube of length l_1 which is open at one end, but connected to a tube of length l_2 of cross-section σ at the other end. This extra tube may either be open or closed (Fig. 28).

Bearing in mind the transformation of the specific impedances (see Chapter VII on acoustic wave-guides), the following equations can be formed for the natural frequencies from formulae (5-45), (5-47) and (5-52):

$$\tan kl_1 = \begin{cases} \frac{S}{\sigma}\cot kl_2 & \text{(closed tube)}, \\ -\frac{S}{\sigma}\tan kl_2 & \text{(open tube)}. \end{cases} \quad (5\text{-}55)$$

If the tube l_2 is short, then for a closed tube

$$\tan kl_1 \approx \frac{S}{\sigma}\frac{1}{kl_2}, \quad \text{or} \quad \cot kl_1 \approx \frac{\sigma}{S} kl_2.$$

If $\frac{\sigma}{S} kl_2 \ll 1$, it follows from the last equation

$$\frac{\pi}{2} - kl_1 \approx \frac{\sigma}{S} kl_2 - n\pi,$$

whence

$$k_n \approx \frac{(2n+1)\frac{\pi}{2}}{l_1 + \frac{\sigma}{S} l_2} \quad \text{or} \quad f_n \approx \frac{c(2n+1)}{4\left(l_1 + \frac{\sigma}{S} l_2\right)}.$$

If the attached tube is very narrow $\left(\frac{\sigma}{S} l_2 \ll l_1\right)$, we get the known formula for a tube which is open at one end and closed at the other. Thus, the connexion of a narrow tube of length l_2 reduces the natural frequency of the main tube.

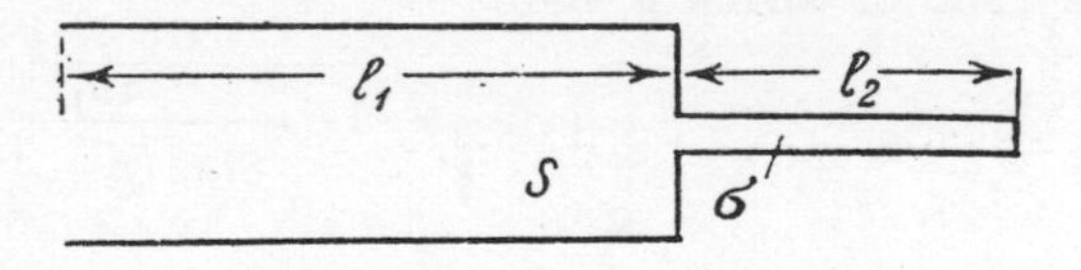

Fig. 28

If $\sigma = S$, then the equation of the natural frequencies takes the form

$$\tan kl_1 = \cot kl_2 \quad \text{(closed tube)},$$

$$\tan kl_1 = -\tan kl_2 \quad \text{(open tube)}.$$

where

$$k(l_1+l_2)=\begin{vmatrix} (2n+1)\frac{\pi}{2} & \text{(closed tube)}, \\ n\pi & \text{(open tube)}. \end{vmatrix}$$

These are known equations for the natural frequencies of a tube of length (l_1+l_2); this result is a check on the correctness of the method used for the analysis.

We will now consider a short open tube l_2 on the assumption that $kl_2<1$. If the tube is very narrow $\left(\frac{S}{\sigma}\gg 1\right)$

so that $\frac{S}{\sigma}kl_2\gg 1$, then

$$\cot kl_1=\tan\left(\frac{\pi}{2}-kl_1\right)=$$

$$=-\frac{\sigma}{S}\frac{1}{\tan kl_2}\approx-\frac{\sigma}{S}\frac{1}{kl_2}\approx-\tan\left(\frac{\sigma}{S}\cdot\frac{1}{kl_2}\right),$$

whence

$$\frac{\pi}{2}-kl_1\approx-\left(\frac{\sigma}{S}\frac{1}{kl_2}+n\pi\right)=-\frac{\sigma}{S}\frac{l_1}{l_2}\frac{1}{kl_1}-n\pi.$$

In order to find kl_1, we obtain a quadratic equation, the positive root of which gives:

$$kl_1=\left(n+\frac{1}{2}\right)\frac{\pi}{2}\cdot\left[1+\sqrt{1+\frac{4\sigma l_1}{Sl_2\pi^2\left(n+\frac{1}{2}\right)^2}}\right].$$

It is quite clear from this formula that the attachment of a thin open tube increases the natural frequencies of the main tube of length l_1. In addition it is obvious that the overtones will be non-harmonic; in fact

$$f_n=\frac{kl_1}{2\pi l_1}c\approx\frac{c(2n+1)}{4l_1}\left[1+\frac{4\sigma l_1}{Sl_2\pi^2(2n+1)^2}\right]. \qquad (5\text{-}56)$$

The increase in natural frequency can be explained as follows. The resonant system of an open tube l_1 can be regarded as a system with lumped constants, so that a certain equivalent mass is concentrated near the open end, and an equivalent elasticity near the closed end. The attachment of an open tube l_2 creates an additional mass at the closed end which is connected with the main mass of the tube via an intermediate elasticity. The total mass is obtained by the parallel connexion of the two masses and is less than the main mass of air in the tube, which causes an increase in the natural frequency of the system. Such a system is known under the name of a "sound mushroom" (Tonpilz in Germany).

It is a different matter if the area of the tube l_2 is not very small and if $\frac{S}{\sigma}kl_2 \ll 1$. Then

$$\tan kl_1 = -\frac{S}{\sigma}\tan kl_2 \approx -\frac{S}{\sigma}kl_2 \approx -\tan\frac{S}{\sigma}kl_2 \ll 1$$

and from (5-55):

$$kl_1 \approx n\pi - \frac{S}{\sigma}kl_2 \quad \text{or} \quad k\left(l_1 + \frac{S}{\sigma}l_2\right) \approx n\pi.$$

This condition corresponds to the natural frequency of a tube of length $l_1 + \frac{S}{\sigma}l_2$, which is open at both ends. For example, if $\frac{S}{\sigma} = 10$; $l_1 = 10$ cm and $l_2 = 1$ cm, then the addition of a small tube l_2 doubles the effective length of the tube and all the natural frequencies are halved.

These arguments are naturally applicable to the study of the effect on natural frequencies of the impedance of a layer covering the walls of a building. If the impedance at the end of the tube has a negative reactive part, then on the basis of (5-54) and from Fig. 27 it will be seen that the first and subsequent natural frequencies of the system are reduced compared with the natural frequencies of a closed tube for which

$$\tan kl = \infty \text{ and } kl = \left(n + \frac{1}{2}\right)\pi.$$

Thus, a negative (elastic) reactance reduces the natural frequencies and is as it were equivalent to an increase in dimensions. On the other hand, with a positive inertial reactance on the wall, it follows from (5-56) that the natural frequencies are increased, i.e. the dimensions of the system are in effect reduced.

We will now consider, using another method, the resonant frequency of a tube which is closed at $x = l$ and has an impedance Z_0 at $x = 0$, with reference to the effect of a front cavity on the performance of a condenser microphone.

Consider the effect of sound on a tube which is closed at one end by a rigid microphone diaphragm of impedance Z_l and which at the open end has a flange of quite a large size (Fig. 29). The boundary at the open end of the tube is assumed to be a flat piston of area $S = \pi r_0^2$ with an impedance

$$Z_0 = S\rho c(R_{10} + jY_{10}),$$

which is calculated by the formulae for a piston diaphragm in Chapter XI.

Suppose that this piston is affected by a force ψ which arises under the action of a plane acoustic wave with pressure amplitude p_0 incident along the axis of the tube. For long waves it can be assumed that an antinode (maximum) of pressure arises at the walls of the flange and in front of the cavity. Consequently,

$$\psi = 2Sp_0 e^{j\omega t}.$$

The impedance at the closed end of the tube Z_l is

assumed to be large. At the end of the tube the velocity is

$$\dot{\xi}(l)=\frac{\psi}{Z_{0l}}=\frac{2Sp_0e^{j\omega t}}{Z_{0l}},$$

and the pressure

$$p(l)=\frac{Z_l\dot{\xi}(l)}{S}.$$

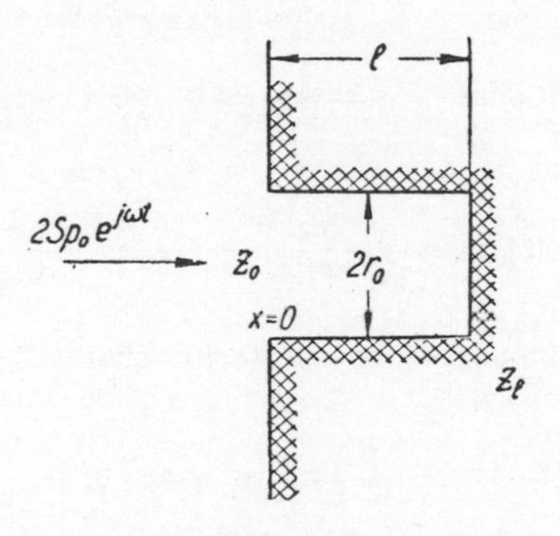

Fig. 29

The quantity Z_{0l} can be calculated from equation (5-42) on the assumption that $Z_l \gg Z_0$ and $Z_0Z_l \gg S^2\rho^2c^2$.

The first of these inequalities is obvious; the second is valid if the impedance $Z_l \gg S\rho c\,\frac{S\rho c}{Z_0}$. Since at low frequencies

$$Z_0 \approx S\rho c k^2 r_0^2$$

(see Chapter XI), we therefore require that $Z_l \gg \frac{S\rho c}{k^2 r_0^2}$, i.e. the impedance Z_l must be considerably greater than

$S\rho c$, since the quantity $\frac{1}{k^2 r_0^2}$ can be in practice of the order of 10^3 or more.

Under these conditions, from formula (5-42):

$$Z_{0l} \approx Z_l \left[\frac{Z_0}{S\rho c} j \sin kl + \cos kl \right]$$

and, consequently,

$$p(l) = \frac{Z_l \cdot 2Sp_0 e^{j\omega t}}{SZ_{0l}} = \frac{2p_0 e^{j\omega t}}{j \sin kl \, [R_{10} + j(Y_{10} - \cot kl)]}. \quad (5\text{-}57)$$

It is assumed that $R_{10} = Y_{10} = 0$ (extremely low frequencies); then

$$p(l) = \frac{2p_0 e^{j\omega t}}{-j^2 \cot kl \cdot \sin kl} = \frac{2p_0 e^{j\omega t}}{\cos kl}.$$

From this expression it is clear that if

$$kl = \left(n + \frac{1}{2}\right)\pi \text{ or } l = \left(n + \frac{1}{2}\right)\frac{\lambda}{2}$$

we get $p(l) = \infty$ and resonance obtains within the tube. This conclusion is in correspondence with the elementary theory of tubes. The lowest resonant frequency will correspond to $n = 0$ and $l = \lambda/4$, and from this

$$f_1 = \frac{c}{4l}.$$

The value $p(l) = \infty$ at resonance is obtained as a result of ignoring the radiation resistance and sound attenuation in the tube. A more exact expression for the condition of resonance can be found from equation (5-57) if we put

$$Y_{10} = \cot kl.$$

This formula corresponds to that obtained previously (see (5-53)).

The solution of this transcendental equation can be found graphically for each particular case. For example, for the cylindrical recess of a condenser microphone of the old type, for which $l=0{\cdot}8$ cm and $r_0=2{\cdot}6$ cm, the first two resonant frequencies are

$$f_1=6670 \text{ c/s and } f_2=32{,}000 \text{ c/s}.$$

The first resonance corresponds to the value $\lambda=6{\cdot}35l$ instead of $\lambda=4l$, as follows from the elementary theory. The second resonance value corresponds almost exactly to the simplified theory $\left(\lambda=\frac{4}{3}l\right)$. At the resonant frequency the pressure at the end of the tube (at the diaphragm of the microphone) is

$$p(l)=\frac{2p_0 e^{j\omega t}}{j \sin kl \cdot R_{10}};$$

the radiation resistance is a function of kr_0, and at the frequency 6670 c/s the denominator will equal $j\times 0{\cdot}41$. For the first resonance we get $|p(l)|=2{\cdot}4\times 2p_0$, i.e. the pressure is 2·4 times greater than in the band of low frequencies where $|p(l)|=2p_0$.

The Transmission of Energy Along Tubes

Let us now consider expressions (5-43) and (5-44). Provided $kl=n\pi$ $(n=1, 2, 3\ldots)$, $Z_{00}=(Z_0+Z_l)$ and $Z_{0l}=(-1)^n(Z_0+Z_l)$. It is clear from this result that the velocities $\dot{\xi}(0)$ and $\dot{\xi}(l)$ will be equal in absolute magnitude. The condition $kl=n\pi$ corresponds to resonance in the tube. Thus a tube with a length equal to a whole number of half-wave lengths transmits the effect of pressure like a rigid bar and the same deformation, $\xi(l)$, can be obtained at great distances as at the point where the force is applied. The conditions for the transmission of energy in this case will be optimum. The load impedance Z_l is as it were transferred to the point where the force is applied and added to the impedance Z_0 of the piston, which is set in motion directly by the force ψ. Of course such an effect can be distinguished clearly only if the degree of attenuation β is small.

Constantinesco* carried out tests on the transmission of large oscillations along water-filled tubes, a system of power transmission analogous to that of electrical energy along conductors, and also designed sound-driven motors for drilling stones.

---

* C.V. Drysdale, *et. al., The Mechanical Properties of Fluids*. London: Blackie, 1925 (see pp.221 ff. and 321).

CHAPTER VI

THEORY OF PROPAGATION OF NON-HOMOGENEOUS WAVES IN A TUBE

Oscillations inside a Rectangular Parallelepiped

We will consider first, as the simplest case, propagation in a tube of rectangular section. In order to explain the method of solution, we will begin with the propagation of a wave inside a volume having the shape of a rectangular parallelepiped with dimensions, a, b, l, along the axes x, y and z (Fig. 30).

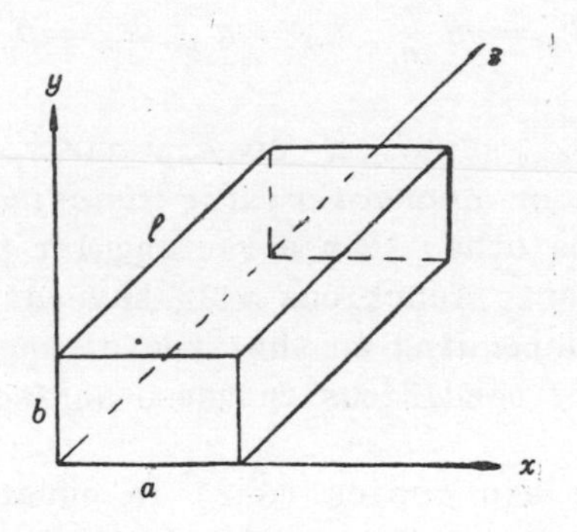

Fig. 30

The wave equation for sinusoidal oscillations has the form (see Chapter I):

$$\Delta\Psi + k^2\Psi = 0. \quad (6\text{-}1)$$

On the rigid faces the condition that the normal velocities vanish must be satisfied:

$$\left.\frac{\partial\Psi}{\partial x}\right|_{\substack{x=0\\x=a}}=0;\quad \left.\frac{\partial\Psi}{\partial y}\right|_{\substack{y=0\\y=b}}=0;\quad \left.\frac{\partial\Psi}{\partial z}\right|_{\substack{z=0\\z=l}}=0.$$

The expression for the velocity potential Ψ which satisfies these boundary conditions can easily be found by splitting the function $\Psi(x, y, z)$ into the product of three functions depending only on x, y, and z respectively. The solutions will have the form;

$$\Psi=A_{mnp}\cdot\cos m\frac{\pi x}{a}\cdot\cos n\frac{\pi y}{b}\cdot\cos p\frac{\pi z}{l}, \tag{6-2}$$

where

$$\left.\begin{matrix}m\\n\\p\end{matrix}\right\}=0,\ 1,\ 2,\ 3\ldots$$

Suppose we put:

$$k_m=m\frac{\pi}{a},\quad k_n=n\frac{\pi}{b},\quad k_p=p\frac{\pi}{l}.$$

The function $A_{mnp}\cdot\cos k_m x\cdot\cos k_n y\cdot\cos k_p z$ is called an *eigenfunction*, or *characteristic function*. For closed volumes of a type other than a rectangular parallelepiped, the characteristic functions will have different mathematical forms depending on the type of boundary surfaces and the boundary conditions on these surfaces.

Substituting expression (6-2) in equation (6-1), we get an expression for the wave number k in terms of k_m, k_n and k_p:

$$k^2=k_m^2+k_n^2+k_p^2=\pi^2\left(\frac{m^2}{a^2}+\frac{n^2}{b^2}+\frac{p^2}{l^2}\right). \tag{6-3}$$

As the formula is of such a form, from now on we will

put k_{mnp} for k. Dividing both sides of the equation by k_{mnp}, we get:

$$\left(\frac{k_m}{k_{mnp}}\right)^2+\left(\frac{k_n}{k_{mnp}}\right)^2+\left(\frac{k_p}{k_{mnp}}\right)^2=1. \qquad (6\text{-}4)$$

It is obvious that all three terms of this expression must be less than unity, or else only one of them can be equal to unity with the other two equal to zero. Suppose we put:

$$\frac{k_m}{k_{mnp}}=\frac{\frac{m}{a}}{\sqrt{\frac{m^2}{a^2}+\frac{n^2}{b^2}+\frac{p^2}{l^2}}}=\cos\alpha;$$

$$\frac{k_n}{k_{mnp}}=\frac{\frac{n}{b}}{\sqrt{\frac{m^2}{a^2}+\frac{n^2}{b^2}+\frac{p^2}{l^2}}}=\cos\beta; \qquad (6\text{-}5)$$

$$\frac{k_p}{k_{mnp}}=\frac{\frac{p}{l}}{\sqrt{\frac{m^2}{a^2}+\frac{n^2}{b^2}+\frac{p^2}{l^2}}}=\cos\gamma.$$

Then instead of equation (6-4), we have:

$$\cos^2\alpha+\cos^2\beta+\cos^2\gamma=1.$$

It follows from (6-5) that the quantities k_m, k_n and k_p can be represented geometrically as the components of a certain wave number vector k_{mnp}, which forms angles α, β, and γ with the coordinate axes; the absolute magnitude of the vector $|k_{mnp}|=\frac{\omega_{mnp}}{c}=\frac{2\pi}{\lambda_{mnp}}$ provides the wave number.

Thus, for each set of the three numbers m, n, and p we have a certain corresponding number k_{mnp}, called the *eigenvalue*, or *characteristic value*, of the parameter k for the given problem; in terms of the k_{mnp} it is possible to define all the natural frequencies of the volume $a\cdot b\cdot l$; these are expressed by the formula

$$f_{mnp}=\frac{\omega_{mnp}}{2\pi}=\frac{k_{mnp}\cdot c}{2\pi}=\frac{c}{2}\sqrt{\frac{m^2}{a^2}+\frac{n^2}{b^2}+\frac{p^2}{l^2}}. \qquad (6\text{-}6)$$

The tip of each wave number vector k_{mnp} with the components k_m k_n and k_p along the coordinate axes may be represented by a point in a three-dimensional space defined by the conditions $x \geqslant 0$, $y \geqslant 0$, and $z \geqslant 0$ (octant). The natural frequencies f_{mnp} can be similarly represented. The oscillations corresponding to the eigenvalues of the wave number k_{mnp}, are called *eigenfunctions* or *normal modes (m, n, p)*.

There is no difficulty in estimating roughly the number of natural frequencies contained between the limits $f = 0$ and the frequency f. Each of the frequencies in this region has a corresponding vector with components $m\frac{c}{2a}$, $n\frac{c}{2b}$, and $p\frac{c}{2l}$. The frequency space can be regarded as having been divided into rectangular volumes which are composed of elementary parallelepipeds with dimensions $\frac{c}{2a}$, $\frac{c}{2b}$, $\frac{c}{2l}$. Each natural frequency corresponds to a vertex of one of these parallelipeds. Thus, the number of natural frequencies in the interval from zero to f is approximately equal to the number of elementary parallelepipeds with the volume

$$V_1=\frac{c}{2a}\cdot\frac{c}{2b}\cdot\frac{c}{2l}=\frac{c^3}{8abl}=\frac{c^3}{8V},$$

where $V= abl$, contained within the octant of a sphere in frequency space of volume $V'\approx\frac{1}{8}\left(\frac{4}{3}\pi f^3\right)$. Thus the number of natural frequencies N at large values of f is approximately:

$$N\approx\frac{V'}{V_1}=\frac{4\pi f^3 V}{3c^3}.$$

The number of natural frequencies between f and $f+\Delta f$ (if $\Delta f \ll f$): is:

$$\Delta N=\frac{dN}{df}\Delta f\approx\frac{4\pi f^2 V}{c^3}\Delta f.$$

By way of example we will now estimate the number of

natural frequencies in a room of volume $V=5\times5\times4$ m^3 in the interval from 1000 to 1001 c/s. This number is very large: $\Delta N\approx 32$.

The minimum natural frequency will correspond to waves which are propagated parallel to the maximum dimension. If $l>a>b$, then if $p=1$, $m=0$ and $n=0$ we get:

$$\Psi_{001}=A_{001}\cos\frac{\pi z}{l} \quad \text{and} \quad f_{001}=\frac{c}{2l},$$

which corresponds to a plane standing wave along the direction of l at the frequency of the fundamental tone of a closed tube of length l.

In exactly the same way plane standing waves are formed along the directions of a or b if $m=1$ and $n=p=0$, $\left(\text{when } f_{100}=\frac{c}{2a}\right)$, and if $n=1$ and $m=p=0$, $\left(\text{when } f_{010}=\right.$ $\left.=\frac{c}{2b}\right)$. For these three cases we have respectively: $\cos^2\gamma=$ $=1$, $\cos^2\alpha=1$, or $\cos^2\beta=1$, i.e. the angles α, β and γ have the values 0 or π. In the case in question $f_{001}<f_{100}<f_{010}$.

It will now be shown that in the general case for any eigenvalue k_{mnp} there is a combination of plane waves whose direction depends on the various combinations of the components k_m, k_n and k_p of the wave vector $\vec{k}_{mnp}$.

Since

$$\cos k_m x=\frac{e^{jk_m x}+e^{-jk_m x}}{2},$$

it follows that having written the corresponding expressions for $\cos k_n y$ and $\cos k_p z$, there is no difficulty in obtaining by transformation the sum of eight expressions of the following type for the velocity potential Φ_{mnp}:

$$\begin{aligned}\Phi_{mnp}=\Psi_{mnp}\cdot e^{j\omega t}=\frac{A_{mnp}}{8}\sum e^{j(\omega t\pm k_m x\pm k_n y\pm k_p z)}=\\ =\frac{A_{mnp}}{8}\sum e^{j[\omega t-k_{mnp}(\mp x\cos\alpha\mp y\cos\beta\mp z\cos\gamma)]}=\\ =\frac{A_{mnp}}{8}\sum e^{j(\omega t-k_{mnp}u)}.\end{aligned} \tag{6-7}$$

The amplitude may be complex: $A_{mnp}=|A_{mnp}|e^{j\varphi_{mnp}}$, i.e. each component Φ_{mnp} has its own phase φ_{mnp}. In expression (6-7), the quantity

$$u=\mp x\cdot\cos\alpha\mp y\cos\beta\mp z\cdot\cos\gamma$$

is the length of a vector directed normal to the front of a certain plane wave and is equal in absolute magnitude to the distance between the origin and the plane of this wavefront.

It will be seen from expression (6-7) that for each eigenvalue k_{mnp} there are eight different possible plane waves corresponding to the eight different combinations of signs in the expression for u. Each of these eight waves has another corresponding wave (of the eight) in the opposite direction. Thus, there are always four different directions of the standing waves inside the volume $a\cdot b\cdot l$.

It is now worthwhile considering terminology for a moment. It will prove very useful if we borrow the word "ray" from optics, but it is of course used in a somewhat different sense. From now on we will refer to each of the plane waves making up the normal mode (m,n,p) as a "ray". The acoustic "ray" with direction cosines (6-5) begins at some point on the face and is reflected from the other faces, its path describing a certain non-planar polygon. When it has returned to the point from which it started, it again begins to describe the same path. *The length of this path is the same from whatever point the path of the "ray" begins and is equal to a whole number of wavelengths.*

The individual sections of these ray polygons are composed of "rays" whose equations are defined by expressions of the type (6-7) with various combinations of signs.

The equality of the path lengths travelled by each ray explains the physical meaning of the eigenvalues of the parameter $k=\frac{2\pi}{\lambda}$. They correspond to definite discrete values of the frequency, which we refer to as *"the natural frequencies"* of the volume. In fact, if the length is the same, each "ray" which leaves some point of the volume $a \cdot b \cdot l$ at an angle which satisfies conditions (6-5), is propagated at velocity c and returns to its starting point in the same period of time T'_{mnp}. This interval of time will be equal to a whole number N of periods T_{mnp} appropriate to natural oscillations of frequency f_{mnp}; it is obvious that $T_{mnp}=\frac{T'_{mnp}}{N}=\frac{1}{f_{mnp}}$.

The general solution for the natural oscillations of any type in a rectangular parallepiped can be represented by the expression:

$$\Phi(x,y,z,t)=\sum_{m=0}^{\infty}\sum_{n=0}^{\infty}\sum_{p=0}^{\infty}\Psi_{mnp}(x,y,z)\cdot e^{j2\pi f_{mnp}t}.$$

Propagation of Sound in an Infinite Rectangular Tube

It will now be assumed that one of the dimensions of the parallelepiped, e.g. l, is infinite. This will then bring us to the case of sound propagation in an infinite tube with a rectangular cross-section. The solution of equation (6-1) is formed from solutions of type (6-2). In this case each term must contain the product of the functions $\cos k_m x$ and $\cos k_n y$, since the velocities on the side faces are then zero. Standing waves also exist in the direction normal to the z axis.

But it is clear that a certain wave motion (with the wave number k_p) must be propagated along the positive direction of the z axis.

In the general case the solution of the equation can be taken in the form:

$$\Phi(x,y,z,t)=\sum_{m=0}^{\infty}\sum_{n=0}^{\infty} B_{mn}\cdot\cos k_m x\cdot\cos k_n y\cdot e^{j(\omega t-k_p z)}. \quad (6\text{-}8)$$

By substitution in the wave equation it is easy to see that for this case as well as for a closed rectangular parallelepiped

$$k^2=k_m^2+k_n^2+k_p^2.$$

Suppose that on the face $z = 0$ there is a certain forced distribution of oscillatory velocity along the z axis given by:

$$\dot{\zeta}(x,y)=\psi_0(x,y)e^{j[\omega t+\varphi(x,y)]}$$

where the angular frequency $\omega=kc$, is that of the driving force. In the special case of pure standing waves, $\varphi(x,y)=0$ or π. We have to expand the function $\psi_0(x,y)$ into a double Fourier series in the eigenfunctions for the oscillations in the direction transverse to the axis of the tube, namely, in the functions $\cos\kappa_m x\cdot\cos\kappa_n y$.

$$\psi_0(x,y)\cdot e^{j\varphi(x,y)}=\sum_{m=0}^{\infty}\sum_{n=0}^{\infty}\alpha_{mn}\cdot\cos k_m x\cdot\cos k_n y,$$

where $k_m=m\frac{\pi}{a}$ and $k_n=n\frac{\pi}{b}$. The coefficients α_{mn} are defined by expressions of the type:

$$\alpha_{mn}=\frac{4}{ab}\int_0^a\int_0^b\psi_0(x,y)\,e^{j\varphi(x,y)}\cdot\cos k_m x\cdot\cos k_n y\cdot dx\,dy; \quad (6\text{-}9)$$

$$\alpha_{m0}=\frac{2}{ab}\int_0^a\int_0^b\psi_0(x,y)\,e^{j\varphi(x,y)}\cdot\cos k_m x\cdot dx\,dy;$$

$$\alpha_{0n}=\frac{2}{ab}\int_0^a\int_0^b \psi_0(x,y)\,e^{j\varphi(x,y)}\cdot\cos k_n y\cdot dx\,dy;$$

$$\alpha_{00}=\frac{1}{ab}\int_0^a\int_0^b \psi_0(x,y)\,e^{j\varphi(x,y)}\cdot dx\cdot dy. \qquad (6\text{-}9)$$

If $\varphi(x,y)=0$ or π, then the coefficients α_{mn} will be real; but if $\varphi(x,y)\neq 0$ or π, then they will be complex. In the first case there will be pure standing waves on the face $z = 0$; but in the second case there will be motion in the form of progressive waves. If the amplitudes of the mutually-opposed progressive waves are equal, then pure standing waves are obtained. In the following we will confine ourselves to processes caused by pure standing waves on the surface $z = 0$, and assume that all α_{mn} are real. That special form of oscillation in the plane of the initial section $z = 0$ which is defined by the numbers m and n and characterized by the amplitude α_{mn}, will be referred to as an oscillation of the "mode (mn)".

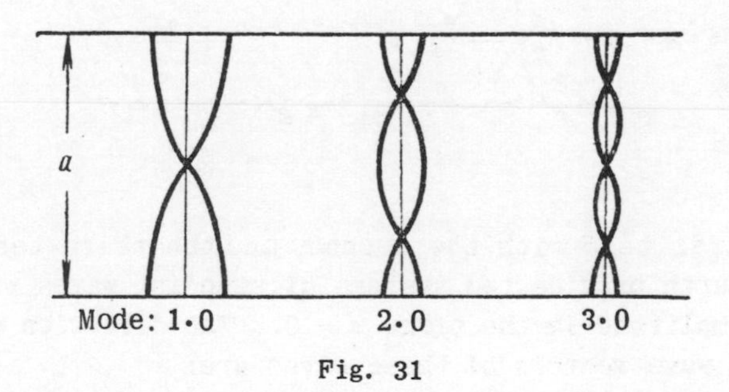

Fig. 31

Figure 31 shows, for example, the distribution of the axial velocities for modes of oscillation 1, 0; 2, 0; and 3, 0.

On the boundary $z = 0$, the particle velocity of the

medium must satisfy the condition

$$-\frac{\partial\Phi}{\partial z}\bigg|_{z=0} = \psi_0(x, y)\, e^{j\varphi(x,y)} \cdot e^{j\omega t},$$

whence

$$\sum_{m=0}^{\infty}\sum_{n=0}^{\infty} B_{mn}\, jk_p \cdot \cos k_m x \cdot \cos k_n y = \sum_{m=0}^{\infty}\sum_{n=0}^{\infty} \alpha_{mn} \cdot \cos k_m x \cdot \cos k_n y.$$

Equating coefficients of terms with corresponding subscripts, we have:

$$B_{mn} = \frac{\alpha_{mn}}{jk_p}. \tag{6-10}$$

Each oscillation mode on the face $z = 0$ is represented by a term of the type $\alpha_{mn} \cos k_m x \cdot \cos k_n y$. The frequency ω is the same for all oscillation modes in the problem in question. In order to elucidate the physical meaning of this expression, it is necessary to transform it slightly:

$$\alpha_{mn} \cdot \cos k_m x \cdot \cos k_n y = \frac{\alpha_{mn}}{4} e^{j(k_m x + k_n y)} + \frac{\alpha_{mn}}{4} e^{j(-k_m x - k_n y)} + \\ + \frac{\alpha_{mn}}{4} e^{j(k_m x - k_n y)} + \frac{\alpha_{mn}}{4} e^{j(-k_m x + k_n y)}.$$

The first term with the second, and the third term with the fourth provide two systems of standing waves with the same amplitude in the plane $z = 0$. The direction cosines of the wave vectors of these waves are:

$$\cos\alpha' = \frac{\pm k_m}{\sqrt{k_m^2 + k_n^2}}; \quad \cos\beta' = \frac{\pm k_n}{\sqrt{k_m^2 + k_n^2}}. \tag{6-11}$$

For the one system of standing waves we take the signs (+, +,) and (−, −), and for the other system (+, −) and (−, +).

Thus:

$$\alpha_{mn}\cdot\cos k_m x\cdot\cos k_n y=\frac{\alpha_{mn}}{4}\sum_4 e^{j[\omega t-\sqrt{k_m^2+k_n^2}(\mp x\cdot\cos\alpha'\mp y\cos\beta')]}=$$

$$=\frac{\alpha_{mn}}{4}e^{j(\omega t-k'_{mn}u')},$$

where $k'_{mn}=\sqrt{k_m^2+k_n^2}$ is the magnitude of a wave vector in the plane $z = 0$ which takes directions corresponding to one of the four possible combinations of signs in expression (6-11), and $u'=\pm x\cos\alpha'\pm y\cos\beta'$ is the section of a line laid off along the direction of the normal to the front of each of the four progressive waves in the plane $z = 0$ and equal in absolute magnitude to the distance between the origin and the wavefront. The angles α' and β' together make 90°. The two systems of standing waves in the plane $z=0$ will intersect at an angle to each other of $2\alpha'=\pi-2\beta'$ The wavelength at the boundary $z = 0$ is

$$\lambda'_{mn}=\frac{2\pi}{k'_{mn}}=\frac{2\pi}{\sqrt{k_m^2+k_n^2}}=\frac{2}{\sqrt{\frac{m^2}{a^2}+\frac{n^2}{b^2}}}=\frac{c'_{mn}}{f},\quad (6\text{-}12)$$

where

$$c'_{mn}=\frac{2f}{\sqrt{\frac{m^2}{a^2}+\frac{n^2}{b^2}}}$$

corresponds to the speed of wave propagation along the plane $z = 0$.

It will be seen that in order to form standing waves of this kind, which represent individual modes of oscillation on the face $z = 0$, their speed of propagation c'_{mn} at the given frequency must be proportional to f and, in addition, that it will be different for different modes (m, n). The free bending waves of real plates and membranes cannot satisfy this condition, since the velocity of transverse waves on membranes is independent of frequency and a constant quantity, whilst for plates it increases in proportion to $\sqrt{f}$. Thus, waves which correspond to individual oscillation modes on the face $z = 0$, can only be formed under forced conditions when an external force which is specially distributed on the plane $z = 0$ is applied, but at frequencies not necessarily equal to the natural frequencies of these modes.

It is clear that we could not expand the function $\psi_0(x, y)$ into a series which contains the products of the functions $\cos k_m x$ by $\sin k_n y$ or $\sin k_m x$ by $\sin k_n y$, since the boundary conditions on the side faces would not then be satisfied. However, this does not imply that the velocities actually cannot be distributed over the face $z = 0$ according to a sinusoidal law for instance. Thus, it is possible to expand motion which in fact has a sinusoidal distribution on the surface of a certain plate or membrane, at a frequency below the fundamental tone, such as is characterized by the function $\sin \frac{\pi x}{a} \cdot \sin \frac{\pi y}{b}$, into a series in $\cos k_m x \cdot \cos k_n y$.

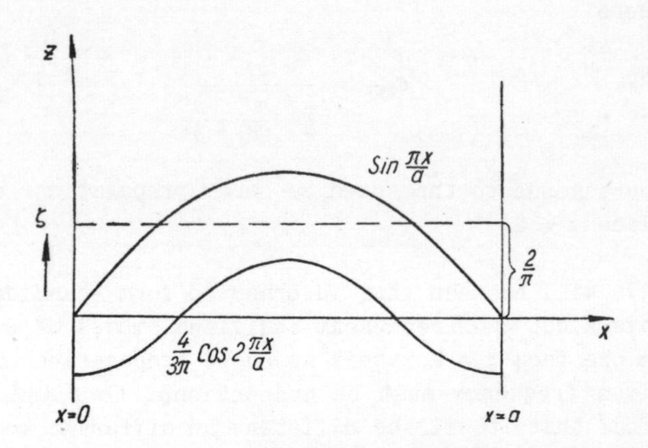

Fig. 32

In the simplest case of a standing wave solely in the direction of the x axis the velocities in the plane $z = 0$ are distributed according to the law $\sin\frac{\pi x}{a}$. The series expansion in cosines has the form:

$$\sin\frac{\pi x}{a}=\frac{2}{\pi}-\frac{4}{3\pi}\cos 2\frac{\pi x}{a}-\frac{4}{15\pi}\cdot\cos 4\frac{\pi x}{a}-\frac{4}{35\pi}\cos 6\frac{\pi x}{a}\dots$$

Thus, motion is composed of a constant term and a number of cosinusoidal components (Fig. 32). The constant term $\frac{2}{\pi}$ excites motion corresponding to a plane wave along the z axis (mode 0,0).

In general, for a symmetrical distribution of velocity about the centre, only those modes of oscillation occur which are defined by even numbers m, n, including the mode (0,0); for an asymmetrical distribution, modes with odd numbers m or n occur. Thus, an oscillation of the type $\cos\frac{\pi x}{a}$, is present only if the excitation in the plane $z=0$ is asymmetric.

The function $\sin\frac{\pi x}{a}\cdot\sin\frac{\pi y}{b}$, which represents the fundamental oscillation of the membrane, is expanded into the series:

$$\sin\frac{\pi x}{a}\cdot\sin\frac{\pi y}{b}=\frac{4}{\pi^2}-\frac{8}{3\pi^2}\left(\cos 2\frac{\pi x}{a}+\cos 2\frac{\pi y}{b}\right)+$$
$$+\frac{16}{9\pi^2}\cos 2\frac{\pi x}{a}\cdot\cos\frac{\pi y}{b}-\frac{8}{15\pi^2}\left(\cos 4\frac{\pi x}{a}+\cos 4\frac{\pi y}{b}\right)+$$
$$+\frac{16}{225\pi^2}\cos 4\frac{\pi x}{a}\cdot\cos 4\frac{\pi y}{b}+\dots$$

Each term in the series expansion of the function Φ in expression (6-8) represents a progressive wave of wave number k_p which is front-modulated (transverse to the z

axis) according to the law $\cos k_m x \cdot \cos k_n y$. This wave process we will call a *wave of mode (m, n)*. Often these waves are called *normal modes with subscript (m,n)* or *of type (m,n)*. Expression (6-8) must satisfy the wave equation (6-1). As we have seen, this leads to the condition (6-3):

$$k^2 = k_m^2 + k_n^2 + k_p^2.$$

However, in the case in question, motion with the frequency ω is defined on the face $z = 0$ and, consequently, $k = \frac{\omega}{c}$ is also given. This implies, that k_p can only have values defined by the following condition for the various "modes" (m, n):

$$k_p = \sqrt{k^2 - (k_m^2 + k_n^2)} = \sqrt{\left(\frac{\omega}{c}\right)^2 - (k_m^2 + k_n^2)} = k_{mn}, \quad (6\text{-}13)$$

and it cannot be selected arbitrarily as in (6-3). It is therefore necessary to ascribe a double and not a triple subscript m, n to the wave number and k_{mn} must be written in place of k_p.

If $k < \sqrt{k_m^2 + k_n^2}$, then $k_p = k_{mn}$ will be imaginary and the phase of the oscillations will be independent of z; only the amplitude of the oscillatory process will depend on z. A curious process of local oscillations arises and this will be considered below.

The wave process in a tube is only excited by oscillations of the mode (m,n) on the face $z = 0$ if

$$k > \sqrt{k_m^2 + k_n^2} \quad \text{or} \quad f > \frac{c\sqrt{k_m^2 + k_n^2}}{2\pi}. \quad (6\text{-}14)$$

Thus a cut-off frequency exists for each mode (m,n)

$$f_{mn}=\frac{c\sqrt{k_m^2+k_n^2}}{2\pi}=\frac{ck'_{mn}}{2\pi}=\frac{c}{2}\sqrt{\frac{m^2}{a^2}+\frac{n^2}{b^2}}, \qquad (6\text{-}14a)$$

below which the wave process in the tube cannot be excited. This cut-off frequency corresponds to the frequency of the natural oscillations (in the direction transverse to the z axis) of the mode $(m,n,)$. In accordance with formula (6-6), the frequencies of these natural oscillations correspond exactly with the critical frequencies (6-14a). The lowest of the critical frequencies will correspond to oscillations parallel with the largest edge of the rectangle ab [mode(1,0), if $a>b$]. If m and n are non-zero, then the oscillations are at an angle to the face ab. Since the frequency $\omega=kc$ and, consequently, the wavelength $\lambda=\frac{2\pi}{k}$ are given, it is possible to rewrite condition (6-14) for the appearance of a wave process in the tube in a slightly different form by taking into account expression (6-12):

$$\frac{2\pi}{\lambda}>\sqrt{k_m^2+k_n^2}=\frac{2\pi}{\lambda'_{mn}}, \quad \text{or} \quad \lambda'_{mn}>\lambda.$$

Consequently, the wave of mode (m,n) can only occur in a tube if the wavelength on the face $z = 0$ is greater than the wavelength, λ, in the medium which fills the tube. It is possible to generalize this conclusion and say that inhomogeneities in the oscillatory forced motion on a scale smaller than the wavelength λ do not excite the higher order wave modes in a tube. Only oscillatory motion with the mode (0,0) for which $k'_{00}=0$ and $\lambda'_{00}=\infty$, will always excite a wave in a tube at any frequency, since the following condition will always be observed

$$\lambda'_{00}>\lambda.$$

For each wave mode (m,n) in (6-8), we obtain an expression for the velocity potential in the form of a sum of four terms:

$$\Phi_{mn}(x,y,z,t)=\frac{B_{mn}}{4}\sum_{4} e^{j(\omega t \mp k_m x \mp k_n y - k_{mn} z)}. \qquad (6\text{-}15)$$

At the given frequency this sum will represent a peculiar wave which travels along the tube (along the z axis) and has a variable velocity potential along the wavefront. *The phase velocity of such a wave along the z axis is:*

$$c_1=\frac{\omega}{k_{mn}}=\frac{\omega}{\sqrt{k^2-(k_m^2+k_n^2)}}=\frac{c}{\sqrt{1-\frac{k_m^2+k_n^2}{k^2}}},$$

i.e. *it is always greater than the speed (c) of waves in free space.* Since a sum of waves of type (6-15) contains pairs of terms with opposite values of the signs of k_m and k_n (if $\varphi(x,y)=0$ or π) whilst the amplitudes $\frac{B_{mn}}{4}$ are equal for all terms in the sum, it follows that there is a stationary spatial distribution of the amplitudes in planes parallel to the z axis, i.e. standing waves. Waves of the type (6-15) will be *amplitude-modulated over the wavefront;* Such waves are often called non-homogeneous or non-uniform. The phase of the velocity potential (and, consequently, that of the acoustic pressure) will only assume the value 0 or π for a given z; the amplitude of the wave is in this case modulated according to the law $\cos k_m x \cdot \cos k_n y$.

Instead of considering waves of the special type (6-15) which are front-modulated and travel along the z axis at an increased phase velocity, it is rather more graphic to regard this process as the sum of plane waves which are propagated at an angle to the axis of the tube and successively reflected from the side faces. The cosines of the angles these plane waves make with the axes x, y, and z, are

$$\cos\alpha=\pm\frac{k_m}{k};\quad \cos\beta=\pm\frac{k_n}{k}; \qquad (6\text{-}16)$$

$$\cos\gamma = \frac{k_{mn}}{k} = \sqrt{1 - \frac{k_m^2 + k_n^2}{k^2}} = \sqrt{1 - (\cos^2\alpha + \cos^2\beta)};$$

$$\sin\gamma = \pm\frac{\sqrt{k_m^2 + k_n^2}}{k} = \pm\frac{\lambda}{\lambda'_{mn}} \qquad (6\text{-}16) \text{ cont.}$$

Expression (6-15) can be written in the form:

$$\Phi_{mn} = \frac{B_{mn}}{4}\sum_4 e^{j[\omega t - k(\pm x\cdot\cos\alpha \pm y\cdot\cos\beta - z\cdot\cos\gamma)]} = \frac{B_{mn}}{4} e^{j(\omega t - ku)}, \qquad (6\text{-}17)$$

where

$$u = \pm x\cdot\cos\alpha \pm y\cdot\cos\beta - z\cdot\cos\gamma$$

is the distance between a certain wavefront plane and the origin. For each of the four waves characterized by the quantity u, the wave number is $\sqrt{k_m^2 + k_n^2 + k_p^2} = k$; consequently, the speed of propagation of the waves is equal to the velocity of sound c in a free medium.

Thus, if we take into account all the combinations of signs in expression (6-15), then the wave mode (m, n) is represented by the sum of the four plane waves or by a pencil of four "rays" which are successively reflected from the four side faces of the tube. The wave field at any point is obtained by the superposition of these waves. As can be seen from equation (6-16), the sine of the angle γ of these plane waves to the axis of the tube is defined by the ratio of the wavelength λ to the wavelength λ'_{mn}, which is just the wavelength of the corresponding mode on the face $z = 0$. An interesting interpretation of this expression will be given below.

The term with the coefficient B_{00} in expression (6-15) corresponds to the values $k_m = k_n = 0$ and $k_{mn} = k$; in addition, $\cos k_m x = \cos k_n y = 1$. The expression for Φ_{00} then simplifies to $\Phi_{00} = B_{00}\, e^{j(\omega t - kz)}$. Thus, the term with the coefficient B_{00} defines that part of the wave motion which is propagated in the form of a plane wave along the z axis.

We will now consider the special case when $k_m \neq 0$, but $k_n = 0$ and the standing waves on the face $z = 0$ are formed with fronts parallel to the y axis (mode m, 0).

$$\Phi_{m0} = B_{m0} \cos k_m x \cdot e^{j(\omega t - k_{m0} z)} = B_{m0}[e^{j(\omega t - k_m x - k_{m0} z)} + \\ + e^{j(\omega t + k_m x - k_{m0} z)}] \tag{6-17a}$$

In this case

$$k_{m0} = \sqrt{k^2 - k_m^2}.$$

The law governing motion on the face $z = 0$ has the form $\dot{\zeta} = \alpha_{m0} \cdot \cos k_m x \cdot e^{j\omega t}$. In this case the tube contains only two plane waves with wave vectors in the plane xz. The directions of these waves are determined by the expressions:

$$\cos \gamma = \pm \frac{k_{m0}}{k} = \sqrt{1 - \frac{k_m^2}{k^2}} = \sqrt{1 - \cos^2 \alpha} = \sin \alpha \tag{6-18}$$

or

$$\sin \gamma = \pm \frac{k_m}{k} = \pm \frac{\lambda}{\lambda'_{m0}},$$

since in the case in question $\lambda'_{m0} = \frac{2\pi}{k_m}$. Thus, the angle γ with the z axis will be $\frac{\pi}{2} - \alpha$.

Figure 33 illustrates the process of wave propagation. If the acoustic waves are regarded as "rays" which leave the face $z = 0$ from a certain point, at an angle $\pm \gamma$ to the axis, the pattern of sound propagation can be obtained by plotting the successive reflections of the rays from the side faces of the tube. It is clear that the angle

γ can vary between the limits 0 (at very large frequencies $k \to \infty$) and $\frac{\pi}{2}$ (if $k=k_m$). Thus, as k tends to k_m, i.e. if the wavelength tends to the quantity λ_{m0} or the frequency to the quantity $f_{m0}=\frac{mc}{2a}$ (which corresponds to the mth overtone of the natural oscillations of a closed tube of length a), the wave modes $(m, 0)$ become increasingly oblique in direction. At the limit, if $f=f_{m0}$, there are only standing waves in the transverse direction (along the x axis) and the flow of acoustic energy along the z axis ceases.

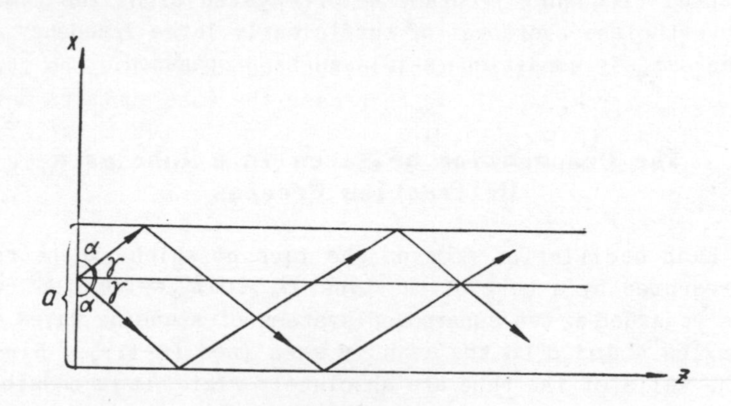

Fig. 33

Waves cannot be propagated along the z axis at frequencies $f<f_{m0}=\frac{mc}{2a}$ if the oscillation mode corresponds to an initial excitation (on the face $z=0$) of the type $\alpha_{m0} \cos m\frac{\pi x}{a}$. There is only a wave process if $f>f_{mo}$ or $\lambda<\lambda_{mo}$.

Frequencies $f_{mn}=\frac{c}{2}\sqrt{\frac{m^2}{a^2}+\frac{n^2}{b^2}}$ correspond to the resonant frequencies of oscillations in the direction transverse to the z axis, whilst the angles with the x and y axis are defined by expression (6-11).

If the oscillations excited in the plane $z = 0$ have an overtone component of frequency $N\omega$, as well as the fundamental component of frequency ω,

$$kN = \frac{2\pi f}{c} N > \sqrt{k_m^2 + k_n^2} = \pi \sqrt{\frac{m^2}{a^2} + \frac{n^2}{b^2}}.$$

If $n = 0$ and $m = 1$, this condition takes the form:

$$kN = \frac{2\pi f}{c} N > \frac{\pi}{a} \quad \text{or} \quad fN > \frac{c}{2a}. \tag{6-19}$$

Consequently, even if $f < \frac{c}{2a}$ and the wave of the fundamental frequency f cannot be propagated along the tube, nevertheless overtones of sufficiently large frequency fN can satisfy condition (6-19) and be propagated.

The Propagation of Waves in a Tube as a Diffraction Process

Each oscillation mode on the face ab, which can be represented by a term of the type $B_{mn} \cos k_m x \cdot \cos k_n y$, can be regarded as two superposed systems of standing waves at angles α' and β' to the x and y axes (see (6-11)). Since the walls of the tube are absolutely rigid, it is possible to regard the system of standing waves as continued beyond the limits of the sides of the rectangle ab owing to the infinite number of mirror reflections from the faces. The whole plane $z=0$ is then covered by a double system of standing waves (Fig. 34), whose normals to the wavefronts are at angles $\pm\alpha'$ and $\pm\beta'$ to the axes x and y.

Thus, it can be assumed that there are no faces a and b and that the oscillatory process inside the rectangle ab is reproduced exactly by the superposition of the two systems of standing waves. Each of these systems of standing waves will radiate sound like an unlimited sinusoidal diffraction lattice of spacing-length λ'_{mn}.

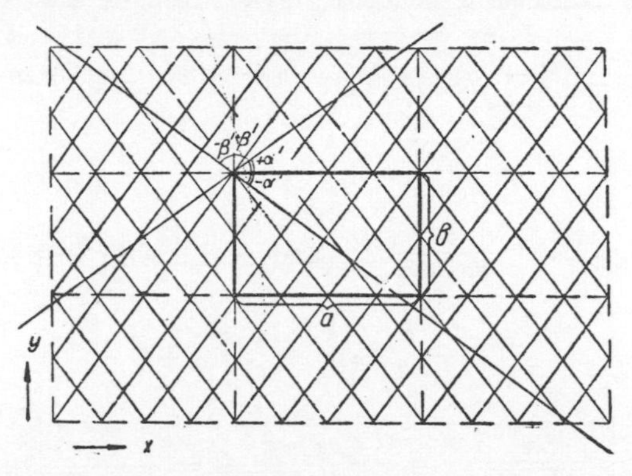

Fig. 34

We will now consider the radiation of sound by a diffraction lattice. Suppose that a plane surface wave is propagated along the x axis in the plane xy at a speed c'. The oscillatory velocity in the direction of the z axis can be expressed by the formula:

$$\dot{\zeta} = \dot{\zeta}_0 e^{j(\omega t - k'x)}, \qquad (6\text{-}20)$$

where

$$k' = \frac{2\pi}{\Lambda} = \frac{\omega}{c'}.$$

This surface wave can be regarded as a progressive diffraction lattice with sinusoidal furrows. It is supposed that the acoustic field produced by this lattice in the half-space $z > 0$ has the form of a plane wave which is propagated at an angle to the plane xy at a speed c, the wave vector lying in the plane xz at an angle γ with the z axis. The velocity potential of this wave is

$$\Phi = Ae^{j(\omega t - x \cdot k \sin \gamma - zk \cos \gamma)} \qquad (6\text{-}21)$$

In order that the wave should produce motion in the plane $z = 0$ corresponding to equation (6-20), it is necessary that the following boundary condition be satisfied

$$-\frac{\partial \Phi}{\partial z}\bigg|_{z=0} = jk \cos\gamma \cdot A \cdot e^{j(\omega t - kx \sin\gamma)} = \dot{\zeta}_0 e^{j(\omega t - k'x)}$$

whence

$$A = \frac{\dot{\zeta}}{jk \cos\gamma} \qquad \text{and} \qquad k \sin\gamma = k',$$

or

$$\sin\gamma = \frac{k'}{k} = \frac{\lambda}{\Lambda} = \frac{c}{c'} \qquad \text{and}$$

$$A = \frac{\dot{\zeta}_0}{j\sqrt{k^2 - (k')^2}} = \frac{\dot{\zeta}_0 c e^{-j\frac{\pi}{2}}}{\omega\sqrt{1 - \frac{c^2}{(c')^2}}} = \frac{\dot{\zeta}_0 \lambda e^{-j\frac{\pi}{2}}}{2\pi\sqrt{1 - \frac{\lambda^2}{\Lambda^2}}}. \qquad (6\text{-}22)$$

It can be seen from these expressions that the wave which arises in the half-space $z > 0$, is similar to a diffraction spectrum or order (+1) for which $\sin\gamma = \frac{\lambda}{\Lambda}$; there is no spectrum of order (-1). If we are given a standing wave on the surface instead of a progressive wave, and its equation is

$$\dot{\zeta} = \dot{\zeta}_0 (e^{jk'x} + e^{-jk'x}) \cdot e^{j\omega t},$$

then we must assume the presence of two superposed plane waves in the space $z > 0$. In this case the expression $-jk \sin\gamma \cdot x$, must stand for one of the exponential arguments and the expression $+jk \sin\gamma \cdot x$ for the other. The second wave will correspond to a spectrum of order minus one, which is symmetric with the spectrum of order plus one about the z axis.

If the wavelength λ in the half-space $z > 0$ exceeds the wavelength Λ on the surface xy, then $\sin\gamma > 1$. Then

$$\cos\gamma = \pm\sqrt{1 - \frac{c^2}{(c')^2}} = \pm j\sqrt{\frac{c^2}{(c')^2} - 1} = \pm j\sqrt{\frac{\lambda^2}{\Lambda^2} - 1},$$

whilst

$$\Phi = e^{\pm\frac{\omega}{c}\sqrt{\frac{c^2}{(c')^2}-1}\cdot z} \cdot e^{j\left(\omega t - \frac{\omega}{(c')^2}x\right)}.$$

Only the minus sign has any physical meaning in the first exponential multiplier of this expression. The wave process in the case in question has the nature of a plane wave which is propagated in the direction of the x axis at a speed c', the amplitude of the wave diminishing along its wavefront due to the damping factor

$$\delta = \frac{\omega}{c}\sqrt{\frac{c^2}{(c')^2}-1} = \sqrt{k^2-(k')^2}.$$

Each wave mode (m,n), which consists of two standing waves in the plane $z = 0$, thus creates four spectra in the tube; the waves corresponding to these spectra form angles γ with the z axis (see formula (6-18)). It is in this way that we can interpret the four plane waves (the pencil of four "rays") which were discussed above. In complicated cases when there are a number of oscillation modes on the face $z = 0$, the wave process in the tube consists of the superposition of similar fourfold pencils of plane waves with different inclinations to the z axis and the x and y axes.

Damped Modes of Oscillation

We will now consider the type of motion which occurs in a tube if the wave number k'_{mn} on the face $z = 0$ is greater than k

$$k'_{mn} = \sqrt{k_m^2 + k_n^2} > k.$$

In this case, it is obvious that k_{mn} is imaginary; suppose we put:

$$k_{mn} = \pm j\mu = \pm j\sqrt{k_m^2 + k_n^2 - k^2}.$$

Then Φ_{mn} can be represented in the form:

$$\Phi_{mn} = B_{mn} e^{\pm \mu z} \cdot \cos k_m x \cdot \cos k_n y \cdot e^{j\omega t}. \qquad (6\text{-}23)$$

In this expression it is only necessary to include the minus sign in the exponential, since the oscillatory process cannot increase indefinitely with increasing distance from the point of excitation. It would of course be possible to write Φ_{mn} in the form (6-17), on the assumption that the cosine of the angle γ with the z axis (equal to $\frac{k_m}{k} = j\frac{\mu}{k}$) is imaginary, i.e. that the angle γ is complex (this assumption has been adopted by some authors). However, this interpretation can in no way be considered graphic. It is easy to show that in this case $\gamma = \frac{\pi}{2} - j \operatorname{arc} \sin \frac{\mu}{k}$. The expression (6-23) can be represented in the form:

$$\Phi_{mn} = \frac{B_{mn}}{4} e^{-\mu z} \sum_{4} e^{j[\omega t - k(\pm x \cdot \cos \alpha' \pm y \cos \beta')]},$$

where the angles α' and β' are defined by formula (6-11). We therefore have two systems of standing waves with wave vectors which are in directions determined by the angles $\pm\alpha'$, and $\pm\beta'$, and these vectors lie in planes transverse to the z axis; however, the amplitudes of these waves diminish with increasing distance from the origin according to the law $e^{-\mu z}$. Thus, the complex angle γ expresses the fact that a curious system of standing waves is produced in which wavefronts of equal phase (parallel to the z axis) are transverse to the wavefronts of equal amplitude (which are transverse to the z axis). A clearer picture can be obtained directly from expression (6-23). It shows that there is no wave process in the tube along the z axis and that the oscillatory motion over the entire length of the tube at the frequency ω is everywhere in phase. The factor $e^{-\mu z}$ shows that the amplitude of the oscillations diminishes exponentially with increasing distance from the beginning of the tube. The oscillations in the direction transverse to the z axis are standing waves with an amplitude which gradually diminishes with increasing z. The direction of the oscillatory motions in the planes transverse to the z axis can be determined by the double system of standing waves whose wave vectors are defined by the angles $\pm\alpha'$ and $\pm\beta'$ in accordance with formula (6-11).

We will now consider what the streamlines will be like in a tube when $k_n = 0$. It is found from equation (6-23) that the components of the velocity of motion along the axes x and z are:

$$\dot{\xi} = -\frac{\partial\Phi_{m0}}{\partial x} = k_m B_{m0} e^{-\mu z} \cdot \sin k_m x \cdot e^{j\omega t},$$

$$\dot{\zeta} = -\frac{\partial\Phi_{m0}}{\partial z} = \mu B_{m0} e^{-\mu z} \cos k_m x \cdot e^{j\omega t},$$

whilst

$$p = j\omega\rho\Phi_{m0} = j\omega\rho B_{m0} e^{-\mu z} \cdot \cos k_m x \cdot e^{j\omega t}.$$

The acoustic pressure thus differs in phase from the particle velocity $\dot{\zeta}$ by $\frac{\pi}{2}$. This implies that the flow of acoustic energy along the z axis is zero. The quantities $\dot{\xi}dt = dx$ and $\dot{\zeta}dt = dz$ represent the projections on the x and z axes of an element of a particle streamline. Dividing $\dot{\zeta}$ by $\dot{\xi}$ we get:

$$\frac{dz}{dx} = \frac{\mu}{k_m} \cot k_m x.$$

Dividing the variables and integrating, we find the equation of the streamlines:

$$z = \frac{\mu}{k_m^2} \ln|\sin k_m x| + C.$$

It is easy to see that C is the coordinate z of the point at which the given streamline intersects the z axis at the antinode of the standing wave, where $k_m x = (2n+1)\frac{\pi}{2}$; this corresponds to values $x = \frac{a}{2m}(2n+1)$. If $k_n = 0$ and $k_m = 2$ (mode 2-0), the streamlines will have the form shown in Fig. 35. The streamlines originate and terminate on two adjacent oscillatory zones on the face $z = 0$ which are separated by nodal lines. The greater the distance from the beginning of the tube, the more the streamlines are spread out. This implies that the particle velocities diminish with increasing distance from the boundary at which the oscillations are excited.

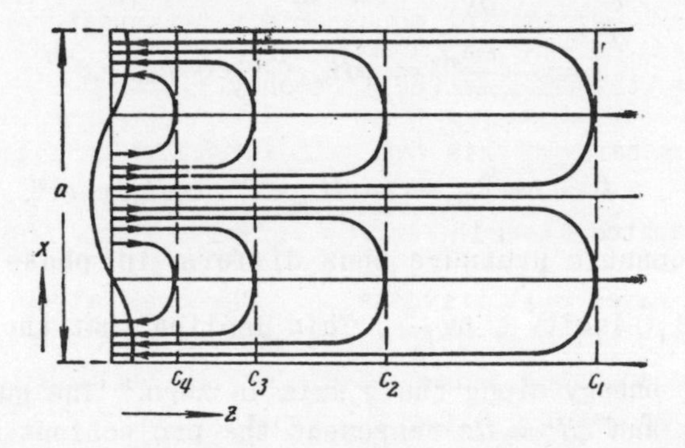

Fig. 35

As we have seen, the critical frequency below which waves of a given mode (m, n) cannot be propagated is defined by expression (6-14a). The lowest cut-off frequency of all is defined by the largest dimension of the tube a and corresponds to the oscillation mode (1, 0):

$$f_{10} = \frac{c}{2a}.$$

If there is ideal "plane" or "piston" oscillatory motion along the z axis at the initial section of the tube, this corresponds to the mode (0, 0). With this oscillation mode the wave number $k'_{mn} = k_{00}$ is always greater than zero and a plane wave is propagated along the tube at any frequency ($\cos\gamma = 1$; $\gamma = 0$). If the motion at the initial section $z = 0$ is non-homogeneous, then this non-homogeneity (in the transverse direction) will exist further on, and it will be transmitted along the z axis, but it will do so according to different laws, depending on whether the scale of the non-homogeneity of the perturbation in the initial section is less or larger than the wavelength λ.

Thus, for example, non-homogeneities which are expressed by the oscillation mode (1,0), are attenuated with increasing distance from the origin at frequencies $f < f_{10} = \frac{c}{2a}$, decaying more rapidly the greater the value of μ, i.e. the smaller the frequency f. If $f = f_{10} = \frac{c}{2a}$ a non-homogeneity of this type will not decay at all and will be propagated along the entire infinite tube. If $f > \frac{c}{2a}$, oblique waves will travel along the tube at an angle to the z axis which is defined by expression (6-16), and the non-homogeneities which exist in the section $z = 0$ will also be propagated along the entire tube.

Non-homogeneities of smaller scale along x and y (for example, $m = 2, 3, \ldots$) will produce short circuited flows at much higher frequencies than if $m = 1$, namely, up to frequencies $f_{20} = 2\frac{c}{2a}$, $f_{30} = 3\frac{c}{2a}$ and so on. Waves begin to be propagated along the tube only at frequencies higher than these cut-off frequencies.

These arguments can be expounded in a slightly different way. Assuming that the frequency f and the velocity distribution in the initial section $\psi_0(x, y)$ are given, it can be said that only those modes of oscillation will be propagated for which

$$f=f_{mn}=\frac{c}{2}\sqrt{\frac{m^2}{a^2}+\frac{n^2}{b^2}}<f.$$

Higher modes for which $f_{mn}>f$, or $\lambda'_{mn}<\lambda$ (in the plane z = 0) is less than in a free medium, will fade out near the origin. Thus, small variations in motion in the plane z = 0 will not be transmitted further.

At a frequency less than the lowest critical frequency, corresponding to the mode (1,0) oscillations of all the higher modes except the mode (0,0), will produce no waves in the tube and will fade out near the origin. No matter how complex the motion at the beginning of the tube, it will always degenerate into a plane wave along the axis of the tube during the course of propagation if $f<f_{10}$. However, higher order wave modes can occur if, as stated above, overtones are present with sufficiently large frequencies Nf.

Application of Theory

The foregoing theory is very useful for analysing the propagation of sound in tubes. If it is necessary to produce a plane wave in a tube for measuring purposes (for example in an acoustic interferometer), then we can rest assured that at low frequencies no appreciable role will be played by non-homogeneities in the excitation at the initial section (z=0). Oscillatory motion of higher modes for which $m>0$ and $n>0$, will be very greatly weakened with increasing distance from the beginning and at a certain distance from the source (for example a loudspeaker affixed to the tube) the motion will be entirely due to the plane wave mode (0,0) excited by the total volume pulsation (current) of the source. Thus, for example, in a tube 15 x 15 cm the lowest mode for non-homogeneous oscillations is obtained at $f_{10}=\frac{3{\cdot}4\times10^4}{2\times15}=1130$ c/s. The damping coefficient of the wave mode (m,n) at a frequency $f < f_{mn}$ is

$$\mu = \pi \sqrt{\frac{m^2}{a^2} + \frac{n^2}{b^2} - 4\frac{f^2}{c^2}}.$$

If the excitation in the initial section is not symmetric about the section centre $\left(\frac{a}{2}, \frac{b}{2}\right)$, then oscillation modes (1,0) and (0,1) will be very pronounced. Suppose we take the case when $m = 1$ and $n = 0$. At the frequency $f = f_{10} = 1130$ c/s, $\mu = 0$, i.e. any non-homogeneity of the mode (1,0) type is propagated along the entire tube. If $f = \frac{f_{10}}{2} = 565$ c/s, we then get $\mu = 0{\cdot}18$ cm^{-1}, i.e. the oscillatory process will decay by a factor $e^{0{\cdot}18 \times 100} = e^{18} \approx 5 \times 10^7$ over a distance of one metre, and will not be significant in practice. Even if $f = 1100$ c/s we still get $\mu = 0{\cdot}05$ cm^{-1} and the attenuation is $e^5 \approx 140$ per m. However, if the exciting sound has overtones, then the same non-homogeneities at the overtone frequencies can produce great distortion in the plane acoustic field in the tube. Thus, for example, a second overtone of 565 c/s with a frequency $2 \times 565 = 1130$ c/s and the oscillation mode (1,0) will give $\mu = 0$ and a non-homogeneity along the entire tube.

If it is desired to introduce attenuation of sound in tubes, e.g. in ventilation channels, it can at once be said that it is very desirable to cover the side walls with sound-absorbing substances since this very greatly damps all higher oscillation modes which are propagated at an angle to the axis of the tube but does not effect the plane part of the wave motion in the tube (mode 0,0) since a plane wave produces no velocity components normal to the side walls. In order to bring about its attenuation, it is necessary to disturb the plane front of the wave in some way. Bends, projections, screens and so on will form higher wave modes; some of the energy of the plane waves will be transmitted to these waves and be absorbed on the side walls if these are lined with a sound-absorber.

The foregoing theory is also important for understanding the operation of the Pierce ultrasonic interferometer. In this instrument the piezoquartz, which operates under conditions of self-oscillation in a valve circuit, radiates waves into a tube which is provided with a plane movable reflector. At resonance of the column of liquid or gas when a whole number of half-waves is packed in the length of the tube and the pressure of the standing wave on the surface of the quartz is a maximum, the tube exerts a powerful reaction on the auto-oscillatory system which leads to the attenuation of the oscillations, and a galvanometer in the anode circuit shows sharp minima of current. The Pierce interferometer had made it possible to measure the wavelength and, consequently, the velocity of sound.

Such an ideal pattern of waves is produced only by the "piston" oscillations of a quartz plate when it radiates pure plane waves. But in quartz plates, bending waves are usually formed whose intensity depends on the nature of the excitation and on the relationship between the width and length of the plate on the one hand and its thickness on the other*. These bending waves create higher order oscillation modes which produce in a tube oblique waves whose wavelengths along the axis of the tube are no longer equal to $\lambda = \frac{c}{f}$, but are functions of the quantities m and n given by the formula

$$\lambda_{mn} = \frac{2\pi}{k_{mn}} = \frac{\lambda}{\sqrt{1 - \frac{\lambda^2}{4\pi^2}(k_m^2 + k_n^2)}}$$

from which it is evident that the wavelengths are greater than λ. Higher order modes may also arise if the area of the piston is smaller than the area of the tube or if the piezo-quartz plate has an inhomogeneous crystal structure.

---

* S.N. Rschevkin, *C.R. Acad. Sci. U.S.S.R.* 16, 267, 1937.

The oblique waves which arise produce resonance if the length of the tube $l=n\frac{\lambda_{mn}}{2}$. These additional resonances can distort the fundamental picture of the maxima and minima in the interferometer and lead to errors in the measurement of wavelength*.

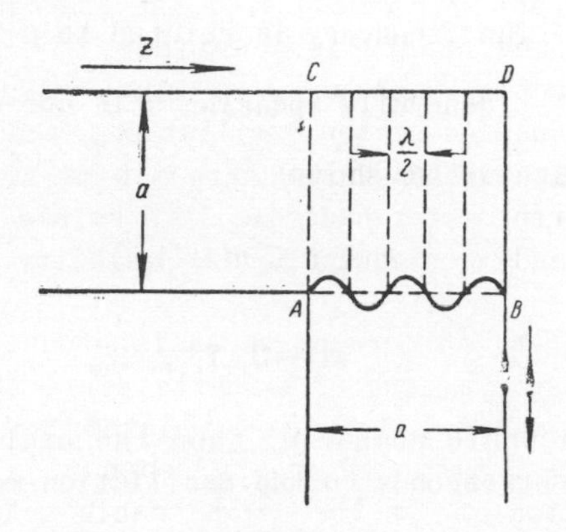

Fig. 36

The foregoing theory is also useful for understanding the wave process at the transmission of sound in tubes with a right-angled bend. The exact solution of this problem is rather complicated and we will confinc ourselves to a qualitative analysis. Suppose that a square tube of sides a has a right-angled bend along the x axis as in Fig. 36. A complex diffraction pattern arises near the right-angled bend and as a result there is a certain distribution of the velocities according to the law $\psi_0(y, z)$, in the section AB, which determines the nature of sound radiation along the infinite tube in the x direction. As a first approximation it can be assumed that standing waves arise in the zone of the bend on reflection from the plane BD, and that in the section AB the velocity distribution along the z

* P.E. Krasnooshkin, *J. Phys. U.S.S.R.* 7, 80, 1943.

axis is governed by the law:

$$\dot{\xi}(z) = A \cdot \cos p \frac{\pi z}{a} = A \cdot \cos kz.$$

The wave number $k = \frac{2\pi}{\lambda} = p\frac{\pi}{a} = \frac{2\pi f}{c}$ and, consequently, $p\frac{\lambda}{2} = a$, i.e. p is the number of half-wave lengths in the section AB. The frequency is related to p by the expression $f = \frac{pc}{2a}$. Generally speaking, p is not a whole number. In such a case we can write:

$$m < p < m + 1,$$

where

$$m = 0,\ 1,\ 2,\ 3...$$

If p is a whole number m, then the excitation in the section AB corresponds to the oscillation mode $(m, 0)$; in this case

$$\sin\gamma = \frac{k_m}{k} = \frac{m\pi/a}{m\pi/a} = 1,$$

i.e. $\gamma = 90°$, and a system of standing waves is established in the entire tube whose fronts are directed along the x axis. These waves are a continuation beyond the bend of the system of waves which are excited in the part of the tube $ABCD$. If p is not a whole number, then we avail ourselves of the following expression which is known from the theory of Fourier series*:

$$\cos pt = \frac{2 \sin p\pi}{\pi}\left[\frac{1}{2p} + \frac{p \cos t}{1^2 - p^2} - \frac{p \cos 2t}{2^2 - p^2} + \ldots + (-1)^{n-1}\frac{p \cdot \cos nt}{n^2 - p^2}\right]. \qquad (6\text{-}24)$$

The largest amplitude in this series is possessed by the

---

* I.M. Ryzhik, *Tables of Integrals, Sums, Series and Products (Tablits a integrolov, summ, rjadov, i proizvedenij)*, Moscow, Gostekhizdat 1951, p.54).

two terms for which the values of n are the nearest whole numbers to p, namely, (m) and $(m + 1)$. The critical frequencies for the modes $(m,0)$ and $(m + 1,0)$ are

$$f_{m0}=\frac{mc}{2a} \text{ and } f_{m+1,0}=\frac{(m+1)\,c}{2a}.$$

A wave of the mode $(m+1,0)$ will not be propagated along the tube and the resulting oscillations will be damped out near the entry section AB of the tube, since for them the frequency is less than the critical frequency of the mode in question $f=p\frac{c}{2a}<(m+1)\frac{c}{2a}$. A wave of the mode $(m,0)$ will however be propagated since for it $f = =p\frac{c}{2a}>m\frac{c}{2a}$. The waves which correspond to the mode $(m,0)$ are at a very great angle to the axis of the tube (almost 90°). The other terms in series (6-24), in particular the first term (mode 0,0), are smaller and do not play any significant role. The wave process is similar to that of a system of standing waves whose fronts extend along the tube (along the x axis). If $p = 1$, then $f=\frac{c}{2a}$ and the first oscillation mode (1,0) is the most powerfully excited of all. The process will consist of vibrations from one wall of the tube to the other; the plane wave of mode (0,0) will of course be superimposed on it as well.

If $p\ll 1$, so that only a small part of a wavelength is contained within the width of the tube, all the sum (6-24) will tend to unity and $\dot{\xi}\approx A$, i.e. purely piston motion is obtained, and after the bend there is a plane wave of mode (0,0). Thus, the smaller the frequency, the easier will the plane wave penetrate beyond the bend.

The reflection at the bend will be the less, the greater the wavelength compared with a, but there is always a small amount of reflection and the wave after the bend will be weaker than it was before it.

The damped oscillation modes of higher order, which arise near the bend, produce a local field of velocities which possesses a certain kinetic energy. This energy is obviously taken from the fundamental plane wave at the moment when the oscillation sets in. Consequently, bends are as it were equivalent to the appearance of a certain "attached" mass. In an electrical line this is analogous to the connection of a number of inductances in series (a coil-loaded line).

The foregoing conclusions are not rigorous and only give a good idea of what is going on. It has definitely been confirmed by experiments that waves are transmitted round bends much more easily at low frequencies and that waves are considerably damped at high frequencies.

It is clear that a layer of porous material (for example, cloth) placed in the middle of the tube along its axis after the bend will intensively absorb acoustic waves corresponding to all the higher oscillation modes $(m>0, n>0)$, which are produced by the bend. Thus, an absorbent layer not occupying any appreciable volume of the tube in conjunction with a bend is an effective sound-absorber. It is also clear that a plane wave in going around a bend transfers part of its energy to higher order wave modes for which the particle velocity has components normal to the walls of the tube (after the bend). Consequently, a sound-absorbing material when placed on the wall in the vicinity of the bend is more effective than when placed on a wall of the straight portion carrying the incident plane wave.

Cylindrical Tube

We will now consider the propagation of sound in cylindrical tubes. The wave equation for the function Ψ can be written in the form

$$\frac{1}{r}\frac{\partial}{\partial r}\left(r\frac{\partial\Psi}{\partial r}\right)+\frac{1}{r^2}\frac{\partial^2\Psi}{\partial\varphi^2}+\frac{\partial^2\Psi}{\partial z^2}+k^2\Psi=0,$$

where φ is the azimuthal angle.

Separating the variables by Fourier's method, we find solutions of this equation in the form:

$$\Psi_p(r,z,\varphi)=[A'_pJ_p(\nu r)+B'_pN_p(\nu r)]\,[A''_p\cos p\varphi+B''_p\sin p\varphi]\times$$
$$\times\left[A'''_pe^{-j\sqrt{k^2-\nu^2}\,z}+B'''_pe^{j\sqrt{k^2-\nu^2}\,z}\right].$$

In this expression J_p and N_p are Bessel and Neumann functions of order p and argument νr; ν is the wave number, the value of which is, as explained previously, defined by the boundary conditions on the side walls of the tube. Since on the axis of the tube Ψ must be finite (and $N_p(0)=-\infty$), it is necessary to put $B'_p=0$. The order p of the Bessel function can obviously only be equal to a whole number or zero ($p=0, 1, 2, 3\ldots$), since otherwise the functions $\cos p\varphi$ and $\sin p\varphi$, and, consequently, Ψ_p will not be single-valued. In addition, solutions which contain the factor $e^{j\sqrt{k^2-\nu^2}\,z}$, should not be used for an infinite tube, since there are no reflected waves. By introducing the multiplier $e^{j\omega t}$ combining A'_p, A''_p, A'''_p in one constant A_p and B'_p, B''_p, and B'''_p in one constant B_p, we get as solutions of the wave equation in an infinite circular tube

$$\Phi_p(r,z,\varphi,t)=(A_p\cos p\varphi+$$
$$+B_p\sin p\varphi)J_p(\nu r)e^{j(\omega t-\sqrt{k^2-\nu^2}\,z)}= \qquad (6\text{-}25)$$
$$=C_pJ_p(\nu r)\cos(p\varphi-\varphi_p)\,e^{j(\omega t-\sqrt{k^2-\nu^2}\,z)},$$

where

$$C_p=\sqrt{A_p^2+B_p^2}\text{ and }\tan\varphi_p=\frac{B_p}{A_p}.$$

The quantity $\cos(p\varphi-\varphi_p)$ shows that there are a number of azimuthal angles φ which define certain diametral planes on which $\Phi_p=0$, and, as this implies, on which the acoustic pressure is also zero. If $p = 0$, then Φ_p and $\frac{\partial \Phi_p}{\partial z}$ are independent of φ, and there are no such planes. If $p = 1$, one nodal plane is formed (for $\varphi = \varphi_1 \pm \frac{\pi}{2}$). The oscillation velocities along the z axis in the two halves of the tube separated by this plane are opposite in phase in each section transverse to the axis. If $p = 2, 3, \ldots$, then there are $2, 3, \ldots$, nodal planes formed respectively and these are disposed at equal angular distances from each other. Generally speaking, p signifies the number of nodal diametral planes along which the acoustic pressure and the axial oscillation velocity are zero in the tube.

On the walls of the tube, $r = r_0$, the radial velocity must always be zero:

$$v_r = -\left.\frac{\partial \Phi_p}{\partial r}\right|_{r=r_0} = 0.$$

This condition leads to the equation:

$$J'_p(\nu r_0) = J'_p(y) = 0, \tag{6-26}$$

which defines the frequencies of the natural oscillations in the direction transverse to the axis of the tube. The natural frequencies are defined in terms of the roots y_p of equation (6-26):

$$f_p = \frac{c}{2\pi} \nu_p = \frac{c}{2\pi r_0} y_p.$$

In the interval from zero to the $(n+1)$-th root (assuming that 0 is the first root of the equation $J'_p(y) = 0$), it is obvious that there are still n roots of the same equation. As can be seen from Fig. 37a and 37b, there are n roots of the equation $J_p(y) = 0$, in the same interval, and each of these roots defines an internal nodal cylindrical surface (of radius $r < r_0$), on which $v_z = 0$. To denote the roots of the equation $J'_p(y) = 0$ we require, besides p, a second subscript n to indicate the number of internal nodal cylinders. Thus, the parameter ν acquires a double index p,n. The equation $J_0'(y)=0$ is always satisfied by the root $y = 0$ which corresponds to a value of the parameter ν which we denote by ν_{00} thus:

$$\nu_{00}=0 \text{ and } f_{00}=0.$$

Each pair of numbers p,n defines a certain wave mode which is propagated along the entire length of the tube without variation.

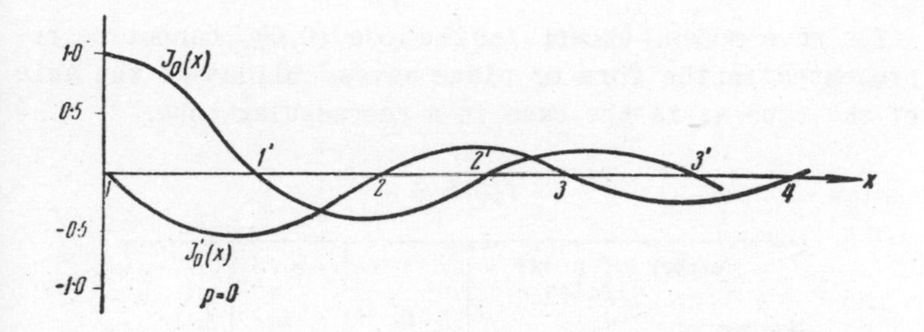

Fig. 37a

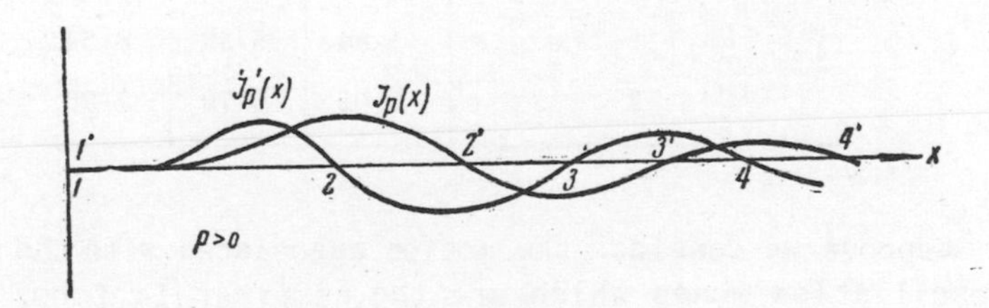

Fig. 37b

The values of the first roots of equation (6-26) for $p = 0,1,2$ and $n = 0,1,2$ are given in Table 4.

If the wave number k in formula (6-25) is greater than ν_{pn}, then the wave number $\sqrt{k^2-\nu_{pn}^2}$ (which defines the wavelength along the axis of the tube) is real, and it is possible for waves to be propagated along the tube with an amplitude which is front-modulated by the function $J_p(\nu_{pn}r)\cdot\cos(p\varphi-\varphi_p)$. If the wave number k is less than ν_{pn}, i.e.

$$f<\frac{c}{2\pi}\sqrt{k^2-\nu_{pn}^2},$$

then the wave modes (p,n) cannot penetrate into the tube and the process is limited to local oscillations which take place in phase at all points and which are attenuated with increasing distance from the beginning of the tube.

The wave modes, except for the mode (0,0), cannot be represented in the form of plane waves oblique to the axis of the tube as is the case in a rectangular tube.

TABLE 4

Number of nodal diameters p \ Number of nodal circles n	0	1	2
0	0	3·83	7·01
1	1·84	5·33	8·54
2	3·05	6·70	9·96

Suppose we consider the motion associated with the first oscillation modes which are the simplest in form. The mode (0,0) which is defined by the root $y=0$, corresponds to the absence of nodal planes and nodal cylinders; in addition $J_0(0)=1$ and the velocity potential takes the form:

$$\Phi_{00}(z,t)=A_{00}e^{j(\omega t-kz)}.$$

This is the equation of a plane wave progressing along the positive z axis. The wave mode (0,0) corresponds to piston motion in the initial section of the tube, and all the elementary theory of wave propagation in tubes which was developed in the previous chapter applies to the wave mode (0, 0).

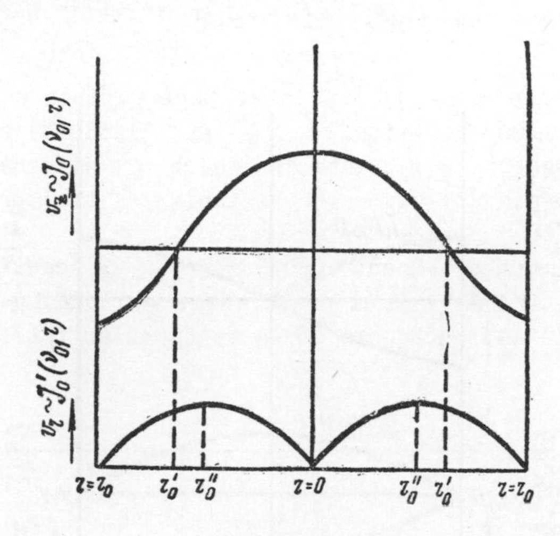

Fig. 38

If $p = 0$ and $n = 1$, then there is only one nodal cylinder and there are no nodal planes. The oscillations are symmetrical about the axis. The potential is

$$\Phi_{01} = A_{01} J_0(\nu_{01} r)\, e^{j(\omega t - \sqrt{k^2 - \nu_{01}^2}\, z)}.$$

The axial velocity v_z will be proportional to $J_0(\nu_{01} r)$, and the radial velocity v_r to $J_0'(\nu_{01} r)$. In order to illustrate the pattern of the oscillations, Fig. 38 shows the behaviour of the functions $J_0(\nu_{01} r)$ and $J_0'(\nu_{01} r)$. It will be seen from the diagram that the radius of the nodal cylinder r_0' is defined by the value of the first root of the equation $J_0(\nu_{01} r) = 0$, which is equal to 2·40:

$$r_0' = \frac{2{\cdot}40}{\nu_{01}} = \frac{2{\cdot}40}{3{\cdot}83} r_0 = 0{\cdot}627 r_0.$$

The radial velocity is maximum at $r_0'' = \frac{1{\cdot}84}{\nu_{01}} = 0{\cdot}48 r_0$; at $r = 0$ and $r = r_0$ it is zero.

For $p = 1$ and $n = 0$, only one nodal plane is obtained and there are no nodal cylinders. The velocity potential in this case has the form:

$$\Phi_{10} = A_{10} J_1(\nu_{10} r) \cos(\varphi - \varphi_1) e^{j(\omega t - \sqrt{k^2 - \nu_{10}^2}\, z)}.$$

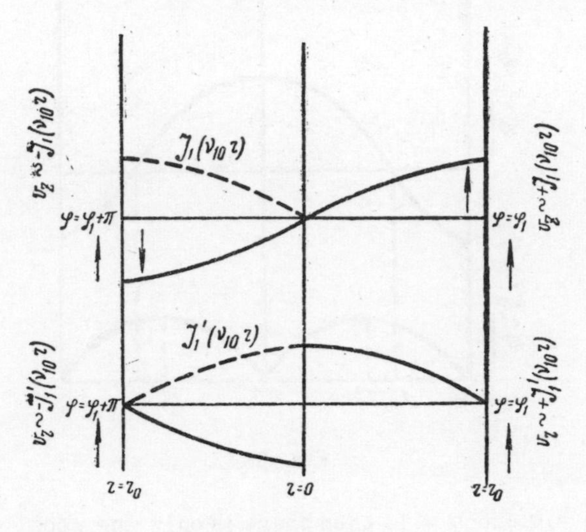

Fig. 39a

The axial velocity is proportional to $J_1(\nu_{10} r) \cos(\varphi - \varphi_1)$, and the radial velocity to $J_1'(\nu_{10} r) \cos(\varphi - \varphi_1)$. Figure 39a shows the distribution of the axial and radial velocities along a line transverse to the nodal plane $\varphi = \varphi_1$, and $\varphi = \varphi_1 + \pi$. Figure 39b shows the pattern of the streamlines in a plane transverse to the axis of the tube.

The general solution of the wave equation for an infinite tube can be represented in the form of a sum of partial solutions of the type (6-25):

$$\Phi = \sum_{p=0}^{\infty} \sum_{n=0}^{\infty} \Phi_{pn},$$

where $p, n = 0, 1, 2, 3, \ldots$

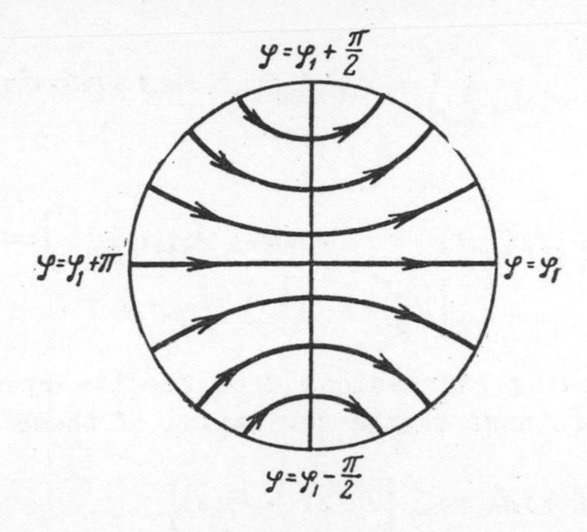

Fig. 39b

In order to determine the numerical coefficients A_{pn} and B_{pn} in the characteristic functions, it is necessary to follow the same procedure as for a rectangular tube and define a certain distribution of the velocities in the initial section

$$\dot{\zeta}=\psi_0(r,\ \varphi)\cdot e^{j\omega t}.$$

The function $\psi_0(r,\varphi)$ can be expanded into a double series in the characteristic functions of the problem in question:

$$\psi_0(r,\ \varphi)=\sum_{p=0}^{\infty}\sum_{n=0}^{\infty}(\alpha_{pn}\cdot\cos p\varphi+\beta_{pn}\sin p\varphi)\cdot J_p(\nu_{pn}r). \tag{6-27}$$

The coefficients α_{pn} and β_{pn} are calculated by the formulae*

$$\alpha_{0n}=\frac{1}{\pi r_0^2 J_0^2(\nu_{0n}r)}\int_0^{r_0}\int_0^{2\pi}\psi_0(r,\varphi)J_0(\nu_{0n}\cdot r)r\,dr\,a\varphi;\ \beta_{0n}=0;$$
$$\alpha_{pn}=\frac{1}{\pi r_0^2 M_{pn}}\int_0^{r_0}\int_0^{2\pi}\psi_0(r,\varphi)\,J_p(\nu_{pn}r)\cos p\varphi\cdot r\,dr\cdot d\varphi; \tag{6-28}$$

* P.M. Morse, *Vibration and Sound*. New York: McGraw-Hill, 1948 (see sect.19).

$$\beta_{pn}=\frac{1}{\pi r_0^2 M_{pn}}\int_0^{r_0}\int_0^{2\pi}\psi_0(r,\varphi)J_p(\nu_{pn}r)\sin p\,\varphi\cdot r dr\,d\varphi, \quad \text{(6-28) cont.}$$

where

$$M_{pn}=\frac{1}{2}\left[J_p^2(\nu_{pn}r_0)-J_{p-1}(\nu_{pn}r_0)\ J_{p+1}(\nu_{pn}r)\right]=$$
$$=\frac{1}{2}\left[\frac{\nu_{pn}^2 r_0^2}{p^2}-1\right]J_{p-1}^2(\nu_{pn}r_0).$$

The following expressions from the theory of Bessel functions are used in the derivation of these formulae:

$$\left.\begin{aligned}
&\int J_0^2(z)\,z\,dz=\frac{z^2}{2}\left[J_0^2(z)+J_1^2(z)\right],\\
&\int J_p^2(z)\,z\,dz=\frac{z^2}{2}\left[J_p^2(z)-J_{p-1}(z)J_{p+1}(z)\right],\\
&\int J_p(z)J_m(z)\,z\,dz=0,\\
&J_{p-1}(z)+J_{p+1}(z)=\frac{2p}{z}\cdot J_p(z),\\
&\frac{dJ_p(z)}{dz}=\frac{1}{2}\left[J_{p-1}(z)-J_{p+1}(z)\right];
\end{aligned}\right\} \quad \text{(6-29)}$$

From the boundary condition

$$v_z(0)=-\left.\frac{\partial\Phi}{\partial z}\right|_{z=0}$$

we find the coefficients A_p and B_p of the series (6-25) for the various values of the additional subscript n in the same way as the coefficients in (6-10) were obtained:

$$A_{pn}=\frac{\alpha_{pn}}{j\sqrt{k^2-\nu_{pn}^2}},\qquad B_{pn}=\frac{\beta_{pn}}{j\sqrt{k^2-\nu_{pn}^2}}. \quad \text{(6-30)}$$

If the perturbation in the section $z = 0$ is symmetrical about the centre, expression (6-27) will contain oscillation modes (0, 1), (0, 2), (0, 3) and so on. At frequencies for which $k>\nu_{01}$, where $\nu_{01}=\frac{3{\cdot}83}{r_0}$ and $f>f_{01}=\frac{2{\cdot}07\times10^4}{r_0}$ (in air) the wave mode (0,1) will be propagated. At the frequency $f=f_{01}$ there will develop along the entire tube intensive resonance oscillations of the mode type (0, 1), and in accordance with formula (6-30) the amplitude of these oscillations will be infinitely large since the formula does not include absorption in the air and the energy loss through the walls. However, considering the smallness of these losses, very intensive oscillations of the mode type (0, 1) can be expected if $f=f_{01}$. If $f<f_{01}$ there can be no propagation of the wave mode (0, 1); oscillatory motion of this type will decay with increasing distance from the beginning of the tube. Motion of arbitrary form which is symmetric about the centre, and is such that the expression (6-27) contains a non-zero constant term corresponding to the mode (0, 0), will cause excitation in the tube of waves with a constant velocity amplitude across the section and these will be propagated along the axis of the tube at the velocity of sound for any frequency, since in this case $k^2-\nu_{00}^2=k>0$. Such a constant term is absent only if the oscillation in the initial section corresponds exactly to a Bessel function of some order p.

If the perturbation in the initial section is non-symmetrical, expression (6-27) must necessarily contain a term of the type (1, 0). At the frequency $f_{10}=\frac{c}{2\pi}\nu_{10}\approx\frac{10^4}{r_0}$ (in air), resonant oscillations will occur in the transverse direction inside the tube. This frequency is roughly half f_{01}. Transverse resonance of this kind occurs in a tube 10 cm in diameter at a frequency of about 2000 c/s. Since it is fairly difficult to achieve symmetrical excitation of oscillations in a tube under real conditions, it follows that at frequencies close to f_{10}, the mode (1, 0) nearly always appears in the expansion of the function $\Phi_0(r, \varphi)$. Marked distortion of the pattern of plane waves (the mode 0, 0) is therefore to be expected owing to the excitation of the wave mode (1, 0). At frequencies $f>f_{10}$ the wave mode (1, 0) begins to be propagated in the tube, but it will be small in amplitude since the resonance in a tube with hard walls is very sharp. Thus, a plane wave, mode type (0, 0), can even be obtained at a frequency higher than f_{10}.

CHAPTER VII

THEORY OF ACOUSTIC WAVE GUIDES

Method of Analysis

In this chapter we will consider the approximate analysis of composite sound conductors in the belief that in the majority of cases this will provide a sufficiently exact solution for a number of problems which are of practical interest. This theory is based on an analogy of the theory of electrical lines and entails the substitution for the actual individual elements of the sound conductor of certain elements with lumped constants (elements of elasticity, mass or friction) or elements of rectangular tubes in which plane waves are propagated. As we shall see, such a treatment is possible if the dimensions of the individual elements and the tube diameters are small compared with the wavelength. No use will be made of tube elements of variable cross-section linking individual volumes or serving as junctions between tubes of different cross-section. All changes in cross-section are assumed to be sudden and abrupt; this involves no appreciable error in the results if the length of the junction is small compared with the wavelength. An approximate analysis has been made of junctions in the form of cones in the book by Stewart and Lindsay.* However, the solutions are quite complicated and difficult to apply in practice. Furthermore, in those solutions no account is taken of the attached mass which results from a change in section. This is a serious omission and in some cases it is prefer-

---

* G.W. Stewart and R.B. Lindsay, *Acoustics*. New York: D. Van Nostrand, 1931.

able to use solutions for abrupt changes in section where the attached mass can be calculated and its effect on the process included.

All the following calculations are based on the determination of the impedance at the input to the system and the transfer impedance, which is defined as the ratio of the force acting at the input to the system to the velocity which is obtained at some element in the system. Knowledge of the input impedance makes it possible to take account of the reflection and absorption of sound, to estimate the radiation of energy, and to include the effect of the load of the waveguide when it is connected to a certain source (telephone, hearing aid, etc.).

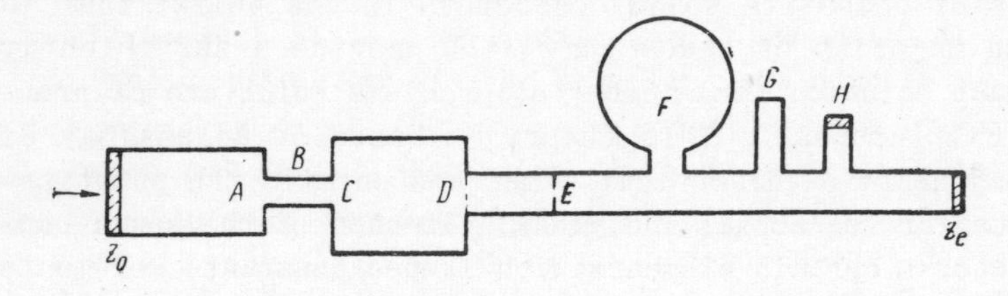

Fig. 40

It is possible to develop a general method of analysing acoustic waveguides consisting of a number of different elements in a row as in Fig. 40. Here tubes of different diameter are connected together with intermediate cavities, partitions with apertures (*E*), frictional elements (*D*) (in the form of thin channels or porous layers), and side branches (*F, G, H*), which lead into cavities or tubes and so on. This requires methods of finding the impedance of the individual elements of the composite waveguide.

Reflection in a Tube Terminated by a Rigid Wall with an Aperture

Suppose that an acoustic wave is incident on the end of a tube which is closed by a rigid screen, in the centre of which there is an aperture of area σ with a mechanical impedance Z_σ (Fig. 41).

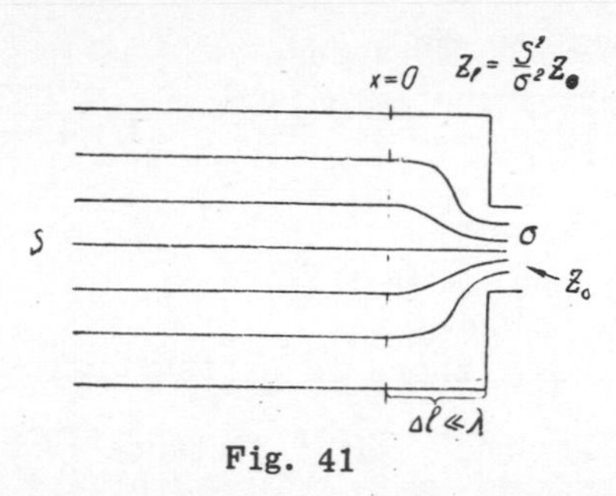

Fig. 41

The reflection from the end of the tube produces a complicated diffraction pattern in the vicinity of the aperture. This phenomenon can be studied rigorously on the basis of the theory of non-homogeneous waves given in Chapter VI. Here we will confine ourselves to showing that in tubes which are rather smaller in diameter than the wavelength the reflected wave becomes plane at a short distance $\Delta l \ll \lambda$ from the aperture. In this region the streamlines are straight lines parallel to the axis of the tube. All the other waves arising as a result of reflection, which together produce the diffraction pattern, rapidly decay in the vicinity of the aperture and are not propagated further.

In the vicinity of a rectangular aperture with sides a and b, in the centre of a partition across a rectangular tube, the non-homogeneities of the velocity fields are balanced out. In fact, as a first approximation the particle velocity in the plane of the partition can be taken to be a constant quantity in the zone of the aperture and zero along the surface of the partition. Such a velocity distribution excites oscillation modes (0,0), (2,0), (0,2), (2,2), (2,4), (0,4), (4,0) and so on. The oscillation mode (0,0) will be propagated along the tube in the form of a plane wave. Higher order oscillation modes will be attenuated near the origin with a damping factor

$$\mu = \sqrt{\left(m\frac{\pi}{a}\right)^2 + \left(n\frac{\pi}{b}\right)^2 - \left(\frac{2\pi}{\lambda}\right)^2}\ .$$

In a square tube with sides a for modes (2,0) or (0,2)

(the least damped) we get:

$$\mu = \sqrt{\left(2\frac{\pi}{a}\right)^2 - \left(\frac{2\pi}{\lambda}\right)^2} = \frac{2\pi}{a} \cdot \sqrt{1 - \frac{a^2}{\lambda^2}}.$$

Provided $\lambda \gg a$

$$\mu \approx \frac{2\pi}{a}.$$

At a distance $x = a$ there is attenuation (in amplitude) by a factor $e^{2\pi} \approx 500$; at a distance $\frac{a}{3}$ by a factor of about 8 and at the distance $\frac{a}{10}$ by a factor of 2. Thus, higher order damped oscillation modes produce distortion of the plane wave only in the zone nearest to the aperture.

Accordingly, we represent the incident and reflected velocity wave and pressure wave as plane waves:

$$p_i = a_0 e^{j(\omega t - \kappa x)}; \quad \dot{\xi}_i = \frac{a_0}{\rho c} e^{j(\omega t - \kappa x)};$$

$$p_r = a_1 e^{j(\omega t + \kappa x)}; \quad \dot{\xi}_r = -\frac{a_1}{\rho c} e^{j(\omega t + \kappa x)}.$$

The origin $(x = 0)$ is selected at a point a short distance Δl from the aperture, where the reflected wave can already be regarded as plane. Bearing in mind that the element Δl is small compared with λ, it can be assumed that the pressure at $x = 0$ will be equal to the pressure p_σ at the input to the aperture with impedance Z_σ; in this case we assume that there is no change in pressure in the non-homogeneous part of the field. (Such an assumption is not strictly correct, since a change in pressure does occur, but this is taken into account later by adding a certain quantity to the impedance of the aperture).

We have, approximately:

$$p_i(0) + p_r(0) = p_\sigma = a_2 e^{j\omega t}. \tag{7-1}$$

The medium in the layer Δl (which is small compared with λ) can be assumed to be incompressible. Then

$$S[\dot{\xi}_i(0) + \dot{\xi}_r(0)] = \sigma \dot{\xi}_\sigma. \tag{7-1a}$$

In addition, the mechanical impedance is

$$Z_\sigma = \frac{\sigma p_\sigma}{\dot{\xi}_\sigma}.$$

Substituting in expressions (7-1) and (7-2) the values

$$p_i(0), \dot{\xi}_i(0), \quad p_r(0), \quad \dot{\xi}_r(0) \text{ and } p_\sigma,$$

we get

$$a_0 + a_1 = a_2,$$

$$\frac{S}{\rho c}\left(a_0 - a_1\right) = \frac{\sigma^2 a_2}{Z_\sigma}.$$

From these equations we can find $\frac{a_1}{a_0}$ and $\frac{a_2}{a_0}$. The reflection coefficient of the pressure wave is

$$r_p = \frac{a_1}{a_0} = \frac{\frac{Z_\sigma}{\sigma\rho c} - \frac{\sigma}{S}}{\frac{Z_\sigma}{\sigma\rho c} + \frac{\sigma}{S}} = \frac{Z_\sigma \frac{S^2}{\sigma^2} - S\rho c}{Z_\sigma \frac{S^2}{\sigma^2} + S\rho c} \tag{7-2}$$

It can be inferred that the mechanical impedance Z_σ in an aperture σ at the end of a tube of area S creates a mechanical impedance Z_l at the end of the tube:

$$Z_l = \frac{S^2}{\sigma^2} Z_\sigma = \frac{Z_\sigma}{u^2}, \tag{7-3}$$

where

$$u = \frac{\sigma}{S}.$$

This expression shows that in going from the section σ to the section S the mechanical impedance increases in the ratio S^2/σ^2 The quantity u can be regarded as *the coefficient of transformation* of a certain mechanical transformer, analogous to an electrical transformer of turn ratio σ/S connected at the end of a line.

It is important to point out that the acoustic impedance at the aperture, which is Z_σ/σ^2, is equal to the equivalent acoustic impedance of the area S, $\overline{Z}_l = \frac{Z_l}{S^2} = \frac{Z_\sigma}{\sigma^2}$, since the pressure and volume velocity remain constant on transformation and their ratio, which is equal to the acoustic impedance also remains unchanged. It is easy to obtain the sound absorption coefficient (for energy) of the impedance Z_a from the expression for r_p; $\alpha = 1 - r_p^2$.

Conductivity of an Aperture

For low frequencies, the kinetic energy of a liquid or gas occupying a tube of length l and section S, and having a velocity $\dot{\xi}$, can be expressed in the form

$$T = \frac{1}{2} M\dot{\xi}^2 = \frac{1}{2}(Sl\rho)\dot{\xi}^2 = \frac{1}{2}\frac{\rho}{S/l}(S\dot{\xi})^2 = \frac{1}{2}\overline{M}\dot{X}^2. \quad (7\text{-}4)$$

The quantity $Sl\rho = M$ is in this case the oscillating mass. When the kinetic energy is expressed in terms of the volume velocity $\dot{X} = S\dot{\xi}$, the mass is expressed in *acoustic units* and is equal to $\overline{M} = \frac{\rho}{S/l} = \frac{M}{S^2}$. The expression for $\overline{M}$ is formally analogous to that for the resistance of an electrical conductor with the specific resistance ρ. The reciprocal of $\overline{M}$ is a measure of the degree of mobility of the medium in the tube. In the following we shall be interested in the relationship between mobility and the geometric constant of the tube, which, in the case in question, is

$$K = \frac{S}{l}.$$

This quantity, which has the dimension of length (cm), is known acoustically as the *conductance*. Introducing the conductance in expression (7-4), we get:

$$T = \frac{1}{2}\frac{\rho S^2}{K}\dot{\xi}^2 = \frac{1}{2}\frac{\rho}{K}\dot{X}^2. \quad (7\text{-}5)$$

It should be pointed out that the term conductivity is not altogether apt, since acoustic conductance is only formally similar to electrical conductance; it is not related to dissipated losses and only characterizes the inertial properties of the flux configuration in question. It would be more correct to call this quantity *mobility*.

There is no difficulty at all in calculating the conductance of a tube. In other cases, where the acoustic fields may be of a more complicated nature, it is first necessary to find the integral of the kinetic energy T over the region and then use formula (7-5) to determine the conductance K or mass $\overline{M}=\frac{\rho}{K}$, by relating it to the volume velocity $\dot{X}$ in the aperture.

In acoustics it is very important to be able to calculate the conductance of an elliptic or circular aperture in an infinitely thin and infinitely extended partition between two half-spaces. This particular problem was solved by Rayleigh*. We will confine ourselves to the physical meaning of the conductance in this case. If an incompressible liquid is made to flow through an aperture in a partition under the action of a pressure difference (steady or fluctuating), a definite streamline pattern is produced in the medium and velocities are in general different at different points in the medium. We are justified in assuming that the velocities are zero at infinity and that the normal component of the velocity is zero at the partition. In the plane of the aperture the velocities are maximum at the edges. In the case of an infinitely thin partition the velocity at the edge is infinite. In order to determine the conductivity, it is necessary to calculate the kinetic energy in the entire infinite region by the following formula:

$$T=\frac{1}{2}\rho\iiint\left[\left(\frac{\partial\Phi}{\partial x}\right)^2+\left(\frac{\partial\Phi}{\partial y}\right)^2+\left(\frac{\partial\Phi}{\partial z}\right)^2\right]dx\,dy\,dz, \qquad (7\text{-}6)$$

---

* Lord Rayleigh, *Theory of Sound*, New York: Dover Publications, 1945 (see vol. II, sect. 306).

where Φ is the velocity potential.

In order to calculate the mean value of T over an interval of time, it is necessary to determine the velocity at all points in the field. If the volume velocity $\dot{X}$ in the aperture is known, the conductance can then be found by formula (7-5). If we put $\dot{X}=\sigma\overline{\dot{\xi}}_0$, where $\overline{\dot{\xi}}_0$ is the mean velocity in the aperture, then the kinetic energy (7-6) can be formally expressed in terms of the mean velocity in the aperture or in terms of the volume velocity across the entire aperture:

$$T=\frac{1}{2}\left(\frac{\rho\sigma^2}{K}\right)\overline{\dot{\xi}}_0^2=\frac{1}{2}\frac{\rho}{K}\dot{X}_0^2. \tag{7-7}$$

Here the quantity

$$\frac{\rho\sigma^2}{K}=M \tag{7-7a}$$

has the dimensions of mass. It is assumed that this mass is moving at the velocity $\dot{\xi}_0$ and has a kinetic energy equal to the entire kinetic energy T of the infinite field. Here, for oscillatory processes, $\dot{X}_0$ and $\overline{\dot{\xi}}_0$ in formula (7-7) have to be regarded as effective values of the velocities and M is the *attached mass of the aperture,* which as we have seen is required in determining the total effective mass.

In fact the actual mass in the aperture of an infinitely thin baffle across a tube is zero (unlike the case considered above where a definite fluid mass oscillated in a tube of length l) and we can only conventionally ascribe the additional kinetic energy (additional to the kinetic energy of the incident plane wave) to a certain fictitious mass M, in accordance with formula (7-7a), which moves with the mean velocity of the medium in the aperture. The bulk of this energy is concentrated in a zone near the aperture and small in size compared with the wavelength. It is obvious that in the case in question, and in any disturbance of a plane flow (in which the streamlines are rectilinear and their density everywhere the same) there must arise a certain additional or attached mass with the inherent property of inertia. Energy has to be expended in order to set this mass in motion. Thus, we can speak of the attached mass of a hole in a partition across a tube or the attached mass of a bend in a tube. Here, in addition to the energy of the plane motion of the medium in the tube, there arises an additional energy related to the velocity field due to the distorting influence of the aperture on the plane wave. The plane wave also possesses energy, but it is largely radiated energy (active); in a plane wave, the phase velocity coincides with the pressure and the attached mass (in the presence of which there must be a certain phase difference between the velocity and pressure) is zero.

According to Rayleigh, the conductivity of an elliptic aperture (of area σ and eccentricity e) in an infinite wall is:

$$K=2\sqrt{\frac{\sigma}{\pi}}\left(1+\frac{e^4}{64}+\frac{e^6}{64}+\dots\right).$$

(The solution is similar to that for the surface charge density on an electrically conducting disc). The conductance of a circular aperture ($e = 0$) is equal to the diameter of the aperture:

$$K=2\sqrt{\frac{\sigma}{\pi}}=2r_0=d. \tag{7-8}$$

For elliptic apertures which are not too eccentric, the conductance is very nearly equal to the diameter of a circle of equivalent area: $K\approx 2\sqrt{\frac{\sigma}{\pi}}$. If the ratio of the semi-axes of the ellipse $\frac{b}{a}=0{\cdot}17$ ($e=0{\cdot}98$) then the conductance is only 20 per cent greater than the quantity

$2\sqrt{\frac{\sigma}{\pi}}$. The conductance of apertures of shapes other than ellipses and circles has been calculated by Ingard*. However, for apertures which are not too extended, it can be assumed that

$$K \approx 2\sqrt{\frac{\sigma}{\pi}} \text{ and } M \approx \frac{\rho\sigma^2}{K}.$$

Since the particle velocity is not uniform over the plane of the aperture, it follows that the volume velocity $\dot{X}$ has to be obtained by integration of the velocity over the area of the aperture.

It is of interest to compare Rayleigh's result with the conductance calculated from the formula for the impedance of a plane piston, i.e. with the conductance for the case where the velocity is uniformly distributed over the entire area of the aperture. In Chapter XI we obtain the following expression for the attached mass of a piston with a flange if $\lambda \gg d$:

$$M_{\text{pist}} = \frac{8}{3}\rho r_0^3 = \frac{1}{3}\rho d^3.$$

If we take a layer of air in an aperture of a partition as a piston with an attached mass on both sides, then

$$T = 2\frac{1}{2}M_{\text{pist}}\dot{\xi}^2 = \frac{1}{2}\rho\frac{2M_{\text{pist}}}{\sigma^2}\dot{X}^2 = \frac{1}{2}\frac{\rho}{K}\dot{X}^2,$$

whence, in accordance with (7-7) we find:

$$K = \frac{\rho\sigma^2}{2M_{\text{pist}}} = \frac{3\pi^2}{32}d = \beta d, \tag{7-9}$$

where

$$\beta = \frac{3\pi^2}{32} = 0{\cdot}925 = \frac{1}{1{\cdot}08}.$$

Thus, for piston motion in an aperture the conductivity is

* U. Ingard, *J. Acoust. Soc. Amer.* 20, 665, 1948.

7·5 per cent less than obtained by formula (7-8), and the mass is roughly an equal amount larger.

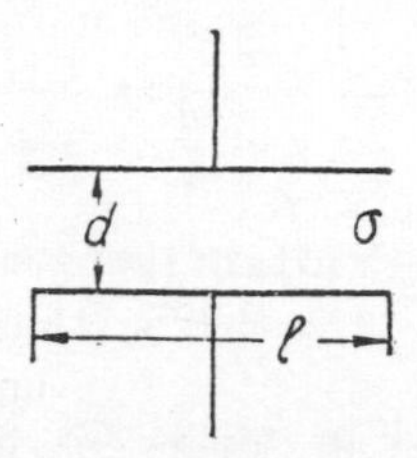

Fig. 42

Using these formulae for the conductance, we can find an expression for the impedance of a tube including the correction for the attached mass at its ends. In the case of long waves ($\lambda \gg d$) it can be assumed that a tube of length l is divided by an infinite partition which stops the flows between its ends (Fig. 42). The case when $l \to 0$, has already been considered by Rayleigh. If $l \neq 0$ it can be assumed that there is at each end an additional attached mass $M' = \frac{\rho\sigma^2}{2K}$ which is to be added to the mass of the medium in the tube, where $2K = 2\beta d = 4\beta r_0$ is the conductivity of one side only of an aperture in an infinite baffle. The total fluctuating mass is

$$M = \rho\sigma l + 2\frac{\beta\sigma^2}{2K} = \rho\sigma\left(l + 2\frac{\sigma}{2K}\right) = \rho\sigma\left(l + 2\frac{\pi}{4\beta}r_0\right).$$

Each end of the tube is as it were elongated by $\frac{\pi}{4\beta}r_0 = \Delta l.$

According to Rayleigh $K = d$ (i.e. $\beta = 1$), and if this is so we get:

$$M = \rho\sigma\left(l + 2\frac{\pi r_0}{4}\right) = \rho\sigma\left(l + \frac{\pi d}{4}\right), \tag{7-10}$$

i.e. an elongation of $\Delta l = \frac{\pi r_0}{4} = 0{\cdot}78\, r_0$ at each end. Thus, the whole tube is effectively elongated by a quarter of the length of its perimeter. The conductance of the tube with the correction for the attached mass at the ends is;

$$K' = \frac{\sigma}{l + \frac{\pi d}{4}} = \frac{\frac{\sigma}{l}}{1 + \frac{\pi d}{4l}}. \qquad (7\text{-}11)$$

If we assume a uniform distribution of velocity over the cross-section and put $\beta = 0{\cdot}925$, then the effective elongation of the tube will be equal to $\frac{\pi d}{4}$ 1·08 and not $\frac{\pi d}{4}$. In the published literature, the usual expression for the conductance of a tube is expression (7-11). However, if it is borne in mind that on the propagation of sound in a tube the velocity distribution over the section is approximately uniform, it is possible that the correction based on formula (7-9) will be better substantiated. We then get:

$$\Delta l = \frac{\pi}{4\beta} r_0 \approx 0{\cdot}85\, r_0.$$

This matter has not yet been adequately explored either theoretically or experimentally and in view of the inaccuracy of this kind of measurement, no data are as yet available to state which formula is nearer the truth.

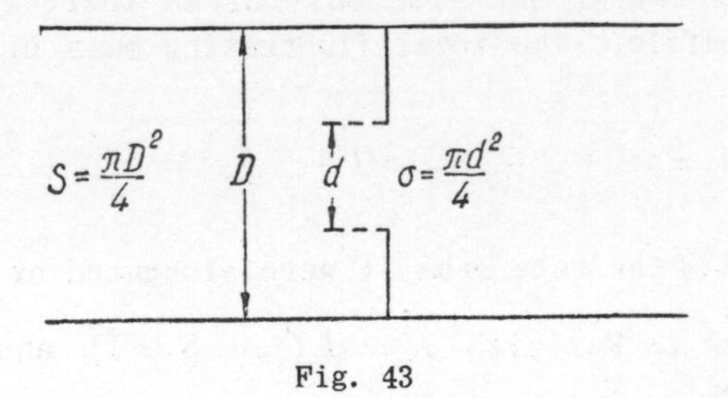

Fig. 43

According to Gutin*, we can assume that the attached mass for the open end of a tube without a flange is $M' \approx 2\rho r_0^3$.

* L.Ya. Gutin, *Zhur. tekh. phys.*, 7, 1096, (1937).

The additional length attributable to this mass is

$$\Delta l = \frac{M'}{\rho\sigma} = \frac{2}{\pi} r_0 = 0{\cdot}64 r_0.$$

It is to be supposed that the conductance of an aperture in a partition across a tube of diameter D (Fig. 43) will be different from that of an aperture in an infinite partition, since the form of the streamlines and the kinetic energy of the reactive flows through the aperture are not the same. If the ratio $\frac{d}{D}$ is small, the problem approximates to the case of an infinite baffle and it can be assumed that $K \approx d$. With an increase in d, when $d \to D$, the conductance must tend to infinity, since the distorting effect of the aperture on the lines of current becomes small and the attached mass disappears.

In accordance with the conclusions reached above and in Chapter VI, the attached mass of a circular aperture in the centre of a partition across a tube can be calculated by formula 7-6, on the assumption of a uniform (piston) velocity distribution over the area of the aperture.

In a tube of radius r_0 (diameter $D = 2r_0$) the velocity potential on one side of a circular centrally disposed piston of radius r_1 (diameter $d = 2r_1$), which oscillates with the velocity amplitude u_0, can be represented in accordance with formula 6-25 by the following series (the time factor $e^{j\omega t}$ is omitted):

$$\Phi(z,r) = \sum_{n=0}^{\infty} C_{on} J_o(\nu_{on}) e^{j\sqrt{k^2 - \nu_{on}^2}\, z} .$$

The coordinate z is marked off from the surface of the piston. The particle velocity in the axial direction is

$$U_z(z,r) =$$

$$= -\frac{\partial\Phi}{\partial z} = \sum_{n=0}^{\infty} j\sqrt{k^2 - \nu_{on}^2}\, C_{on} J_o(\nu_{on} r)\, e^{-j\sqrt{k^2 - \nu_{on}^2}\, z}$$

The particle velocity in the radial direction is

$$U_r(z,r) = -\frac{\partial\Phi}{\partial r} = \sum_{n=0}^{\infty} \nu_{on} C_{on} J_1(\nu_{on} r) e^{-j\sqrt{k^2 - \nu_{on}^2}\, z}$$

The total velocity is $u = \sqrt{u_r^2 + u_r^2}$.

The boundary condition for $z = 0$ is written as follows

$$U_z(0,r) = \sum_{n=0}^{\infty} j\sqrt{k^2 - \nu_{on}^2}\, C_{on} J_o(\nu_{on} r) =$$

$$\left\{ \begin{matrix} U_o \text{ if } 0 < r < r_1 \\ 0 \text{ if } r_1 < r < r_o \end{matrix} \right\}.$$

Multiplying both sides by $J_o(\nu_{om}, r)$ and integrating over the cross section of the tube, we get:

$$2\pi \sum_{n=0}^{\infty} j\sqrt{k^2 - \nu_{on}^2}\, C_{on} \int_0^{r_o} J_o(\nu_{on} r) J_o(\nu_{om} r) r\, dr =$$

$$= 2\pi u_o \int_0^{r_1} J_o(\nu_{om} r) r dr.$$

From the theory of Bessel functions

$$\int_0^{r_0} J_0(\nu_{on} r) J_0(\nu_{om} r) r\, dr = \left\{ \begin{array}{l} 0 \text{ if } m \neq n \\ \dfrac{r_0^2}{2} J_0^2(\nu_{on} r_0) \text{ if } m = n \end{array} \right\}.$$

This formula also applies to $\int_0^{r_0} J_1(\nu_{on} r) J_1(\nu_{om} r) r dr$ if $m = n$.

Using these relationships, we find

$$C_{oo} = \frac{r_1^2}{jkr_0^2} u_o, \quad C_{on} = \frac{2r_1 J_1(\nu_{on} r_1 u_o}{j\sqrt{k^2 - \nu_{on}^2}\ \nu_{on} r_0^2\ J_0^2(\nu_{on} r_0)} =$$

$$= \frac{2r_1 J_1(\nu_{on} r_1)\ u_o}{\sqrt{1 - \frac{k^2}{\nu_{on}^2}}\ (\nu_{on} r_0)^2 J_0^2(\nu_{on} r_0)} \approx$$

$$\approx \frac{2\ r_1 J_1(\nu_{on} r_1)\ u_o}{(\nu_{on} r_0)^2 J_0^2(\nu_{on} r_0)}, \quad k \ll \nu_{on}.$$

In calculating the kinetic energy it is only necessary to take into account higher oscillation modes (n = 1, 2, 3, ...) which decay with increasing distance from the oscillating piston. For long waves ($k \ll \nu_{on}$)

$$u^2 = u_z^2 + u_r^2 = \sum_{n=1}^{\infty} C_{on}^2 \nu_{on}^2 J_o^2(\nu_{on} r) e^{-2\nu_{on} z} +$$

$$+ \sum_{n=1}^{\infty} C_{om}^2 \nu_{om}^2 J_1{}^2(\nu_{om} r) e^{-2\nu_{om} z} +$$

$$+ 2 \sum_{n=1}^{\infty} \sum_{m=1}^{\infty} C_{on} C_{om} \nu_{on} \nu_{om} J_o(\nu_{on} r) J_o(\nu_{om} r) e^{-(\nu_{on} + \nu_{om}) z}$$

$$+ 2 \sum_{n=1}^{\infty} \sum_{m=1}^{\infty} C_{on} C_{om} \nu_{on} \nu_{om} J_1(\nu_{on} r) J_1(\nu_{om} r) e^{-(\nu_{on} + \nu_{om})}$$

The kinetic energy in the whole volume of the tube from $z = 0$ to $z = \infty$ (at the instant of maximum velocity) is

$$T_1 = \frac{1}{2} \, 2\pi\rho \int_0^{\infty} dz \int_0^{r_o} u^2 \, r dr.$$

The integrals of the third and fourth terms in the expression for T_1 are zero by virtue of the stated properties of integrals of Bessel functions; the values of the integrals of the Bessel functions in the first and second terms (is $n = m$) have been given above. Bearing in mind that

$$\int_0^{\infty} e^{-2\nu_{on} z} dz = 1/(2\nu_{on})$$

and substituting the value C_{on} obtained above, we get

$$T_1 = \frac{1}{2}\pi\rho \sum_{n=1}^{\infty} C_{on}{}^2 \nu_{on} r_o{}^2 J_o^2(\nu_{on} r_o) =$$

$$= 2\pi r_1{}^2 r_o \rho u_o^2 \sum_{n=1}^{\infty} \frac{J_1{}^2(\nu_{on} r_1)}{(\nu_{on} r_o)^3 J_o{}^2(\nu_{on} r_o)}$$

A certain fictitious attached mass M_1 which oscillates with velocity amplitude u_0, can be associated with the kinetic energy thus obtained:

$$T_1 = \frac{1}{2} M_1 u_0^2.$$

The acoustic field for higher modes on the other side of the aperture is of identical structure, being as it were a specular image of the first side. Thus, on the other side of the aperture, where piston motion occurs, there arises the same attached mass M_1 and the total attached mass of the aperture is

$$M = 2M_1 = 4\pi r_1^2 r_o \rho \sum_{n=1}^{\infty} \frac{J_1^2(\nu_{on} r_1)}{(\nu_{on} r_o)^3 J_o^2(\nu_{on} r_o)} =$$

$$= \frac{4\pi r_1^3 \rho}{\xi} \sum_{n=1}^{\infty} \frac{J_1^2(\nu_{on} r_o \xi)}{(\nu_{on} r_o)^3 J_0^2(\nu_{on} r_o)},$$

where $\xi = r_1/r_o = d/D$.

On increasing the radius of the tube ($D \rightarrow \infty$) we arrive at the case of a piston radiator with an infinite flange for which at the limit $M_1 = 8/3\ r_1^3 \rho$ (see Chapter XI) and, consequently, the attached mass of the aperture if $\xi \rightarrow 0$ must tend to the quantity

$$M_o = \frac{16}{13} r_1^3 \rho = \rho\sigma^2/K_o \psi\ (o),$$

where in the limit $\xi = o$ the conductance is $K_o = (3\pi^2/32)d$ (see formula 7.9). When ξ is small the conductance is $K = K_o\,\psi(\xi)$ I.

The problem of the attached mass of a circular aperture in a partition across a tube can be solved without assuming piston motion of the medium in the aperture in the same way as Rayleigh approached a circular aperture in an infinite partition. This problem has been solved by Fok*. Without introducing a complicated solution, we will merely give the final expression for the attached mass of the circular aperture in the partition

$$M' = \rho\sigma^2/d\,\psi'(\xi) = \rho\sigma^2/K'(\xi).$$

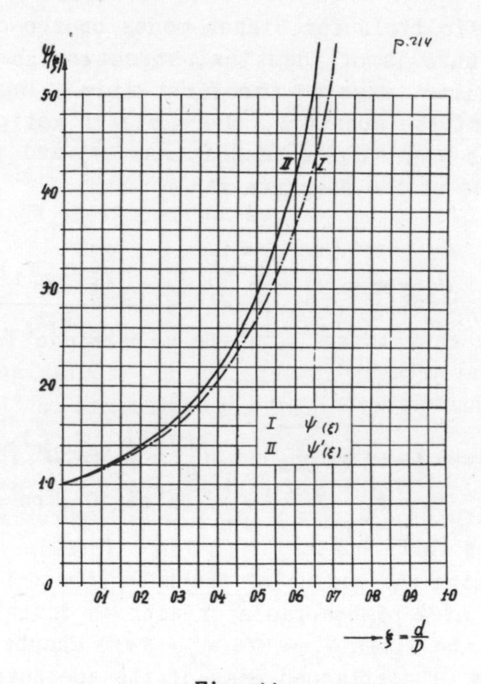

Fig. 44

* V.A. Fok, 1941, *Dokl. Akad. Nauk SSSR*, 31, (9).

The conductance $K'(\xi)$ is equal to $d\psi'(\xi)$, where

$$\psi'(\xi) = 1 + a_1\xi + a_2\xi^2 + \ldots$$

and

$a_1 = -1\cdot40925;$		$a_7 = +0\cdot03015;$
$a_2 = 0;$		$a_8 = -0\cdot01641;$
$a_3 = +0\cdot33818;$		$a_9 = +0\cdot01729;$
$a_4 = 0;$		$a_{10} = -0\cdot01248;$
$a_5 = +0\cdot06793;$		$a_{11} = +0\cdot01205;$
$a_6 = -0\cdot02287;$		$a_{12} = -0\cdot00985.$

Fok's function $\psi'(\xi)$, like the function $\psi(\xi)$, is always greater than unity. If $\xi \rightarrow 1$ it tends to infinity, i.e. the attached mass tends to zero (see Fig. 44, curve II), but if $\xi \rightarrow 0$, it tends to unity. There is very little difference between curves I and II if ξ is small*

If $\frac{d}{D} < 0{\cdot}2$ it can be assumed approximately that $K \approx d$, i.e. $M' \approx \frac{\rho a^2}{d}$. Conversely, if $\frac{d}{D} > 0{\cdot}8$, it can be assumed that K is a very large quantity and we can ignore the effect of the attached mass. For a circular aperture in a tube of square section with a side a, it can be assumed that the value of the function $\psi\left(\frac{d}{D'}\right)$, where D' is the diameter of a circle of area a^2, will be of approximately the same order as that obtained from Fok's formula.

---

* V.S. Nesterov(19) (*Dokl. Akad. Nauk SSSR*, 31, No.3, 1941), experimentally investigated the conductance of circular apertures as a function of the quantity $\xi = d/D$ and found good agreement with Fok's formula. The accuracy of the measurements was not however sufficient to determine which of the formulae $\psi(\xi)$ or $\psi'(\xi)$ agreed best with the tests.

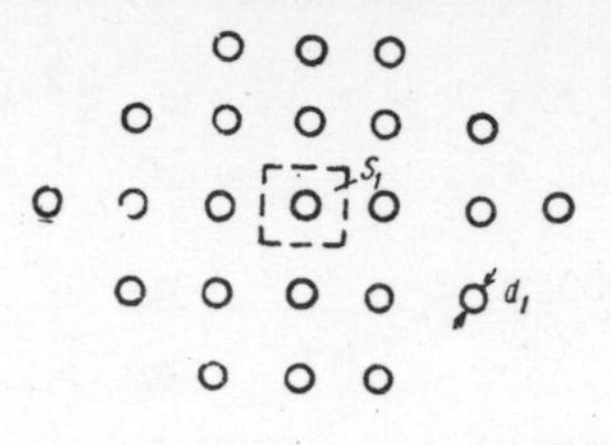

Fig. 45

Suppose we require to determine the conductance of a number (n) of apertures which are disposed on an area S of a partition in a tube. If the apertures of diameter d_1 in an infinite partition are distributed uniformly over the area and are not very close to each other, i.e. $d_1 < 0{\cdot}2D_1$, where $D_1 = 2\sqrt{\frac{S_1}{\pi}}$, and S_1 is the area belonging to one aperture (Fig. 45), then on the basis of Fok's conclusions it can be assumed that the conductance of each aperture is approximately independent of the distance between them and that it is equal to $K_1 = d_1$. The kinetic energy of the reactive flows in the zone occupied by the apertures is equal to the sum of the attached kinetic energies of the individual apertures:

$$T = \frac{1}{2} nM_1 \dot{\xi}_1^2 = \frac{1}{2} n \frac{\rho\sigma_1^2}{K_1} \dot{\xi}_1^2 = \frac{1}{2} \frac{\rho}{nK_1} \dot{X}^2 = \frac{1}{2} \frac{\rho}{K} \dot{X}^2,$$

where K_1 is the conductivity of one aperture and $\dot{\xi}_1$ the velocity in the apertures.

The total conductance is

$$K = nK_1 \approx nd_1,$$

and the total attached mass

$$M = nM_1 = n\frac{\rho\sigma_1^2}{K_1}.$$

In acoustic units the attached mass of one aperture is

$\overline{M}_1 = \frac{\rho}{K_1}$, and the attached mass of n holes is

$$\overline{M} = \frac{\rho}{K} = \frac{\rho}{nK_1} = \frac{\overline{M}_1}{n}.$$

Electrically this is analogous to the fact that the inductance of n identical parallel circuits is n times less than the inductance of one circuit.

If the apertures are arranged close to each other, the attached mass of each aperture tends to zero, as can be seen both from Fok's formula (7-12) and from the curve in Fig. 44, and all the n apertures can be taken together as one aperture with a total area S. If the perforated area is not very extensive, its conductance is equivalent to that of a circle of diameter $d = 2\sqrt{\frac{S}{\pi}}$, and it can be calculated as for a single aperture of diameter d by the formula $K \approx d$.

In the case of a mesh* it can be assumed that the free area of the individual cells is approximately the same as the area of each cell and also that the conductance of the individual cells is infinite. It is only necessary to include the frictional resistance of the apertures, whilst the inertance of the cells can be ignored. If the mesh is used to cover an aperture of diameter d, its conductance is calculated in the same way as for a free aperture which is not covered by a mesh.

The Transmission of Sound from a Tube of One Section into an Infinitely Long Tube of Another Section

Suppose that a plane wave is incident from left to right

---

* S.N. Rschevkin and S.T. Terosipiants, *Zhur. tekh. phys.* 11 (1-2), 149, 1941.

in the tube S_1 in Fig. 46 and that it is reflected back from right to left. A plane transmitted wave will then pass from left to right in the tube S_2. Such an assumption

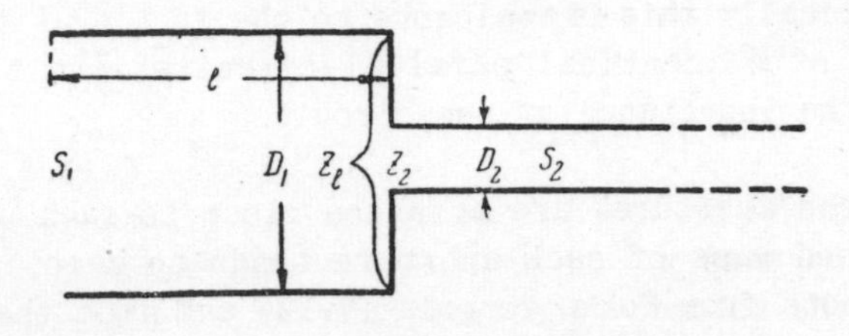

Fig. 46

is valid approximately only for points which are some distance away from the spot where the section S_1 is joined to the section S_2. Plane motion will be disturbed in the neighbourhood of the junction at $x \approx l$ and as we have seen, will produce the attached mass M which we ascribe to the aperture of the smaller tube S_2. In the case in question (see p.214) the attached mass is

$$M = \frac{\rho S_2^2}{2D_2\psi\left(\frac{D_2}{D_1}\right)}.$$

The formation of a reflected wave in the tube S_1 can be formally ascribed to the effect of a certain impedance Z_l which is positioned at the end of the tube S_1 (at $x = l$). Since the irregular part of the acoustic field is concentrated within a very small element $\Delta l \ll \lambda$, it can be assumed that the equations of the plane wave are approximately satisfied right up to the point of change in the section and on the other side. But we have to take account of the pressure drop across the inertance due to the attached mass. The pressures at the boundary of the tubes S_1 and S_2 can be regarded as matched if the following condition is satisfied:

$$p_1(l) = p_2(l) + j\frac{\omega M}{S_2}\dot{\xi}_2(l). \quad (7\text{-}13)$$

Here $p_1, \dot{\xi}_1$ and $p_2, \dot{\xi}_2$ are the pressure and particle velocity in the tubes S_1 and S_2 respectively. On the right-hand side of equation (7-13) we have the term $j\omega\frac{M}{S_2}\dot{\xi}_2(l)$, representing the pressure drop across the inertance due to the attached mass M. We can also write the condition under which the volume velocity will be constant on passing from one section to the other:

$$S_1\dot{\xi}_1(l) = S_2\dot{\xi}_2(l).$$

The impedance at the end of the tube is:

$$Z_l = \frac{S_1 p_1(l)}{\dot{\xi}_1(l)} = \frac{S_1 p_1(l)}{\dot{\xi}_2(l)\frac{S_2}{S_1}} = \frac{S_1^2}{S_2^2} S_2 \frac{p_2(l) + \frac{j\omega M\dot{\xi}_2(l)}{S_2}}{\dot{\xi}_2(l)}.$$

Since for the second tube $\frac{p_2(l)}{\dot{\xi}_2(l)} = \rho c$, it follows that

$$Z_l = \frac{S_1^2}{S_2^2}(S_2\rho c + j\omega M). \quad (7\text{-}14)$$

The impedance $(S_2\rho c + j\omega M)$ is the sum of the wave impedance of the tube $S_2\rho c$ and the impedance of the attached mass of the output aperture of the tube $j\omega M$. There is no difficulty in showing that by taking formula (7-8) for the conductance, expression (7-14) (when $D_1 \gg D_2$) can be written in the form:

$$Z_l = \frac{S_1^2}{S_2^2} S_2\rho c\left(1 + j\frac{\pi}{8}kD_2\right),$$

where

$$k = \frac{\omega}{c} = \frac{2\pi}{\lambda}.$$

The multiplication of the impedance at the input to the second tube by $\frac{S_1^2}{S_2^2}$ is analogous to the transfer of this impedance from the secondary circuit into the primary circuit of a stepdown voltage transformer.

If sound is transmitted from a narrow tube S_1 into a wide tube S_2 additional energy is also formed in the intermediate section, the amount of energy being the same as in the previous case, for corresponding amplitudes of motion. The expression for the attached mass will have the form

$$M = \frac{\rho S_1^2}{2D_1 \psi\left(\frac{D_1}{D}\right)}.$$

The impedance at the end of a narrow tube (of section S_1) which connects into a wide tube (of section S_2) is expressed in a slightly different form, namely:

$$Z_l' = \frac{S_1^2}{S_2^2} S_2 \rho c + j\omega M = \frac{S_1^2}{S_2^2}\left[S_2 \rho c + j\omega M \frac{S_2^2}{S_1^2}\right], \quad (7\text{-}15)$$

or

$$Z_l' = \frac{S_1^2}{S_2^2} S_2 \rho c\left[1 + j\frac{\pi}{8} kD_1 \frac{S_2}{S_1}\right].$$

The quantity $M\frac{S_2^2}{S_1^2}$ is the attached mass of the aperture of the narrow tube expressed in terms of the section of the wide tube. On passing from the wide tube into the narrow tube (formula (7-14)), the ratio of the active component of the impedance (resistance) to the reactive component is:

$$\frac{R_l}{Y_l} = \frac{1}{\frac{\pi}{8} kD_2} = \frac{4}{\pi^2} \frac{\lambda}{D_2}.$$

When $\lambda \gg D_2$, the active component is correspondingly larger than the reactive component and $Z_l \approx \frac{S_1^2}{S_2^2} S_2 \rho c$. On transition from the narrow tube into the wide tube, we get from expression (7-15)

$$\frac{R_l'}{Y_l'} = \frac{1}{\frac{\pi}{8} kD_1 \frac{S_2}{S_1}} = \frac{4}{\pi^2} \frac{\frac{\lambda}{D_1}}{\frac{S_2}{S_1}}.$$

If the ratio of S_2/S_1 is large, the ratio R_l'/Y_l' can be of the order of unity or even less. The inertial component of impedance may be predominant at the end of a narrow tube which passes into a wide tube. If $S_2 \to \infty$, i.e. on transition into an open medium, the reactive component (as is known from the theory of the piston diaphragm) is greater than the active (resistive) component. In these calculations no account has been taken of the effect of friction, which considerably alters the picture in narrow tubes.

If S_1 and S_2 are only slightly different from each other in section, then the attached mass M will be small and it can be assumed in both cases that $Z_l \approx \frac{S_1^2}{S_2^2} S_2 \rho c$. The reflection coefficient of the intermediate section for the pressure wave is in this case:

$$r_p = \frac{Z_l - S_1 \rho c}{Z_l + S_1 \rho c} = \frac{\frac{S_1^2}{S_2^2} S_2 \rho c - S_1 \rho c}{\frac{S_1^2}{S_2^2} S_2 \rho c + S_1 \rho c} = \frac{S_1 - S_2}{S_1 + S_2}. \qquad (7\text{-}16)$$

This simple formula is the one which is usually given in textbooks, but as we have seen, it is not always suitable.

In accordance with equation (7-16), on the reflection of sound propagated in a tube of large section at a junction with a tube of small section ($S_1 > S_2$), no abrupt change will occur in the phase of the pressure, but there will be a sudden change equal to π in the phase of the particle velocity (as in the case of reflection from a medium with a large acoustic impedance $\rho_2 c_2$). If $S_1 < S_2$ an abrupt change will occur in the phase of the pressure wave, but no change will take place in the phase of the velocity wave (as in the case of reflection from a medium with a small acoustic impedance $\rho_2 c_2$).

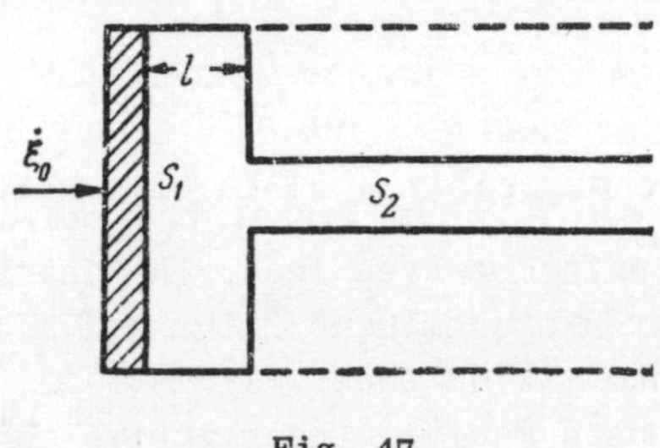

Fig. 47

We will now compare from the energy point of view the radiation which takes place when a piston of cross-section S_1 is vibrating at the beginning of an infinite tube of the same cross-section with that which takes place on transfer from a tube of cross-section S_1 into a narrow tube of cross-section S_2. It is assumed that the length of the wide tube l is small compared with the wavelength (Fig. 47). The second configuration is an idealized representation of the transfer chamber of a horn loudspeaker, since a horn of initial cross-section S_2 has an output impedance of approximately $S_2 \rho c$. The impedance at the input to the wide tube of constant section S_1 is $S_1 \rho c$, and the radiated power is

$$\Pi_1 = \frac{1}{2} S_1 \rho c \dot{\xi}_0^2,$$

where $\dot{\xi}_0$ is the velocity amplitude of the piston. The input impedance Z in the second case is $(S_2 \rho c + j\omega M)\frac{S_1^2}{S_2^2}$,

where M is the attached mass in the section S_2, $M \approx \frac{\rho S_2^2}{D_2}$.

The active (resistive) component is then, as we have seen, much greater than the reactive component.

The radiated power is:

$$\Pi_2 \approx \frac{1}{2}\frac{S_1^2}{S_2^2} S_2 \rho c \dot{\xi}_0^2 = \frac{1}{2} S_1 \rho c \dot{\xi}_0^2 \left(\frac{S_1}{S_2}\right).$$

Thus, in the second case the radiated power is $\frac{S_1}{S_2}$ times greater. The use of a transformation air chamber makes it possible to increase the radiated power of a horn loudspeaker very considerably. It is of course assumed that $\dot{\xi}_0$ is the same in both cases, which corresponds to a source with a very large internal impedance whose performance is unaffected by the size of the load. It is easy to prove that the converse applies if the internal impedance of the source is small, in which case the value of $\dot{\xi}_0$ is greatly dependent on the load. In this case the radiated power would be decreased by a factor of $\frac{S_1}{S_2}$ as a result of using a transformation air chamber in the narrow tube. The method which has been described corresponds to the use of a transformer to approach the optimum load of an electrical generator.

The Input Impedance Z of an Aperture (of Area S) and a Volume V, Terminated in an Impedance Z_σ Concentrated on an Area σ

In the case of long waves ($\lambda \gg \sqrt[3]{V}$) it can be assumed that the volume velocity across the section S (Fig. 48a) is equal to $\dot{X}_0 = S\dot{\xi}_0$, and that it can be divided into two parts, namely, $\dot{X}_\sigma$ the volume velocity across the area σ, of impedance Z_σ, and $\dot{X}_v$, the volume velocity which flows into the volume V owing to its compressibility:

$$\dot{X}_0 = \dot{X}_v + \dot{X}_\sigma. \tag{7-17}$$

The elastic impedance of the volume V is $\frac{\rho c^2 S^2}{j\omega V}$, and consequently,

$$\dot{X}_v = S\frac{p_0}{\frac{\rho c^2 S^2}{j\omega V}} = \frac{p_0}{\frac{\rho c^2}{j\omega V}},$$

and

$$\dot{X}_\sigma = \sigma\dot{\xi}_\sigma = \frac{\sigma^2 p_0}{Z_\sigma} = \frac{p_0}{Z_\sigma/\sigma^2}.$$

In these expressions p_0 denotes the acoustic pressure prevailing in the entire cavity V from the internal edge of the input aperture to the impedance Z_σ; this assumption of uniform pressure is valid for a cavity of which the typical dimension is small compared with λ. The input impedance of the aperture S is $Z = \frac{Sp_0}{\dot{\xi}_0} = \frac{S^2 p_0}{\dot{X}_0}$, assuming that the input aperture produces no pressure drop, i.e. if its own impedance is neglected, which is of course not quite correct. Expression (7-17) takes the form:

$$S^2\frac{p_0}{Z} = \frac{p_0}{\frac{\rho c^2}{j\omega V}} + \frac{p_0}{\frac{Z_\sigma}{\sigma^2}},$$

whence

$$\left.\begin{aligned} \frac{1}{Z} &= \frac{1}{\frac{\rho c^2 S^2}{j\omega V}} + \frac{1}{Z_\sigma\frac{S^2}{\sigma^2}} = \frac{1}{Z_v} + \frac{1}{Z'_\sigma} \\ &\text{or} \\ Z &= \frac{Z_v Z'_\sigma}{Z_v + Z'_\sigma}, \end{aligned}\right\} \qquad (7\text{-}18)$$

where $Z'_\sigma = Z_\sigma\frac{S^2}{\sigma^2}$ is the mechanical impedance of the aperture σ, transferred to the area S of the input aperture. It is easy to see that the acoustic impedance at the input $\overline{Z} = \frac{p_0}{\dot{X}_0} = \frac{Z}{S^2}$ can be written as a simpler expression:

$$\frac{1}{\overline{Z}}=\frac{1}{\frac{\rho c^2}{j\omega V}}+\frac{1}{\frac{Z_\sigma}{\sigma^2}}=\frac{1}{\overline{Z}_v}+\frac{1}{\overline{Z}'_\sigma}, \tag{7-18a}$$

where $\overline{Z}'_\sigma=\frac{Z_\sigma}{\sigma^2}$ is the acoustic impedance of the aperture σ. The acoustic impedance at the input aperture to the volume V is thus expressed as the impedance of the parallel connexion of the acoustic impedance of the volume and the acoustic impedance $\overline{Z}'_\sigma$. The electrical analogue of the parallel connexion of $\overline{Z}_v$ and $\overline{Z}'_\sigma$ (formula (7-18a)) is illustrated in Fig. 48b; the corresponding analogue for formula (7-18) is more complicated (Fig. 48c) since a transformer has to be included.

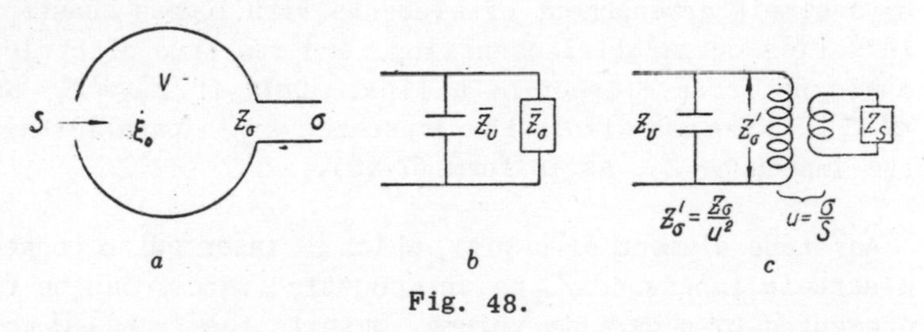

Fig. 48.

The impedance of the volume V in series with the impedance Z_σ concentrated on the area σ on the right-hand side can be found from the formula for the input impedance of a tube of section S, as in Chapter V (formula (5-3)), in which $Z_l=\frac{S^2}{\sigma^2}Z_\sigma=Z'_\sigma$. If $kl\ll 1$ it can be assumed that $\cos kl\approx 1$ and $\sin kl\approx kl$, whence

$$Z_{00}\approx S\rho c\,\frac{Z_l+jS\rho c kl}{S\rho c+jZ_l kl}=Z_l\frac{1+j\frac{S\rho c}{Z_l}kl}{1+j\frac{Z_l}{S\rho c}kl}=\frac{\rho c^2S^2}{j\omega(Sl)}\cdot\frac{Z_l+j\omega\rho Sl}{\frac{\rho c^2S^2}{j\omega(Sl)}+Z_l}.$$

The quantity $j\omega\rho(Sl)$ is the inertance Z_m of an element of tube of length l, i.e. $Z_m = j\omega M$; $Z_v = \frac{\rho c^2 S^2}{j\omega(Sl)}$ is the elastic impedance of the volume $V = Sl$. Thus:

$$Z_{00} = Z_v \frac{Z_l + Z_m}{Z_v + Z_l} = \frac{Z_v Z_l}{Z_v + Z_l}\left(1 + \frac{Z_m}{Z_l}\right). \tag{7-19}$$

If Z_σ is not very small and the section of the tube S is considerably greater than σ, then $Z_l = \frac{S^2}{\sigma^2} Z_\sigma$ will be large. However, if the frequency is small, then $Z_m/Z_l \ll 1$ and equation (7-19) changes into (7-18). If the frequency is increased Z_m increases and cannot be ignored. The calculation then has to be performed by the more accurate formula (7-19). Thus, a tube which connects an input of area S with an impedance Z_l in general cannot be represented by a simple arrangement of elements with lumped constants in series or parallel connexion, and its true electrical analogue is an element of a line. Only if $Z_l \gg Z_m$ and $kl \ll 1$ do we get simply the impedance Z_v in parallel with the impedance Z_l, as in form (7-18).

Any tube element or cavity, which is inserted to connect a certain impedance Z_l to an acoustic system, can be represented by a certain volume. Despite the fact that this volume stands in series with the impedance geometrically, its impedance (at least at low frequencies) is in parallel with Z_l. *It is impossible to connect an elastic impedance in series in an acoustic (or for that matter a mechanical) circuit.* This important conclusion reveals the difficulties involved in constructing electrical analogues for many acoustic systems.

It follows from what has been said that any connecting tube is, generally speaking, a fourpole. The impedance $\hat{Z}_{00}$ at the input to the whole system, if $|Z_l| \gg \omega\rho(Sl)$, is that of a parallel connexion of the impedance Z_l and the elastic impedance. Conversely, if $|Z_l| \ll \omega\rho(Sl)$ and

$Z_l < Z_v$, the tube plays the role of a series inertance $j\omega\rho Sl$. If the quantities Z_l and $\omega\rho Sl$ are of the same order, a connecting tube cannot be unambiguously represented in the form of some simple system of elements with lumped constants as in formula (7-19). A similar situation also occurs for ultra-short electrical waves.

Finally, we will consider the case of a closed tube of of length l, which comes under the same category if $Z_l = \infty$ and $S = \sigma$. Here

$$Z_{00} = -jS\rho c \cot kl.$$

As shown in Chapter V (formula (5-43)), if $kl \ll 1$ we get:

$$Z_{00} \approx \frac{\frac{\rho c^2 S^2}{Sl}}{j\omega} = \frac{E}{j\omega},$$

i.e. a short tube acts like an elastic impedance of volume $V = Sl$. With an increase in frequency there is an increase in kl, so at higher frequencies more terms of the series expansion of cot kl must be used. A second approximation is:

$$Z_{00} = \frac{\frac{\rho c^2 S^2}{Sl}}{j\omega} + j\omega\rho \frac{Sl}{3}. \qquad (7\text{-}20)$$

Thus, not only does the elasticity of the volume have a part to play in a closed tube, but also so does the inertance corresponding to 1/3 of the mass of air contained in the tube. If $kl = \frac{\pi}{2}$, i.e. $l = \frac{\lambda}{4}$, we get $Z_{00} = 0$. Given that $Z_{00} = 0$, using the approximate formula (7-20) we get $kl = \sqrt{3}$ or $\lambda = 3{\cdot}62l$, which underestimates the resonant wavelength of a tube open at one end by 10 per cent. The correct value is $(\lambda = 4l)$.

The connexion of an element of a tube of length equal to a quarter wavelength makes it possible to satisfy the condition of acoustic short circuit $(Z = 0)$ quite satisfactorily. This however cannot be done completely by an open aperture in free air owing to the impedance caused by the reaction of the radiation field.

Frictional Elements in Acoustic Waveguides

If the fluid in a tube possesses internal friction, the motion of the fluid along the tube is laminar at small velocities, that is, the motion is uniform in each cylindrical layer, the layers moving at different velocities depending on their distances from the wall. The boundary layer at the wall is at rest, and the axial layer moves with the maximum velocity. Owing to the friction between the layers moving with different velocities, additional losses and additional inertance occur in the propagation of sound. We will now enquire into the effect of viscosity on the oscillatory motion of a plane layer. Suppose that fluid is in contact with an infinite plane wall (XY) vibrating in a direction x lying in the plane. The viscosity imparts motion from one layer to another and curious transverse waves occur in the fluid which are propagated in the direction normal to the plane XY. The vibrational particle velocity $\dot{\xi}$ along the x axis diminishes with increasing z according to the law:

$$\dot{\xi}=f(z).$$

and is $\xi_0 e^{j\omega t}$ on the wall.

We will now consider the motion of a plane element of area equal to unity and of thickness dz, the normal to which coincides with the normal to the moving plane (Fig. 49).

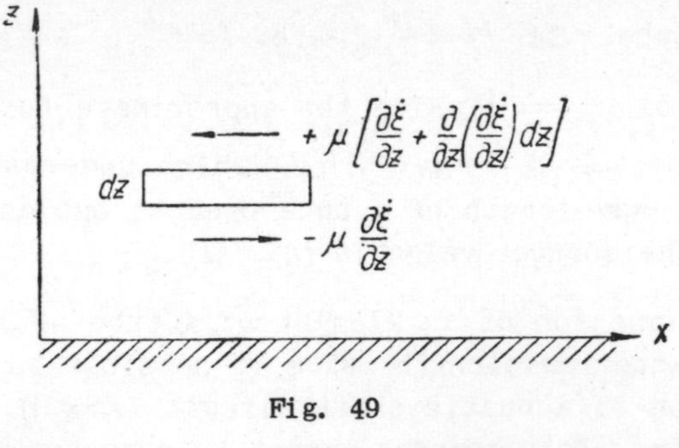

Fig. 49

The lower side of the element will be affected by the

frictional force $-\mu\frac{\partial\dot{\xi}}{\partial z}$, where μ is the coefficient of viscosity. The frictional force on the upper side is

$$\mu\left[\frac{\partial\dot{\xi}}{\partial z}+\frac{\partial}{\partial z}\left(\frac{\partial\dot{\xi}}{\partial z}\right)\right]dz.$$

The total frictional force due to the effect of viscosity on an element 1 cm^2 in area is

$$-\mu\frac{\partial\dot{\xi}}{\partial z}+\mu\frac{\partial\dot{\xi}}{\partial z}+\mu\frac{\partial}{\partial z}\left(\frac{\partial\dot{\xi}}{\partial z}\right)dz=\mu\frac{\partial^2\dot{\xi}}{\partial z^2}dz$$

along the X axis. The mass of the element is $\rho\, dz$.

The equation of motion takes the form:

$$\rho\frac{\partial\dot{\xi}}{\partial t}=\mu\frac{\partial^2\dot{\xi}}{\partial z^2}.$$

Assuming that the solution of this equation is in the form

$$\dot{\xi}=\dot{\xi}_0{}^{j(\omega t-k'z)}$$

and substituting it in the equation of motion, we find:

$$k'=\pm\beta(1+j)=\pm\frac{2\pi}{\lambda'}(1+j),\text{ where }\beta=\sqrt{\frac{\rho\omega}{2\mu}};$$

then

$$\dot{\xi}=\dot{\xi}_0e^{\mp\beta z}\cdot e^{j(\omega t\mp\beta z)}.$$

Thus, a curious wave is obtained in which the damping factor β is numerically equal to the wave number. The solution represents viscous waves of the transverse type which decay in the direction z. The concept of viscous waves was first introduced by the English physicist Stokes. Over a length $x=\frac{1}{\beta}=\sqrt{\frac{2\mu}{\rho\omega}}$, the wave is attenuated in amplitude by a factor e.

On the other hand, the wavelength of the viscous wave is

$$\lambda' = \frac{2\pi}{\beta} = 2\pi \sqrt{\frac{2\mu}{\omega\rho}};$$

and the speed of these waves is

$$c' = \frac{\omega}{\beta} = \sqrt{\frac{2\mu\omega}{\rho}},$$

rather less than the speed of sound c. A viscous wave is already attenuated by a factor e over a length $\frac{1}{\beta} = \frac{\lambda'}{2\pi} \approx \frac{\lambda'}{6}$ Assuming (for air) $\mu = 2 \times 10^{-4}$, at 500 c/s ($\omega = 2\pi \times 500 = 3140$) we get $\lambda' = 0{\cdot}6$ mm. It is obvious that viscous waves at audio frequencies in air will occupy only a very thin layer on the surface of the moving body. In water the wavelength of Stokes' viscous waves will be still less, e.g. at 500 c/s, $\lambda' = 0{\cdot}14$ mm.

The frictional force on an area of 1 cm^2 is

$$R = -\mu \left(\frac{\partial \dot{\xi}}{\partial z}\right)_{z=0} = \mu\beta (1 + j)$$

and has, of course, a passive (inertial) component as well as an active (resistive) component.

For the average input impedance per unit cross-sectional area of a circular tube of radius r_0 and length l in the presence of internal friction, Crandall* found:

$$Z_1' = R_1' + j\omega M_1' = \frac{j\omega\rho l}{1 - \frac{2J_1(k' r_0)}{k' r_0 J_0(k' r_0)}}. \qquad (7\text{-}21)$$

Here

$$k' = \sqrt{\frac{j\omega\rho}{\mu}} = \frac{2\pi}{\lambda'}(1 + j),$$

* I.B. Crandall, *Theory of Vibrating Systems and Sound,* New York: D. Van Nostrand, 1926 (see pp. 229 ff.).

λ' is the wavelength of a viscous Stokes' wave, and J_0 and J_1 are zero and first order Bessel functions. The impedance of a tube of section S will be SZ_1'.

If $|k'r_0| < 2$, i.e. when $r_0 < \frac{\lambda'}{\pi}$, which is satisfied for air if $r_0^2 f < 0{\cdot}1$, we get approximately:

$$Z_1' = R_1' + j\omega M_1' \approx \frac{8\mu l}{r_0^2} + j\frac{4}{3}\rho l\omega. \tag{7-22}$$

The expression $R_1' = \frac{8\mu l}{r_0^2}$ corresponds to Poiseuille's law of resistance in laminar motion of a viscous fluid along a narrow tube. In the case of narrow tubes, the resistance in expression (7-22) is greater than the reactance and the total impedance is independent of the frequency. The quantity $M_1' = \frac{4}{3}\rho l$ represents the effective mass taking part in the vibrations and is 1/3 greater than the actual mass of the medium in a tube of 1 cm^2 in section, i.e. there is an attached mass due to the effect of viscosity.

If the radius or frequency is increased for given values of μ and ρ, there will be an accompanying increase in $|k'r_0|$, and the approximate formula (7-22) loses its validity. An analysis by an exact formula* is illustrated by the curves in Fig. 50, which shows γ (the ratio of the quantity R_1' for air to the value obtained from Poiseuille's formula, namely $R_1' = \frac{8\mu l}{r_0^2}$, as a function of the frequency for four values of the diameter, $2r_0 = 0{\cdot}02$, $0{\cdot}004$, $0{\cdot}1$ and $0{\cdot}2$ cm. Two frequency scales are marked off along the base for two values of μ; the value $\mu = 2\times10^{-4}$ corresponds to a fully thermo-insulated wall, and $\mu' \approx 4\times10^{-4}$ corresponds

---

* S.N. Rschevkin and S.T. Terosipiants, *Zhur. tekh. phys.* 11, (1-2), 149, 1941.

to a wall of very great heat conductivity (metal walls)*. For tubes of diameter smaller than 0·02 cm, the resistance is practically the same as Poiseuille's value over the entire acoustic range and it is independent of the frequency.

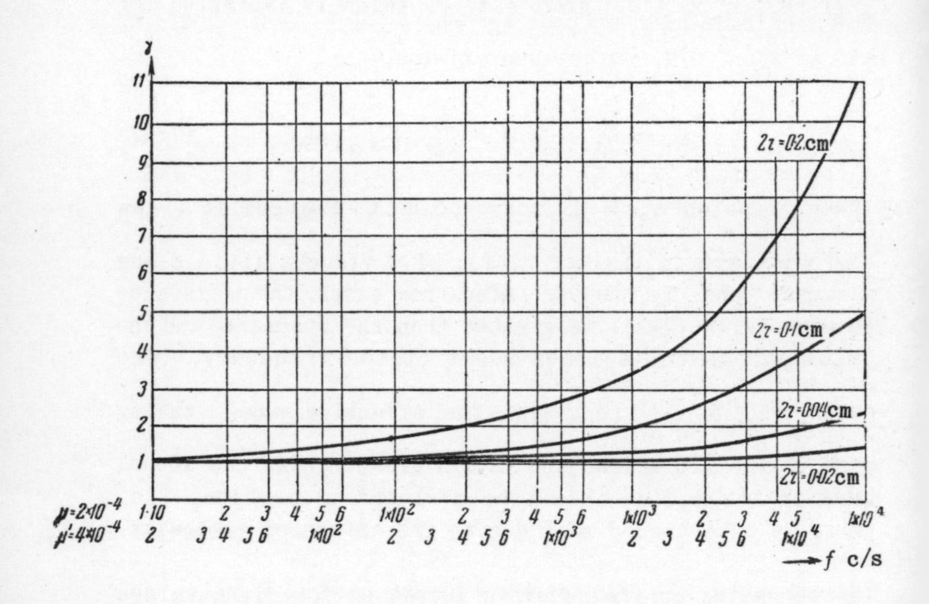

Fig. 50

At large values of r_0 and ω (if $|kr_0| > 10$) we can use approximate expressions for the Bessel functions,

$$\frac{J_1(x\sqrt{-j})}{J_0(x\sqrt{-j})} \approx -j;$$

---

* The value of μ' can be calculated by Kirchoff's formula

$$\sqrt{\mu'} = \sqrt{\mu}\left[1 + (\gamma - 1)\left(\frac{\nu}{\mu c_p}\right)^{1/2}\right],$$

where ν is the coefficient of thermal conductivity of the gas and $\gamma = \frac{c_p}{c_v}$.

and the expression for Z_1' then takes the form:

$$Z_1' \approx \frac{l}{r_0}\sqrt{2\rho\mu\omega} + j\omega\rho l\left(1 + \frac{1}{r_0}\sqrt{\frac{2\mu}{\rho\omega}}\right).$$

The magnitude of the specific resistance $R_1' \approx \frac{l}{r_0}\sqrt{2\rho\mu\omega}$ is to a great extent frequency-dependent. This expression for the resistance was found by Helmholtz.

For an infinitely wide rectangular slot of depth d and length l the specific impedance is, as in (7-21),

$$Z_1' = \frac{j\omega\rho l}{1 - \dfrac{\tan\dfrac{k'd}{2}}{\dfrac{k'd}{2}}} = R_1'(\omega) + jY_1'(\omega),$$

where

$$k' = \sqrt{\frac{\omega\rho}{j\mu}}. \qquad \text{If } k'd < 1$$

$$Z_1' \approx \frac{12\mu l}{d^2} + j\omega\frac{6}{5}\rho l.$$

The quantity $\frac{12\mu l}{d^2}$ corresponds to Poiseuille's value for circular tubes. Figure 51 shows values of $R_1'(\omega)\Big/\frac{12\mu l}{d^2}$, as a function of frequency for various values of d (0·01, 0·025, 0·05, 0·075 and 0·1 cm) with the two frequency scales as in Fig. 50*.

For a number of parallel tubes each of area σ, (the zone area of each tube being S_1) we get for the impedance per cm^2:

$$Z_1 = Z_1'\sigma\frac{S_1^2}{\sigma^2}\cdot\frac{1}{S_1} = Z_1'\frac{S_1}{\sigma} = \frac{Z_1'}{N\sigma},$$

where N is the number of apertures per unit area. Using

* S.N.Rschevkin and S.T.Terosipiants, *Zhur. tekh. phys.* 11, (1-2), 149, 1941.

this formula we can estimate the resistance R_1 for metal meshes, taking its cells (of area σ) as circular tubes of radius $r_0 = \sqrt{\frac{\sigma}{\pi}}$ having a length approximately equal to twice the diameter of the wires from which the grid is woven.

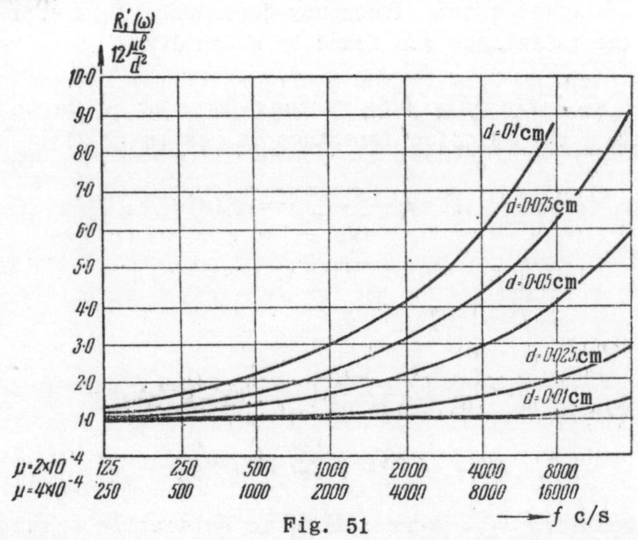

Fig. 51

Capillary tubes and systems of tubes and slots can be used as standards of resistance since their resistance is independent of frequency over a wide range and can be calculated quite accurately. It is impossible to calculate the resistance of cloth, wadding, or other fibrous and porous substances with channels of irregular shape and its value has to be found experimentally. For this purpose gas is blown through the substance at a constant rate and the pressure drop Δp across the specimen in question and the velocity u of the gas are measured. The specific resistance is:

$$R_1 = \frac{\Delta p}{u}.$$

It is measured in mechanical ohms per cm^2 and has the dimensions of $\left[\frac{\text{dyne/cm}^2}{\text{cm/sec}}\right]$. The reactance of thin porous layers (cloth, gauze) is practically negligible; the reactive component of impedance must however be taken into account for thick layers of porous material.

If the velocity u of the gas is increased, there is not only a marked pressure drop due to friction, but also a hydrodynamic drop due to the expansion and contraction of the flow. A hydrodynamic drop in pressure at the inlet from a large cavity into a narrow tube is equal to $\frac{\rho u^2}{2}$, and this must obviously be added to the drop $R_1 u$ caused by the friction in the narrow part of the tube. The total pressure drop is:

$$\Delta p = R_1 u + \frac{\rho u^2}{2}.$$

The experimentally determined resistance

$$R_1' = \frac{\Delta p}{u} = R_1 + \frac{\rho u}{2}, \qquad (7\text{-}23)$$

depends on the velocity of the gas u. It has been found experimentally* that the relationship between the resistance and velocity is similar to equation (7-23).

Table 5 shows the specific resistance of various porous materials.

Roughly speaking the resistance of several layers of porous material is equal to the sum of the resistances of the individual layers.

Table 6 shows the impedance of various acoustic systems, together with sketches of the systems and diagrams of the equivalent electrical circuits.

---

* L. Sivian, *J. Acoust. Soc. Amer.* 7, 94, 1935; R.L. Brown and R.H. Bolt, *J. Acoust. Soc. Amer.* 13, 337, 1942; S.N. Rschevkin, and S.S. Tumanskii, *Zhur. tekh. phys.* 17 (6), 681.

TABLE 5

Material	Specific frictional resistance, mech.ohm/cm^2
Gauge (1 layer)	0.4 – 0.5
Industrial calico	1
Flimsy cotton cloth	3 – 5
Copper mesh (mesh 0.12 mm, hole diameter 0.05 mm)	3
Flimsy chintz	6
Fine (ribbed) metal mesh	8 – 10
Wool felt	30
Siberian cambric	40 – 80
Glass cloth (various grades)	3 – 100
Woolen cloth	100 – 500

Side Branches in a Sound Conductor

It is assumed that the width of a side branch of section σ at the point $x = 0$ (Fig. 52) is very small compared with λ and, consequently, that the pressure at the outlet of the element of the main tube (of section S) is the same as at the inlet to the branch tube and at its point of continuation past the branch tube. At the branch point the incident wave gives rise to a reflected wave, a wave which is transmitted along the main tube and an oscillatory process at the impedance Z_σ (at the inlet to the side tube).

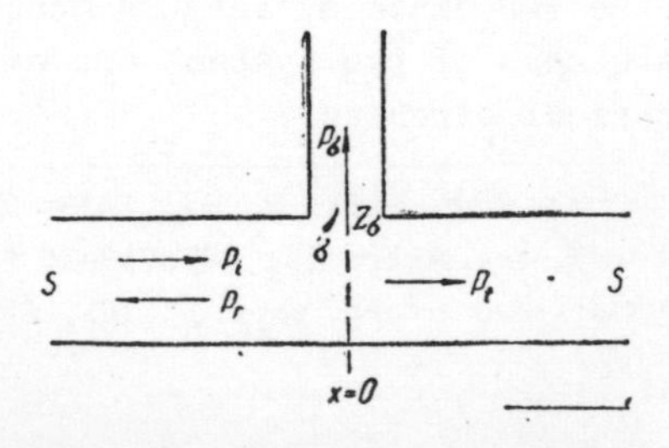

Fig. 52

Suppose that we take the following expressions for the pressures and velocities of all these processes (the factor $e^{j\omega t}$ being suppressed):

Incident wave $\begin{cases} p_i = A_i e^{-jrx} \\ \dot{\xi}_i = \dfrac{A_i}{\rho c} e^{-jkx} \end{cases}$

Reflected wave $\begin{cases} p_r = A_r e^{jkx} \\ \dot{\xi}_r = -\dfrac{A_r e^{jkx}}{\rho c} \end{cases}$

Transmitted wave $\begin{cases} p_t = A_t e^{-jkx} \\ \dot{\xi}_t = \dfrac{A_t}{\rho c} e^{-jkx} \end{cases}$

Input to branch tube $\begin{cases} p_\sigma = A_\sigma \\ \dot{\xi}_\sigma = \dfrac{\sigma A_\sigma}{Z_\sigma} \end{cases}$

At the branch point ($x = 0$) we can write the following boundary conditions if we ignore the additional masses in the intermediate section:

(1) $A_i + A_r = A_t = A_\sigma$ (continuity of pressure). This condition is equivalent to assuming that at the branch point there is no additional impedance (for example, an inertance or elastic impedance) which would cause a pressure drop;

(2)

$$\frac{SA_i}{\rho c} - \frac{SA_r}{\rho c} = \frac{SA_t}{\rho c} + \frac{\sigma^2 A_\sigma}{Z_\sigma} \tag{7-24}$$

(continuity of the volume velocity).

TABLE 6

System	Schematic drawing	Electrical equivalent of system impedance	Mechanical impedance	Acoustical impedance
Infinite tube of section S	S	$r = S\rho c$	$Z = S\rho c$	$\overline{Z} = \frac{\rho c}{S}$
Tube of length l and section S terminated in impedance Z_l	ℓ, S, Z_l	Z_l	$Z = S\rho c \frac{Z_l \cos kl + jS\rho c \sin kl}{S\rho c \cos kl + jZ_l \sin kl}$. if $kl \ll 1$, $Z_l \gg S\rho c$ $Z \approx \frac{Z_l Z_v}{Z_l + Z_v}$, where $Z_v = \frac{\rho c^2 S^2}{j\omega l S}$	$\overline{Z} = \frac{\rho c}{S} \cdot \frac{Z_l + j\frac{\rho c}{S}\tan kl}{\frac{\rho c}{S} + jZ_l \tan kl}$
Closed tube of length l and section S	ℓ, S	ℓ Section of line open at end	$Z = -jS\rho c \cot kl = \frac{S\rho c}{j \tan kl}$ if $l \ll \lambda$ $Z \approx \frac{\rho c^2 S^2}{j\omega V} + j\omega\left(\frac{1}{3} Sl\rho\right)$, $V = Sl$ (volume of tube)	$Z = -j\frac{\rho c}{S} \cot kl.$ if $l \ll \lambda$ $Z \approx \frac{\rho c^2}{j\omega V} + j\omega\left(\frac{1}{3}\frac{l\rho}{S}\right)$

continued

System	Schematic drawing	Electrical equivalent of system impedance	Mechanical impedance	Acoustical impedance
Tube of length l and section S open at the far end	l, S	l Section of line short circuited at end	$Z = jS\rho c \cdot \tan kl$ if $l \ll \lambda$ $Z \approx j\omega Sl\rho = j\omega M$, $M = \rho Sl$ (mass of air in tube)	$\overline{Z} = j\frac{\rho c}{S}\tan kl$ if $l \ll \lambda$ $\overline{Z} \approx j\omega\frac{l\rho}{S} = j\omega\frac{M}{S^2}$
Closed volume V with neck of section S (for $\lambda \gg \sqrt[3]{V}$)	S, V	Capacitance	$Z = \frac{\rho c^2 S^2}{j\omega V} = \frac{E}{j\omega}$ $E = \frac{\rho c^2 S^2}{V}$ (stiffness of the volume)	$\overline{Z} = \frac{\rho c^2}{j\omega V}$
Tube of length l ($l \gg \lambda$) and section S in infinite wall (end conductivities included)	l, S, d	Inductance	$Z = j\omega\frac{\rho S^2}{K} = j\omega M$, $M = \frac{\rho S^2}{K} = \rho S^2\left(\frac{l}{S} + \frac{1}{\beta d}\right) = \rho Sl\left(1 + \frac{\pi d}{\beta \cdot 4l}\right)$	$\overline{Z} = j\omega\frac{\rho}{K}$, $K = \frac{S}{l}\cdot\frac{1}{1 + \frac{\pi d}{\beta 4l}}$. if $l \gg d$; $K \approx S/l$ if $d \gg l$; $K \approx d$;
			$\beta = 1$ for $l = 0$ and $\beta \approx \frac{3\pi^2}{32} = 0{\cdot}92$ for long tube	

continued

System	Schematic drawing	Electrical equivalent of system impedance	Mechanical impedance	Acoustical impedance
Resonator of volume V with neck in form of a tube of length l and diameter d (for $\lambda \gg \sqrt[3]{V}$)	d S V $d = 2r_0$	L C	$Z = j\rho S^2 \left(\frac{\omega}{K} - \frac{c^2}{\omega V}\right)$ $K = S/l',\ l' = l + \Delta l_1 + \Delta l_2;$ $\Delta l_1 \approx \frac{4d}{3\pi} = 0{\cdot}85 r_0$ — for internal end $\Delta l_2 \approx \frac{d}{\pi} = 0{\cdot}64 r_0$ — for free end	$\overline{Z} = j\rho \left(\frac{\omega}{K} - \frac{c^2}{\omega V}\right)$
Circular hole of diameter d in an infinitely thin screen (radiation on one side included, but not friction)	S d	L R	$Z = \frac{\rho\omega^2 S^2}{2\pi c} + j\omega \frac{\rho S^2}{K} =$ $= \rho\omega S^2 \left(\frac{1}{\lambda} + j\frac{1}{K}\right)$ if $d \ll \lambda,\ K \approx d$ $Z \approx j\omega\rho \frac{S^2}{d}$	$\overline{Z} = \frac{\rho\omega^2}{2\pi c} + j\omega \frac{\rho}{K} =$ $= \rho\omega \left(\frac{1}{\lambda} + j\frac{1}{K}\right).$ if $d \ll \lambda$ $\overline{Z} \approx j\omega \frac{\rho}{d}$

continued

System	Schematic drawing	Electrical equivalent of system impedance	Mechanical impedance	Acoustical impedance
Circular hole of diameter d in screen across a tube of diameter D (radiation resistance and friction neglected)	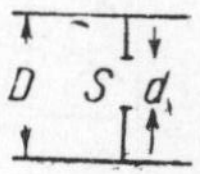 D S d	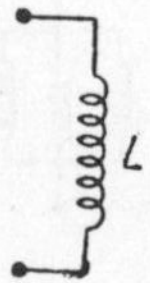 L	$Z = j\omega\rho \dfrac{S^2}{d} \psi\left(\dfrac{d}{D}\right)$ $\psi\left(\dfrac{d}{D}\right) = \left(1 - 1{\cdot}40925\,\xi + 0{\cdot}33818\,\xi^3 + 0{\cdot}06793\,\xi^5 + \ldots\right)^{-1}$ (Fok's function) if $d \ll D$ $\psi\left(\dfrac{d}{D}\right) \approx 1$ if $d \to D$ $\psi\left(\dfrac{d}{D}\right) \to 0$,	$\overline{Z} = j\omega \dfrac{\rho}{d} \psi\left(\dfrac{d}{D}\right)$
Capillary tube of length l and section S. Diameter $d = 2\sqrt{\dfrac{S}{\pi}} = 2r_0$	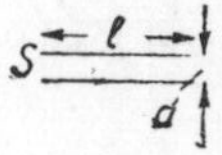 S l d	 L R	$Z \approx S\left(\dfrac{8\mu l}{r_0^2} + j\omega \dfrac{4}{3} l\rho\right)$ $\left(\text{provided } r_0^2 f < \dfrac{2\mu}{\pi\rho}\right)$. $\mu \approx 2 \times 10^{-1}$ for air ($t = 18°$) if walls thermally insulated; $\mu \approx 4 \times 10^{-4}$ if walls heat-conducting	$Z \approx \dfrac{1}{S}\left(\dfrac{8\mu l}{r_0^2} + j\omega \dfrac{4}{3} l\rho\right)$

continued

System	Schematic drawing	Electrical equivalent of system impedance	Mechanical impedance	Acoustical impedance
Narrow slot of length l, breadth b, and height h $S = bh;\ h \ll b$	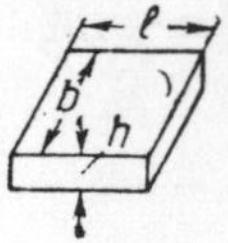		$Z = S\left(\frac{12\mu l}{h^2} + j\omega \frac{6}{5} l\rho\right)$	$\overline{Z} = \frac{1}{S}\left(\frac{12\mu l}{h^2} + j\omega \frac{6}{5} l\rho\right)$
			$\left(\text{provided}\ \ h^2 f < \frac{8\mu}{\pi\rho}\right)$	
			$\mu \approx 2 \times 10^{-4}$ for air at 18°C with thermally insulated walls; $\mu \approx 4 \times 10^{-4}$ if walls good heat conductors	
Number (n) of round holes with area $\sigma_1 = \frac{\pi d_1^2}{4}$ in an infinite thin plate (frictional resistance neglected) if $d_1 < 0{\cdot}2\sqrt{\frac{S_1}{\pi}}$ (S_1 is zone area of one hole)	 n holes	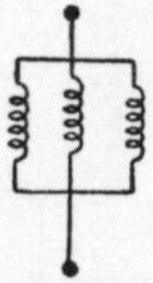 n branches	$Z \approx j\omega M_1 n$, where $M_1 \approx \frac{\rho\sigma_1^2}{d_1}$	$\overline{Z} = j\omega \frac{\overline{M}_1}{n}$, where $\overline{M}_1 = \frac{\rho}{K_1} \approx \frac{\rho}{d_1} = \frac{M_1}{\sigma_1^2}$

continued

System	Schematic drawing	Electrical equivalent of system impedance	Mechanical impedance	Acoustical impedance
Number (n) of round holes of diameter $d_1 > 0{\cdot}7\sqrt{\frac{S_1}{\pi}}$, (where S_1 is the zone area of one hole). Total circular area occupied by holes $S = \frac{\pi d^2}{4}$	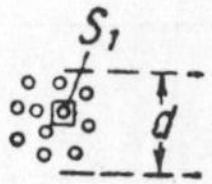 S_1, d, n holes	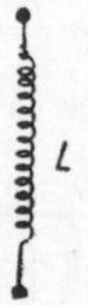 L	$Z \approx j\omega \frac{\rho S^2}{d}$	$\bar{Z} \approx j\omega \frac{\rho}{d}$
Impedance at end of tube of area S with attached impedance Z_σ, in centre, concentrated on an area $\sigma = \frac{\pi d^2}{4}$	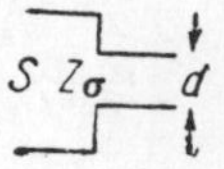 S Z_σ d	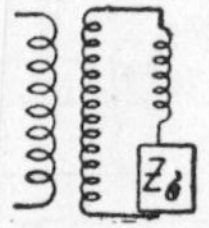 Z_σ	$Z \approx \frac{S^2}{\sigma^2}\left(Z_\sigma + j\omega \frac{\rho\sigma^2}{2d}\right) = \frac{S^2}{\sigma^2}(Z_\sigma + j\omega M)$, $M \approx \frac{\rho\sigma^2}{2d}$	$\bar{Z} = \bar{Z}_\sigma + j\omega\bar{M}$, $\bar{Z}_\sigma = \frac{Z_\sigma}{\sigma^2}$; $\bar{M} = \frac{M}{\sigma^2}$

If $d < 0{\cdot}2 \times 2\sqrt{\frac{S}{\pi}}$

If $d > 0{\cdot}7 \times 2\sqrt{\frac{S}{\pi}}$ it can be assumed that $M \approx 0$

continued

System	Schematic drawing	Electrical equivalent of system impedance	Mechanical impedance	Acoustical impedance
Impedance at inlet (area S) to volume V with impedance Z_σ on an area of the wall of V (for $\lambda \gg \sqrt[3]{V}$)	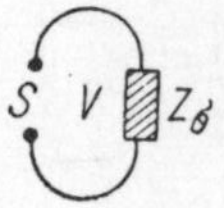 S, V, Z_σ; $\sigma = \frac{\pi d^2}{4}$	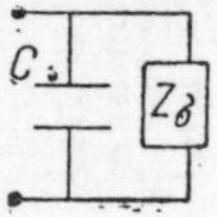 C, Z_σ	$\frac{1}{Z} \approx \frac{1}{Z_v} + \frac{1}{Z'_\sigma}$, $Z_v = \frac{\rho c^2 S^2}{j\omega V}$, $Z'_\sigma = \frac{S^2}{\sigma^2} Z_\sigma$	$\frac{1}{\bar{Z}} \approx \frac{1}{\bar{Z}_v} + \frac{1}{\bar{Z}_\sigma}$, $\bar{Z}_v = \frac{\rho c^2}{j\omega V}$, $\bar{Z}_\sigma = \frac{Z_\sigma}{\sigma^2}$
Impedance of tube (of section S) branched into tubes of sections $\sigma_1, \sigma_2, \sigma_3 \ldots$ with impedances $Z_1, Z_2, Z_3 \ldots$	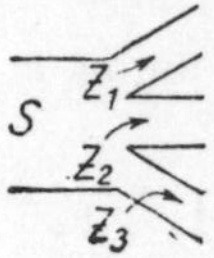 S, Z_1, Z_2, Z_3	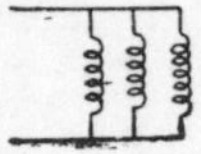	$\frac{S^2}{Z} = \frac{\sigma_1^2}{Z_1} + \frac{\sigma_2^2}{Z_2} + \frac{\sigma_3^2}{Z_3} + \ldots$	$\frac{1}{\bar{Z}} = \frac{1}{\bar{Z}_1} + \frac{1}{\bar{Z}_2} + \frac{1}{\bar{Z}_3} + \ldots$ $\bar{Z}_1 = \frac{Z_1}{\sigma_1^2}$, $\bar{Z}_2 = \frac{Z_2}{\sigma_2^2}$, $\bar{Z}_3 = \frac{Z_3}{\sigma_3^2}$.

Hence, the reflection coefficient is

$$r=\frac{A_r}{A_i}=\frac{-\frac{1}{2}\frac{S\rho c}{Z_\sigma\frac{S^2}{\sigma^2}}}{1+\frac{1}{2}\frac{S\rho c}{Z_\sigma\frac{S^2}{\sigma^2}}},$$

and the transmission coefficient

$$t=\frac{A_t}{A_i}=\frac{A_i+A_r}{A_i}=1-\frac{\frac{\sigma^2\rho c}{2SZ_\sigma}}{1+\frac{\sigma^2\rho c}{2SZ_\sigma}}=\frac{1}{1+\frac{1}{2}\frac{S\rho c}{Z_\sigma\frac{S^2}{\sigma^2}}}.$$

The same problem can be solved by calculating the reflection from an impedance consisting of impedances $S\rho c$ and Z_σ in parallel. In the absence of an aperture $Z_\sigma=\infty$, $r=0$ and $t=1$, i.e. the sound is transmitted unhindered. With an aperture which leads into free space or a tube of length $\frac{\lambda}{4}$, it can be assumed that $Z_\sigma\approx 0$; we get $r\approx -1$ and $t=0$, i.e. total reflection. If $Z_\sigma=R_\sigma+jY_\sigma$ is the impedance of a resonator with small attenuation, then $Z_\sigma=R_\sigma$ at the resonant frequency and, since R_σ is a small quantity, we also get in this case $r\approx -1$ and $t\approx 0$. This is the principle of a Quincke filter which consists of a number of side tubes of length $l=\frac{\lambda}{4}$. At resonant frequency there is no sound transmitted through the main tube; the oscillations finish at the resonator and the wave is reflected back completely. At frequencies where $l=n\frac{\lambda}{2}$, the sound will be transmitted through the tube unhindered, nor will open side tubes of length $\left(n+\frac{1}{2}\right)\frac{\lambda}{2}$ have any great effect on the transmission of sound since Z_σ is very large for them.

Branching of a Tube of Cross-section S into Two Branches with Impedance Z_1 and Z_2 Concentrated on Areas σ_1 and σ_2

For this case, as before, we write the boundary conditions:

$$A_i + A_r = A_1 = A_2,$$

$$\frac{SA_i}{\rho c} - \frac{SA_r}{\rho c} = \frac{\sigma_1^2 A_1}{Z_1} + \frac{\sigma_2^2 A_2}{Z_2} = \left(\frac{\sigma_1^2}{Z_1} + \frac{\sigma_2^2}{Z_2}\right)A_1,$$

where A_i, A_r, A_1 and A_2 are the corresponding pressure amplitudes. Suppose we introduce the quantity

$$\frac{\dot{X}_{in}}{p_{in}} = \frac{1}{\overline{Z}} = \frac{\sigma_1^2}{Z_1} + \frac{\sigma_2^2}{Z_2} = \frac{1}{\overline{Z}_1} + \frac{1}{\overline{Z}_2} = \frac{S^2}{Z},$$

where $\overline{Z}_1 = \frac{Z_1}{\sigma_1^2}$; $\overline{Z}_2 = \frac{Z_2}{\sigma_2^2}$ are the acoustical impedances of the apertures σ_1 and σ_2, Z is the mechanical impedance at the inlet and $\overline{Z}$ the acoustic impedance at the inlet. The reflection coefficient is found from the boundary conditions:

$$r = \frac{A_r}{A_i} = \frac{Z - S\rho c}{Z + S\rho c} = \frac{\overline{Z} - \frac{\rho c}{S}}{\overline{Z} + \frac{\rho c}{S}}.$$

It should be pointed out that the connexion of the mechanical impedances Z_1 and Z_2 in "parallel" produces the mechanical impedance

$$Z = \frac{\frac{S^2}{\sigma_1^2} Z_1 \frac{S^2}{\sigma_2^2} Z_2}{\frac{S^2}{\sigma_1^2} Z_1 + \frac{S^2}{\sigma_2^2} Z_2} \quad \text{and not} \quad \frac{Z_1 Z_2}{Z_1 + Z_2}.$$

The acoustical impedance is

$$\overline{Z} = \frac{\overline{Z}_1 \overline{Z}_2}{\overline{Z}_1 + \overline{Z}_2},$$

i.e. a formula is obtained for the connexion of impedances Z_1 and Z_2 in parallel.

For the velocity amplitudes at the inlets Z_1 and Z_2 we get:

$$\dot{\xi}_1 = \frac{\sigma_1 A_1}{Z_1} = \frac{\sigma_1 A_i}{Z_1} \frac{2Z}{Z + S\rho c} = A_i \frac{2\frac{\sigma_1}{Z_1}}{1 + \frac{\rho c}{S}\left(\frac{\sigma_1^2}{Z_1} + \frac{\sigma_2^2}{Z_2}\right)};$$

$$\dot{\xi}_2 = \frac{\sigma_2 A_2}{Z_2} = \frac{\sigma_2 A_i}{Z_2} \frac{2Z}{Z + S\rho c} = A_i \frac{2\frac{\sigma_2}{Z_2}}{1 + \frac{\rho c}{S}\left(\frac{\sigma_1^2}{Z_1} + \frac{\sigma_2^2}{Z_2}\right)}.$$

If $\bar{Z} = \frac{\rho c}{S}$ (or $Z = S\rho c$) then $r = 0$, i.e. there is no reflection at the branch and all the sound is transmitted into impedances Z_1 and Z_2. If the tube branches into two infinite tubes, the same result is obtained provided that

$$\frac{\sigma_1^2}{\sigma_1 \rho c} + \frac{\sigma_2^2}{\sigma_2 \rho c} = \frac{S}{\rho c}$$

or

$$\sigma_1 + \sigma_2 = S.$$

In order to avoid sound reflection on branching into two infinite tubes, it is necessary to make the sum of their areas equal to the area of the main conductor S. If the main tube branches into infinite tubes of different diameter, no reflection will occur if:

$$\sum_{i=1}^{n} \sigma_i = S.$$

Excitation of Sound Waves by a Membrane or Plate

Wave motion is often initiated by membranes or plates, their surfaces vibrating flexurally according to more or less complicated laws.

It was shown in Chapter VI that for long waves the radiation in distant parts of the tube is propagated in the form of a plane wave excited by the total volume pulsation of the membrane and that it is independent of spatial variations in the membrane oscillations. The impedance of an oscillating plate or membrane, which is a distributed system, is conventionally defined relative to the centre of a system whose motion is characterized by a certain velocity u_0. Taking into account the kinetic, potential and dissipated energy of the system, we introduce certain equivalent parameters M', E' and R' for the mass, stiffness and friction of the system which we conventionally "reduce to the centre". Thus, we replace the distributed system by a system with one degree of freedom and an equivalent mass M', stiffness E' and coefficient of friction R'. In addition, the force exerted on the system over its entire area is replaced by an equivalent force ψ_0, at the centre which does the same work. The volume pulsation (current) produced by the membrane or plate is a source of the plane wave, but the higher oscillation modes of the surface produce additional oscillations in the surrounding medium. At long wavelengths, the higher modes do not produce waves which are propagated in the tube, they excite only an oscillatory process in the zone near the source. This leads to the appearance of additional energy connected with these oscillations, and this can be formally expressed in terms of an additional or "attached" mass moving as a unit with the velocity u_0 of the membrane (or plate) centre. For oscillations in air this additional mass is usually small and can be ignored. It cannot however be ignored in a liquid. The magnitude of the equivalent parameters M', E' and R' depends on the form of the oscillations of the membrane or plate. This topic has been investigated in detail for circular plates and membranes*. For a circular membrane of radius r_0, the distribution of the oscillation amplitude as a function of the polar coordinate r,

---

* S.N. Rschevkin, *Zhur. tekh. phys.* 5, 1440, 1935; S. Timoshenko, *Vibration Problems in Engineering*, New York: D.Van Nostrand, 1928 (see chap. IV)

both for static deformation (strain) and forced low frequency oscillations due to a force uniformly distributed over the entire area, is governed by the law:

$$u = u_0 f(r) = u_0 \left(1 - \frac{r^2}{r_0^2}\right),$$

where u_0 is the amplitude at the centre. In the case in question

$$f(r) = 1 - \frac{r^2}{r_0^2}.$$

For the first resonant frequency of the membrane, when all of its area oscillates in the same phase,

$$f(r) = J_0\left(2{\cdot}40 \frac{r}{r_0}\right).$$

For a plate which is clamped around the circumference at low frequencies

$$f(r) = \left(1 - \frac{r^2}{r_0^2}\right)^2,$$

and at the first resonant frequency

$$f(r) = \frac{J_0\left(3{\cdot}196 \frac{r}{r_0}\right) + \lambda J_0\left(j 3{\cdot}196 \frac{r}{r_0}\right)}{1 + \lambda},$$

where

$$j = \sqrt{-1} \qquad \text{and} \qquad \lambda = 0{\cdot}056.$$

For a plate which is resting on its circumference so that its edges cannot move normal to the plate but are free to bend around the circular line of rest (at low frequencies)

$$f(r) = 1 - \frac{r^2}{r_0^2},$$

i.e. the distribution is governed by the same law as for

a membrane. The natural frequencies of such plates have been calculated by Ostroumov*.

The equivalent mass is found by equating the kinetic energy of an equivalent system moving like a piston with velocity u_0, to the actual kinetic energy of the whole system, defined by integration over the area. Since the velocity at the centre is the maximum velocity, equality between the kinetic energy of a piston moving with velocity u_0 and the total kinetic energy can be obtained if we assume that the equivalent mass M' is equal to a certain part β of the total mass M of the membrane or plate:

$$M' = \beta M.$$

The coefficient β is called the *mass coefficient* and is defined in terms of the mean square of the oscillation velocity over the area:

$$\beta = \frac{1}{\pi r_0^2}\left[2\pi \int_0^{z_0} f^2(r)\, r\, dr\right].$$

The volume velocity produced by the oscillating membrane of area S will be less than Su_0 and equal to $\dot{X}_0 = \gamma S u_0$, where γ (the *area coefficient*) is calculated by the formula:

$$\gamma = \frac{1}{\pi r_0^2}\left[2\pi \int_0^{r_0} f(r) \cdot dr\right].$$

In order to calculate the power which is radiated in the form of a plane wave along the tube, excited by the oscillations of the plate or membrane, it is necessary to use the mean velocity over the area S as explained in Chapter VI. The power Π is

$$\Pi = \frac{1}{2}\rho c\,(\gamma S)^2 u_0^2.$$

---

* G.A. Ostroumov, *Zhur. tekh. phys.* 5, (6), 947, 1935.

In order to calculate the stiffness coefficient of a cavity of volume V in which oscillations are excited by a membrane of area S, it is necessary to use the equivalent area γS:

$$E = \frac{\rho c^2 (\gamma S)^2}{V}.$$

The equivalent stiffness E' of a membrane or plate excited by a uniform pressure or by a force concentrated at the centre is calculated roughly by ascertaining the elastic energy of the deformed membrane or plate and representing it in the form $V = \frac{1}{2} E' u_0^2$. The results of the calculations of the equivalent stiffness E' are shown in Table 7, where τ is the tension coefficient of the membrane, μ Poisson's coefficient, and E_Y Young's modulus. This table also includes other constants for membranes and plates.

The total work done by an external force distributed according to a certain law over the surface of the membrane or plate can be replaced by the work done by an equivalent force referred to the centre. Thus, for example, the work done by a uniform pressure p_0 in displacing the centre of a plate or membrane, which oscillates according to the law $a = a_0 f(r)$, a distance δa_0 is:

$$\delta W = \int_0^{r_0} p_0 \delta a_0 f(r) \cdot 2\pi r dr = 2\pi p_0 \delta a_0 \int_0^{r_0} f(r) r dr = p_0 (\gamma S) \delta a_0.$$

Thus, it is clear that the equivalent force at the centre is:

$$\psi_0 = p_0 (\gamma S),$$

and not $p_0 S$, as might have been thought at first sight.

TABLE 7

Type of system	Mass coefficient β	Area coefficient γ	Equivalent stiffness at the centre, E'	Equivalent force at the centre ψ_0
Circular membrane under uniform pressure, at low frequencies	$\frac{1}{3} = 0{\cdot}333$	$\frac{1}{2} = 0{\cdot}5$	$2\pi\tau$	$\frac{1}{2} Sp_0$
As above, at the frequency of the fundamental tone	0·269	0·432	$1{\cdot}558\,\tau$	$0{\cdot}432\, Sp_0$
Circular plate clamped round the edge, of thickness d, under uniform pressure p_0, at low frequencies	$\frac{1}{5} = 0{\cdot}20$	$\frac{1}{3} = 0{\cdot}333$	$\frac{16\pi E_y d^3}{9r_0^3(1-\mu^2)}$	$\frac{1}{3} Sp_0$
As above, at the frequency of the fundamental tone	0·183	0·306	$5{\cdot}02\frac{E_y d^3}{r_0^2(1-\mu^2)}$	$0{\cdot}306\, Sp_0$
Circular plate clamped round the edge under a force ψ_0, concentrated at the centre, at low frequencies	$\frac{7}{54} = 0{\cdot}13$	$\frac{1}{4} = 0{\cdot}25$	$\frac{4}{3}\pi\frac{E_y d^3}{r_0^2(1-\mu^2)}$	ψ_0
Circular plate resting on its edge but not clamped under uniform pressure p_0, at low frequencies	$\frac{1}{3} = 0{\cdot}333$	$\frac{1}{2} = 0{\cdot}5$	—	$\frac{1}{2} Sp_0$
As above, at the frequency of the fundamental tone	0·30	0·451	—	—

Resonant Sound Absorber

In order to illustrate the use of the proposed methods of calculation, we will now consider the performance of a resonant sound absorber which has been developed by acousticians in the U.S.S.R.*.

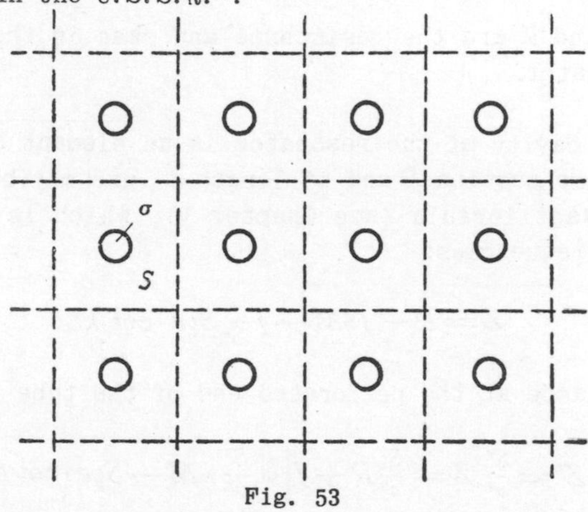

Fig. 53

It is assumed that resonators are arranged on the surface of a wall at the nodes of a square lattice (Fig. 53), and that each resonator occupies an area S. If sound is incident on this system normal to the surface of the wall, it is therefore clear by virtue of symmetry that the propagation of sound is in no way affected if we divide the whole space into channels of square cross-section with rigid walls along the surfaces of the cells occupied by the individual resonators (the dashed lines in Fig. 53). In studying the behaviour of the system in the case of normal incidence of sound, it is immaterial whether or not the resonators are separated from each other by real partitions. Thus, we can consider the propagation of sound in a tube of area S with an aperture of area σ at the end, which leads

* S.N. Rschevkin, *Usp. fis. nauk.*, 30 (1-2), 40, 1946; S.N. Rschevkin, *Zs. Hochfr. U. Elektroak.* 67, 128, 1958.

into the cavity of the resonator of volume V. At low frequencies, the impedance at the inlet to the resonator (if $\lambda \gg \sqrt[3]{V}$) is

$$Z = R + j\omega M - j\frac{\rho c^2 \sigma^2}{\omega V},$$

where R and M are the resistance and mass in the neck of the resonator.

If the cavity of the resonator is an element of a tube of the same section S and of length l, use may be made of a more exact formula (see Chapter V), which is suitable for any frequencies:

$$Z = R + j\omega M - j\frac{\sigma^2}{S^2} S\rho c \cdot \cot kl.$$

The impedance at the perforated end of the tube is

$$Z' = \frac{S^2}{\sigma^2} Z = \frac{S_2}{\sigma^2} R + j\left[\omega \frac{S^2}{\sigma^2} \cdot M - S\rho c \cdot \cot kl\right].$$

The "dimensionless impedance" at the end of the tube, expressed as a fraction of ρc and calculated per unit area of the tube, is:

$$Z_1 = \frac{Z'}{S\rho c} = \frac{Z}{\frac{\sigma^2}{S}\rho c} = R_1 + j(\omega M_1 - \cot kl),$$

where

$$R_1 = \frac{R}{\frac{\sigma^2}{S}\rho c}; \quad M_1 = \frac{M}{\frac{\sigma^2}{S}\rho c} = \frac{\frac{\rho \sigma^2}{K}}{\frac{\sigma^2}{S}\rho c} = \frac{1}{c}\frac{S}{K}.$$

Here R_1 represents the "dimensionless resistance", and M_1 the "dimensionless mass". The quantity $\cot kl$ is the dimensionless impedance of an element of tube of length l. The coefficient of sound reflection from the wall covered with the resonators is

$$r_p = \frac{Z_1 - 1}{Z_1 + 1} = \frac{R_1 - 1 + j(\omega M_1 - \cot kl)}{R_1 + 1 + j(\omega M_1 - \cot kl)}. \quad (7\text{-}25)$$

If

$$R_1 = 1 \left(\text{or } R = \frac{\sigma^2}{S}\rho c \right) \text{and } \omega M_1 = \cot kl \left(\text{or } \frac{kS}{K} = \cot kl \right)$$

we get $r = 0$, i.e. *sound absorption is complete.* In this case the coefficient of sound absorption (for energy) $\alpha = 1 - |r_p|^2$ is equal to unity.

A plot of α as a function of ω shows the maxima, equal to $\frac{4R_1}{(R_1+1)^2}$, which occur at frequencies given by the roots of the equation $\omega M_1 = \cot \frac{\omega l}{c}$, and the minima, equal to zero, occurring when $\frac{\omega l}{c} = n\pi$, or $l = n\frac{\lambda}{2}$ (Fig. 54).

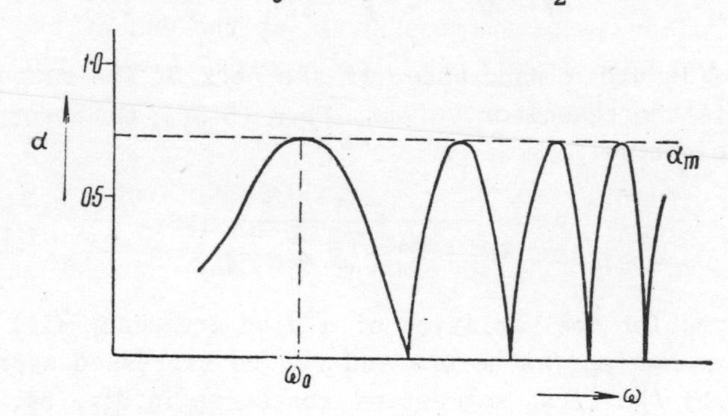

Fig. 54

In order to obtain $r = 1$, it is necessary to match the frictional resistance at the aperture, selecting σ and S in accordance with the formula $R = \frac{\sigma^2}{S}\rho c$. Such a selection is practically always possible.

We will now consider the case of long waves $(kl \ll 1)$ in somewhat greater detail. In this case $\cot kl \approx \frac{c}{\omega l} = \frac{E_1}{\omega}$ and

$$Z_1 = R_1 + j\left(\omega M_1 - \frac{E_1}{\omega}\right). \tag{7-26}$$

The quantity $E_1 = \frac{c}{l}$ can be called the "dimensionless stiffness" per unit area of the tube. It is easy to see that $E_1 = \frac{E}{\frac{\sigma^2}{S}\rho c}$, where $E = \frac{\rho c^2 \sigma^2}{V}$ is the "stiffness coefficient" of the resonator in mechanical ohms.

The resonant frequency of the system, at which maximum absorption is obtained, is

$$\omega_0 = \sqrt{\frac{E_1}{M_1}} = c\sqrt{\frac{K}{Sl}} = c\sqrt{\frac{K}{V}},$$

where K is the conductance of the neck of the resonator and V is the resonator volume. From (5-30), the absorption coefficient is

$$\alpha = \frac{4R_1}{(R_1+1)^2 + \left(k\frac{S}{K} - \frac{1}{kl}\right)^2}.$$

The curve for the variation of α with frequency will have the same maximum as before and can be expressed approximately by the first segment of the curve in Fig. 54. The width of the resonance curve depends upon the attenuation decrement of the system.

The maximum absorption is $\alpha_m = \frac{4R_1}{(R_1+1)^2}$. It can be obtained at two different values of R_1, which can be found by regarding the expression for α as a quadratic equation in R_1, assuming α_m to be a parameter. The equation has the form:

$$R_1^2 - 2\,\frac{2-\alpha_m}{\alpha_m} \times R_1 + 1 = 0.$$

The two roots $R_1^{(1)}$ and $R_1^{(2)}$ of this equation are related by the expression $R_1^{(1)} \times R_1^{(2)} = 1$. One of these roots will be greater than unity, and the other less. In the first case the resonance curve has a gradual slope and in the second case an acute one. In practice it is important to have the maximum possible absorption over a wide frequency band, and therefore it is necessary to make $R_1 > 1$. The parameters of the resonant systems, S, σ, l, K and R have to be determined accordingly.

Consider the impedance diagram in Fig. 55. If the frequency changes, the point representing the impedance of the system will move along the straight line Z' parallel to the ordinate in accordance with equation (7-26), intersecting the R_1 axis at the point R_1', which corresponds to a frequency $\omega = \omega_0$, at which the reactance is zero (resonance). Suppose that the absorption coefficient is α_m at $\omega = \omega_0$. The larger of the two possible values of R_1 is taken, which corresponds to the more highly damped resonator. This value, R_1', is the centre of a certain circle of constant absorption $\alpha = \alpha_1$, the radius of which (see Chapter V) is:

$$R_1' = \frac{\frac{S^2}{\sigma^2} R}{S\rho c} = \frac{r_1 \sigma}{\frac{\sigma^2}{S}\rho c} = \frac{r_1}{\rho c}\,\frac{S}{\sigma},$$

and the abscissa of the centre

On the other hand

$$\frac{2-\alpha_1}{\alpha_1} = \frac{r_1}{\rho c}\,\frac{S}{\sigma},$$

hence

$$\left.\begin{aligned} \rho' &= \frac{2\sqrt{1-\alpha_1}}{\alpha_1}, \\ R_1' &= \frac{2-\alpha_1}{\alpha_1}. \end{aligned}\right\} \qquad (7\text{-}27)$$

where r_1 is the specific resistance in the neck of the resonator. Expressing α_m in terms of α_1, we get:

$$\alpha_m = \alpha_1 (2 - \alpha_1), \quad \text{or} \quad \frac{\alpha_m}{\alpha_1} = 2 - \alpha_1. \qquad (7\text{-}28)$$

This quantity specifies the non-uniformity of sound absorption in a certain frequency band between the frequencies f_1 and f_2 (on the rising and falling portions, respectively, of the resonance curve) at which $\alpha = \alpha_1$. Suppose we require the value of the absorption coefficient to be $\alpha = \alpha_1$ at the angular frequency $\omega_1 = 2\pi f_1$ (below resonance) corresponding to the lowest point of the circle $\alpha = \alpha_1$ (point B), and at the frequency $\omega_2 = 2\pi f_2$ (above resonance) corresponding to the highest point of the circle (point A, Fig. 55). It is obvious that in this case $\alpha > \alpha_1$ over the widest possible frequency band. At points A and B the reactive part Y_1 must be equal either to $+\rho'$ or $-\rho'$.

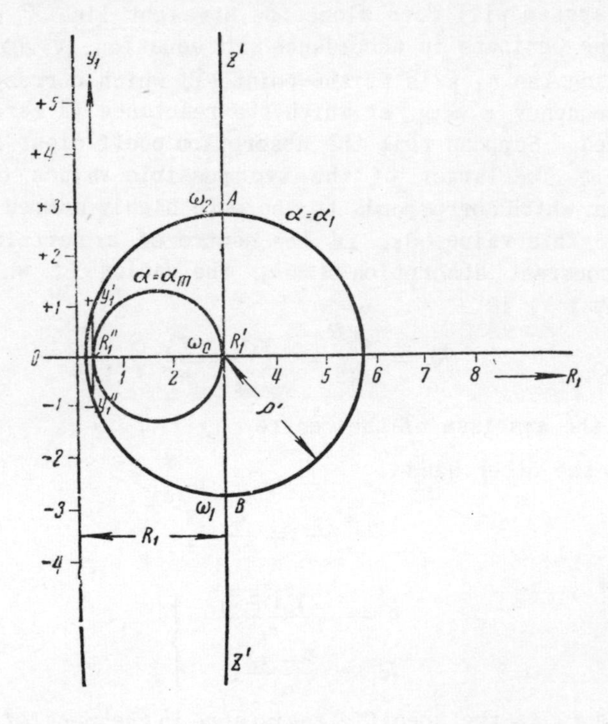

Fig. 55

Consequently,

$$\omega_1 M_1 - \frac{E_1}{\omega_1} = -\frac{2\sqrt{1-\alpha_1}}{\alpha_1},$$

$$\omega_2 M_1 - \frac{E_1}{\omega_2} = +\frac{2\sqrt{1-\alpha_1}}{\alpha_1}.$$

From these two equations we find:

$$l = \frac{c\alpha_1}{4\pi\sqrt{1-\alpha_1}} \cdot \frac{f_2 - f_1}{f_1 f_2}, \tag{7-29}$$

$$\frac{S}{K} = cM_1 = \frac{c\sqrt{1-\alpha_1}}{\pi\alpha_1} \frac{1}{f_2 - f_1}. \tag{7-30}$$

In accordance with expression (7-11), if we ignore the correction indicated by $\psi\left(\frac{d}{D}\right)$ according to Fok's formula, (i.e. if $d < 0{\cdot}2\sqrt{\frac{S}{\pi}}$) then it can be assumed that

$$K = \frac{\frac{\sigma}{b}}{1 + \frac{\pi d}{4b}},$$

where d is the diameter of the neck of the resonator, and b its length. Equations (7-27) and (7-30) can be regarded as a set of two equations in the unknowns $d = 2\sqrt{\frac{\sigma}{\pi}}$ and $a = \sqrt{S}$. Substituting the value of K into equation (7-30), we find:

(1) the diameter of the resonator neck:

$$d = \frac{4}{\pi^2 \rho} r_1 \frac{\sqrt{1-\alpha_1}}{2-\alpha_1} \frac{\frac{1}{f_1}}{\frac{f_2}{f_1} - 1} - \frac{4}{\pi} b, \tag{7-31}$$

(2) the distances between the centres of the apertures of the resonators:

$$a = \sqrt{S} = \sqrt{\frac{\pi\rho c}{4}}\, d \sqrt{\frac{2-\alpha_1}{r_1 \alpha_1}}. \tag{7-32}$$

Formulae (7-29), (7-31) and (7-32) make it possible to calculate the geometric parameters of a resonant sound absorber, namely, the depth of the layer of resonators l, the diameter of the apertures d and the distance between the apertures a, provided that $\alpha > \alpha_1$ in the frequency band from f_1 to f_2. It is obvious that given α_1, the degree of non-uniformity in absorption $\frac{\alpha_m}{\alpha_1}$ over the given frequency band is fixed in advance in accordance with expression (7-28). The specific resistance r_1 can be assumed to be given; it can vary within wide limits. It is also necessary to choose in advance the thickness of the front wall b which fixes the length of the necks of the resonators. The calculation described above is valid only if $f_2/f_1 < 1 \cdot 5$.

It is outside the scope of this chapter to consider the absorption coefficient of a resonant sound absorber if the sound is incident at an angle to the normal.

In order to obtain a high degree of uniform absorption over a wide frequency band, use is made of multi-layer resonant absorbers (Fig. 56), in which the resonant system consists of a number of resonators in series (separated by distances l_1, l_2, l_3,..., the nth being a distance l_n from the exterior wall). These resonators are connected together by apertures of resistances R_1, R_2, R_3,... In order to analyse such a system, use is made of the formula for the input impedance of a closed tube terminated by an impedance Z_l (see Chapter V). All the impedances are expressed per unit area of the tube S and as a fraction of ρc, i.e. we take dimensionless impedances. The input impedance has the form:

$$Z_{00} = Z_0 + \frac{j \sin kl + Z_l \cos kl}{j Z_l \sin kl + \cos kl}. \qquad (7\text{-}33)$$

For the nth layer (the first from the wall) for which $Z_l = \infty$, it is necessary to take the impedance of the aperture in the partition of the nth layer as Z_0 and l_n as l in this formula.

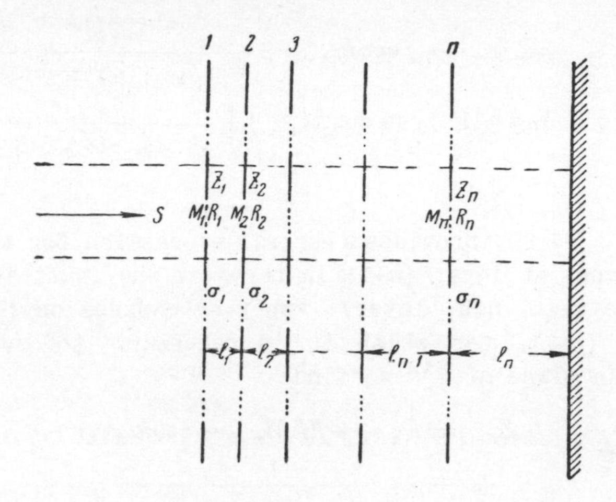

Fig. 56

Using the notation in Fig. 56, the impedance at the inlet to the nth layer is:

$$\left.\begin{aligned} Z_n^{\text{in}} &= R_n + j(kM_n - \cot kl) = Z'_n - j\cot kl_n, \\ \text{where} \quad R_n &= \frac{r_n \cdot S}{\sigma_n \cdot \rho c} \text{ and } M_n = \frac{S}{K_n}. \end{aligned}\right\} \quad (7\text{-}34)$$

For the layer (n-1) (i.e. the second from the wall) the impedance is:

$$Z'_{n-1} = R_{n-1} + jkM_{n-1},$$

where R_{n-1} and M_{n-1} are defined as in expression (7-34). After applying the transformation indicated by (7-33), the input impedance of the (n-1)th layer is obtained in the form:

$$\begin{aligned} Z_{n-1}^{\text{in}} &= Z'_{n-1} + \frac{j\sin kl_{n-1} + Z_n^{\text{in}}\cos kl_{n-1}}{Z_n^{\text{in}}\, j\sin kl_{n-1} + \cos kl_{n-1}} = \\ &= Z'_{n-1} - j\cot kl_{n-1} + \end{aligned} \quad (7\text{-}35)$$

$$+ \frac{j\cot kl_{n-1}(Z_n^{\text{in}} j\sin kl_{n-1} + \cos kl_{n-1}) + j\sin kl_{n-1} + Z_n^{\text{in}}\cos kl_{n-1}}{Z_n^{\text{in}} j\sin kl_{n-1} + \cos kl_{n-1}} =$$

$$=Z'_{n-1}-j\cot kl_{n-1}+\frac{\frac{j}{\sin kl_{n-1}}}{j\sin kl_{n-1}(Z_n^{\text{in}}-j\cot kl_{n-1})}=$$

$$=R_{n-1}+j(kM_{n-1}-\cot kl_{n-1})+\frac{1}{\sin^2 kl_{n-1}(Z_n^{\text{in}}-j\cot kl_{n-1})}. \quad \text{(7-35) cont.}$$

Formula (7-35) provides a general expression for the input impedance at layer (n-1) in terms of the input impedance at the next, nth, layer. Applying expression (7-35) to layer (n-2), for which it is necessary to substitute Z_{n-1}^{in} in place of Z_n^{in} we find:

$$Z_{n-2}=R_{n-2}+j(kM_{n-2}-\cot kl_{n-2})+$$
$$+\frac{1}{\sin^2 kl_{n-2}\left[Z_{n-1}+\frac{1}{\sin^2 kl_{n-1}\cdot Z_n}\right]}.$$

Continuing the procedure to find the impedance at the input to the first layer, we obtain eventually the impedance at the input to the entire absorber in the form of a continued fraction:

$$Z^{\text{in}}=Z_1+\cfrac{1}{\sin^2 kl_1\left\{Z_2+\cfrac{1}{\sin^2 kl_2\left[Z_3+\cfrac{1}{\sin^2 kl_3\left(Z_4+\cdots\cdots+\cfrac{}{\sin^2 kl_{n-1}\cdot Z_n}\right)}\right]}\right\}}. \quad \text{(7-36)}$$

Here $Z_1=R_1+j(kM_1-\text{ctg}kl_1)$, and the quantities Z_2, Z_3, Z_4,..., are defined by formulae (7-35). They represent the impedances of the partial systems which are obtained when all the apertures except one are closed. Thus, Z_i is composed of the impedance of the ith aperture Z_i' together with the impedances of tubes of length l_i and l_{i-1} attached to it on either sides. Nesterov, who proposed formulae (7-35) and (7-36), gave detailed methods of calculating the input impedance of multi-layer systems by special nomograms*. The response of multi-layer resonant systems can also be calculated by impedance diagrams. The theory of resonant sound-absorbers has been dealt with in a large number of papers. Two-layer and three-layer systems have been analysed by Rschevkin** and in detail by Nesterov***.

Acoustic Filters

A tube element can be treated as a symmetric fourpole (see Chapter V) and, like its electrical analogue, can be described by the following equations:

$$\left.\begin{aligned} V_0 &= AV_l + BI_l, \\ I_0 &= CV_l + DI_l, \\ A = D = \cosh\gamma l;\ B &= \frac{\rho c}{S}\sinh\gamma l;\ C = \frac{\sinh\gamma l}{\rho c/S}. \end{aligned}\right\} \quad (7\text{-}37)$$

where

The quantity $\gamma = \beta + j\alpha$ (see Chapter V) is the *propagation constant.***** An element of a tube is a *symmetrical fourpole* since its coefficients A and D are equal and the coefficients A, B, C and D are related by the expression

$$AD - BC = 1 \quad (7\text{-}38)$$

(which also holds for a non-symmetrical fourpole). If these conditions are satisfied, it is possible to eliminate two parameters and thus use only two of the four parameters

* V.S. Nesterov, *Dokl. Akad. Nauk SSSR*, 31 (3), 237, 1941.

** S.N. Rschevkin, *Dokl. Akad. Nauk SSSR*, 22, (9), 568, 1939.

*** V.S. Nesterov, *Zhur. tekh. fiz.* 9 (19), 1727; 1939; *ibid.* 10 (8), 617, 1940.

**** Here we are using the same notation as in the theory of electrical lines and filters. The following theory of acoustic filters is quite analogous to the theory of electrical lines and filters.

A, , B, C and D to characterize a symmetric fourpole. It is convenient to use two new parameters. As one of these parameters, suppose we take the *wave impedance or the characteristic impedance of the fourpole* Z_0. For a tube of length l, terminated in an infinite tube of the same section, the wave impedance at the termination is $Z_l = \frac{V_l}{I_l} = \frac{\rho c}{S}$. In this case it follows from expressions (7-37) and (7-38) that

$$Z_0 = \frac{V_0}{I_0} = \frac{\cosh\gamma l \cdot \frac{V_l}{I_l} + \frac{\rho c}{S}\sinh\gamma l}{\frac{\sinh\gamma l}{\frac{\rho c}{S}}\frac{V_l}{I_l} + \cosh\gamma l} = \frac{\rho c}{S} = \frac{V_l}{I_l} = Z_l,$$

i.e. the wave impedance (in acoustic units) of a tube element terminating in the wave impedance, is also equal to $\frac{\rho c}{S} = Z_l$.

As the second parameter we take the natural logarithm of the ratio $\frac{V_0}{V_l}$ (which is equal to $\frac{I_0}{I_l}$ where I_0 is the equivalent current through Z_0). This parameter is known as the *propagation constant of the fourpole* Γ. The quantities Z_0 and Γ fully characterize a symmetrical fourpole.

Suppose we wish to determine the values of Z_0 and Γ for a symmetrical fourpole, and hence put $Z_l = \frac{V_l}{I_l} = Z_0$. Then

$$Z_0 = \frac{V_0}{I_0} = \frac{A\frac{V_l}{I_l} + B}{C\frac{V_l}{I_l} + A} = \frac{AZ_0 + B}{CZ_0 + A},$$

whence

$$Z_0 = \sqrt{\frac{B}{C}}. \tag{7-39}$$

In order to find Γ we have to put $\frac{V_0}{V_l} = e^{\Gamma}$. We then get:

$$e^{\Gamma}=\frac{AV_l+BI_l}{V_l}=A+\frac{B}{Z_0}=A+\sqrt{BC}=A+\sqrt{A^2-1}\,.$$

Since $e^{\Gamma}=\cosh\Gamma+\sinh\Gamma$, it follows that

$$A=D=\cosh\Gamma;\sqrt{BC}=\sqrt{A^2-1}=\sinh\Gamma,$$

or

$$B=Z_0\sinh\Gamma \quad \text{and} \quad C=\frac{\sinh\Gamma}{Z_0}.$$

Thus

$$\Gamma=\text{arc}\cosh A=\text{arc}\sinh(BC)^{1/2}. \qquad (7\text{-}39a)$$

By formula (7-37) we can find the *short-circuit impedance* Z_k and the no load impedance Z_∞, of the fourpole by putting $I_l=0$ or $V_l=0$ as appropriate:

$$Z_k=\frac{B}{A} \quad \text{and} \quad Z_\infty=\frac{A}{C}.$$

These expressions provide the important formula:

$$Z_kZ_\infty=\frac{B}{C}=Z_0^2 \quad \text{or} \quad Z_0=\sqrt{Z_kZ_\infty}\,.$$

All the expressions which have been formed here, as well as the theory of filters which is to follow, are suitable not only for a tube element, but also for any symmetrical fourpoles which satisfy (7-38) provided that $A = D$.

If an arbitrary impedance Z_l is connected at the output of a symmetrical fourpole, then by (7-37)

$$\frac{V_0}{V_l}=\cosh\Gamma+\frac{Z_0}{Z_l}\sinh\Gamma=\cosh\Gamma\left(1+\frac{Z_0}{Z_l}\tanh\Gamma\right),$$

$$\frac{I_0}{I_l}=\cosh\Gamma+\frac{Z_l}{Z_0}\sinh\Gamma=\cosh\Gamma\left(1+\frac{Z_l}{Z_0}\tanh\Gamma\right),$$

i.e. $\frac{V_0}{V_l}\neq\frac{I_0}{I_l}$; but if $Z_0=Z_l$, then $\frac{V_0}{V_l}=\frac{I_0}{I_l}$.

The impedance Z_0' at the inlet will no longer be equal to Z_0:

$$Z_0' = Z_0 \frac{\tanh\Gamma + \frac{Z_l}{Z_0}}{\tanh\Gamma \frac{Z_l}{Z_0} + 1}. \qquad (7\text{-}40)$$

If the attenuation Γ is considerable ($\tanh \Gamma \approx 1$) it is then found from (7-40) that $Z_0' \approx Z_0$ independently of the impedance Z_l at the outlet.

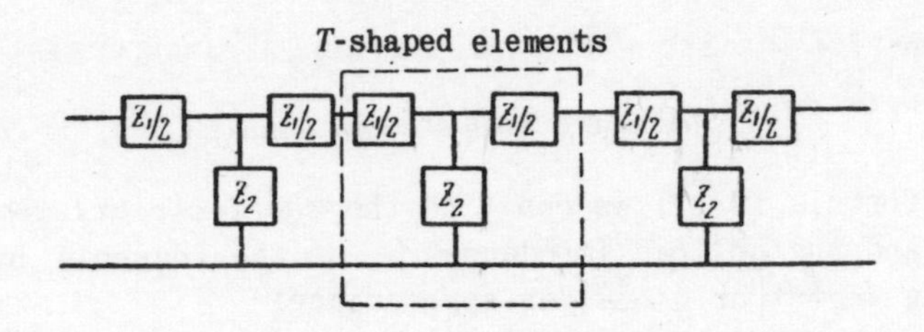

Fig. 57

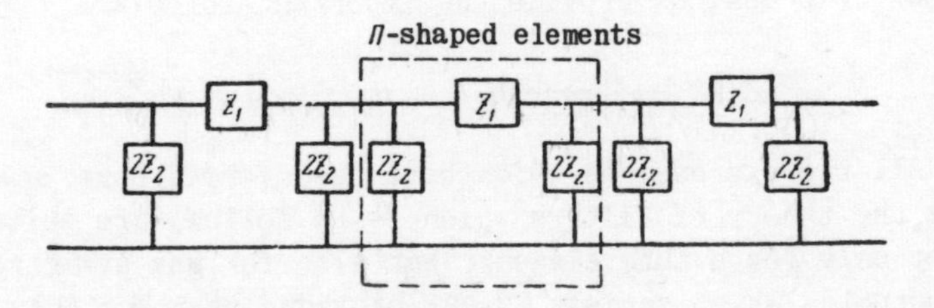

Fig. 58

We will now form a system of acoustic impedances in the form of a set of identical cells which are interconnected, in the form of an infinite chain. Figures 57 and 58 illustrate the electrical analogues of such chains. Figure 57 shows a chain consisting of T-shaped meshes; one cell (delineated by a dotted line) contains two impedances, $\frac{Z_1}{2}$ in the series branch and Z_2 in the parallel branch. The chain in Fig. 58 consists Π-shaped meshes; Z_1 in the series branch and $2Z_2$ in the parallel branches. It is obvious that the two series impedances $\frac{Z_1}{2}$ in the middle meshes of the T-chain can be combined into one impedance Z_1 so that individual impedances $\frac{Z_1}{2}$ remain only at the ends. Likewise, in the Π-chain the middle impedances $2Z_2$ which are in parallel are transformed into Z_2 and the elements $2Z_2$ remain only at the ends of the parallel branch. Figures 59 and 60 show acoustic realizations of such chains of individual cells.

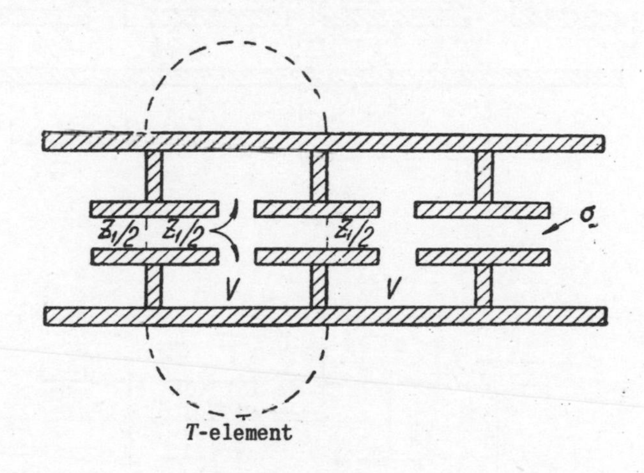

Fig. 59

The series branches Z_1 consist of tube elements and the parallel branches are apertures in the tube walls, or volumes V opening laterally into the tube through such apertures.

We will now find the parameters Z_0 and Γ for T- and Π-chains. For the Π-link there are definite relationships between the pressures $\frac{V_0}{V_l}$ and volume currents (velocities) $\frac{I_0}{I_l}$ at the input and output. These relationships can easily be found from the equivalent electrical network (Fig. 61) provided that the impedance at the input to the mesh is equal to Z_0 when the output impedance is also Z_0:

$$I_0 = \frac{V_0}{2Z_2} + \frac{V_l}{2Z_2} + I_l;$$

$$V_0 - \left(I_0 - \frac{V_0}{2Z_2}\right) Z_1 = V_l.$$

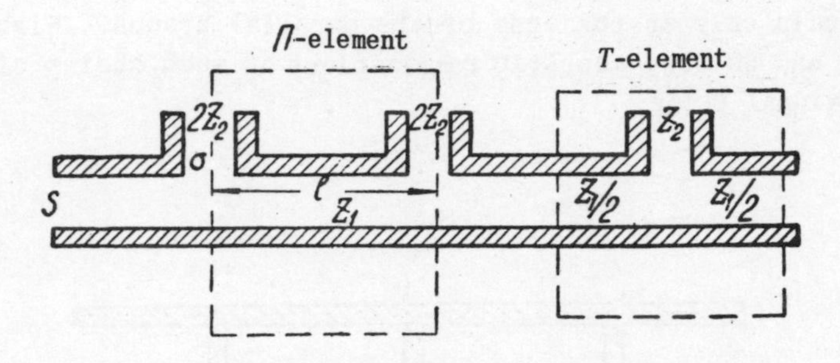

Fig. 60

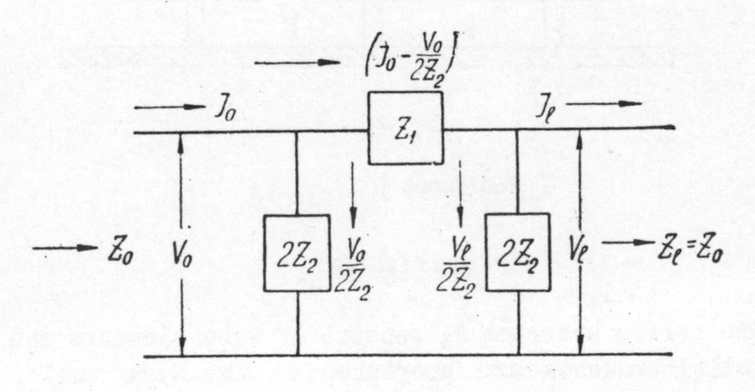

Fig. 61

Solving these equations for V_0 and I_0, we find:

$$V_0 = \left(1 + \frac{Z_1}{2Z_2}\right) V_l + Z_1 I_l,$$

$$I_0 = \frac{1 + \frac{Z_1}{4Z_2}}{Z_2} V_l + \left(1 + \frac{Z_1}{2Z_2}\right) I_l.$$

It is clear from these equations that the coefficients of a П-chain have the following values:

$$A=D=1+\frac{Z_1}{2Z_2};\quad B=Z_1;\quad C=\frac{1+\frac{Z_1}{4Z_2}}{Z_2}.$$

The wave impedance is

$$Z_0^{\Pi}=\sqrt{\frac{B}{C}}=\sqrt{\frac{Z_1Z_2}{1+\frac{Z_1}{4Z_2}}},\qquad (7\text{-}41)$$

and the propagation constant on one mesh is found from the expressions

$$\left.\begin{aligned}\cosh\Gamma_1=A=1+\frac{Z_1}{2Z_2};\ \sinh\Gamma_1=\sqrt{BC}=\sqrt{\frac{Z_1}{Z_2}\left(1+\frac{Z_1}{4Z_2}\right)};\\ \sinh\frac{\Gamma_1}{2}=\sqrt{\frac{\cosh\Gamma_1-1}{2}}=\frac{1}{2}\sqrt{\frac{Z_1}{Z_2}}.\end{aligned}\right\}\qquad (7\text{-}42)$$

For a T-chain we find in the same way:

$$Z_0^{T}=\sqrt{Z_1Z_2}\cdot\sqrt{1+\frac{Z_1}{4Z_2}}.$$

The quantity Γ_1 for a T-chain can be found by the same equa-
For one mesh of either type we have:

$$V_0=\cosh\Gamma_1\cdot V_l+Z_0\sinh\Gamma_1\cdot I_l,$$
$$I_0=\frac{\sinh\Gamma_1}{Z_0}V_l+\cosh\Gamma_1\cdot I_l,$$

on condition that the impedance $Z_l=Z_0$, at the output is equal to the wave impedance.

For a chain of n meshes the propagation constant is $\Gamma=n\Gamma_1$. The impedance at the input to such a chain equals Z_0 as in the case for one cell.

If the impedances Z_1 and Z_2 are purely reactive, we can then put:

$$Z_1=jX_1\quad\text{and}\quad Z_2=jX_2,$$

where X_1 and X_2 can be positive (an inertance) or negative (an elastic impedance). In this case

$$\left.\begin{aligned} Z_0^{\Pi} &= \frac{\sqrt{-X_1X_2}}{\sqrt{1+\frac{X_1}{4X_2}}} = j\frac{2X_2}{\sqrt{1+\frac{4X_2}{X_1}}}, \\ Z_0^{T} &= \sqrt{-X_1X_2}\cdot\sqrt{1+\frac{X_1}{4X_2}} = j\,\frac{X_1}{2}\sqrt{1+\frac{4X_2}{X_1}}. \end{aligned}\right\} \quad (7\text{-}43)$$

The propagation constant for meshes of both types is found from the expressions:

$$\cosh\Gamma_1 = 1+\frac{X_1}{2X_2}; \qquad \sinh\frac{\Gamma_1}{2} = \frac{1}{2}\sqrt{\frac{X_1}{X_2}}. \quad (7\text{-}44)$$

If X_1 and X_2 have the same sign, i.e. if the series and parallel branches contain only inertances or elastic impedances, then in accordance with (7-44) $\cosh\Gamma_1 > 1$ and Γ_1 will be real. The chain will damp the amplitude without changing the phase. Such chains are called *attenuators*. A chain which consists solely of active resistances will also behave in exactly the same way.

If X_1 and X_2 have different signs, then the quantity $\cosh\Gamma_1$ is real, but it is less than unity and can even become less than zero. In this case Γ_1 is complex:

$$\Gamma_1 = b + ja, \quad (7\text{-}45)$$

where b is the transmission loss, and a the phase constant calculated for one cell. The phase velocity (the number of cells traversed by a wave per unit of time) is $\frac{\omega}{a}$.

If $\cosh\Gamma_1 > 1$, then Γ_1 is real and $a = 0$, whilst the phase velocity is infinite. A wave process in such circuits (attenuators) is impossible. If $\cosh\Gamma_1 < 1$, then, bearing (7-45) in mind, we get

$$\begin{aligned} \cosh\Gamma_1 &= \cosh b\cdot\cosh ja + \sinh b\cdot\sinh ja = \\ &= \cosh b\cdot\cos a + j\sinh b\cdot\sin a. \end{aligned} \quad (7\text{-}45\text{a})$$

In accordance with (7-44), the quantity $\cosh\Gamma_1$ is always real, but if X_1 and X_2 are different in sign it is less than unity. In accordance with (7-45a) the quantity cosh Γ_1 has a real value in two cases:

$$\begin{array}{lll} 1)\ \sinh b=0, & \text{or} & \cosh b=1, \\ 2)\ \sin a=0, & \text{or} & \cos a=\pm 1. \end{array}$$

First case. In the first case it is obvious that $b = 0$. The quantity Γ_1 is found from the expression

$$\cosh\Gamma_1=\cosh b\cdot\cos a=\cos a=1+\frac{X_1}{2X_2}=1-\frac{1}{2}\frac{|X_1|}{|X_2|}. \quad (7\text{-}46)$$

In this case there is no damping ($b = 0$), *but only a phase change on transmission through each mesh by an amount a.* In order that a should be real in value, it is obvious that the following condition must be fulfilled: $1>\cos a>+1$, i.e.

$$-1\leqslant 1-\frac{|X_1|}{2|X_2|}\leqslant +1 \quad \text{or} \quad 0\leqslant\frac{|X_1|}{|X_2|}\leqslant 4. \quad (7\text{-}47)$$

This condition is applicable to Π, and T-filters. Since X_1 and X_2 are functions of frequency, it follows that condition (7-47) can only be realised in a definite frequency band. The particular band depends on the type of functions $X_1(\omega)$ and $X_2(\omega)$. It can be seen from formula (7-43) that if condition (7-47) is satisfied, the wave impedance of the chain is purely active (resistive).

Second case. In the second case $\sin a=0$, i.e. $a=0$ or $a=\pi$, whilst $b\neq 0$ If $\cos a=+1$ (when $a=0$) we get:

$$\cosh\Gamma_1=\cosh b=1-\frac{1}{2}\frac{|X_1|}{|X_2|}. \quad (7\text{-}48)$$

If $\cos a = -1$ (when $a=\pi$)

$$\left.\begin{array}{l} \cosh\Gamma_1=-\cosh b=1-\dfrac{1}{2}\dfrac{|X_1|}{|X_2|}, \\ \text{or} \\ \cosh b=\dfrac{1}{2}\dfrac{|X_1|}{|X_2|}-1. \end{array}\right\} \quad (7\text{-}49)$$

The condition $a=0$ and $\cosh \Gamma_1 \geq 1$ is satisfied only if $\frac{|X_1|}{|X_2|}=0$, i.e. if either $X_1=0$, or $X_2=\infty$. This case obviously can arise only at certain discrete values of the frequency ω. The condition $a=\pi$ is fulfilled if

$$\frac{|X_1|}{|X_2|} \geqslant 4. \qquad (7\text{-}50)$$

It can be satisfied throughout the entire frequency band.

The pressure and velocity in the second case are attenuated on each mesh of the chain by a factor e^b if either $\frac{|X_1|}{|X_2|}=0$, or $\frac{|X_1|}{|X_2|} \geqslant 4$. It is of interest that if $a=\pi$ the phase is reversed in each succeeding mesh. The wave impedance at either $a=0$ or $a=\pi$ is purely reactive in accordance with formulae (7-43).

A chain in which X_1 and X_2 have different signs behaves quite differently in two different frequency bands. The chain transmits wave motion without attenuation in the frequency band for which condition (7-47) is satisfied, and in this case the phase changes by a on each mesh. The quantity a is defined by formula (7-46) and lies within the limits from 0 to π. The circuit thus transmits waves freely; this is the *transmission region. In this region the wave impedance of the chain is purely resistive.*

In the frequency band where condition (7-50) is satisfied there is attenuation in each link by a factor of e^b, where

$$b = \operatorname{arc\,cosh}\left[\frac{|X_1|}{2|X_2|}-1\right]$$

and a change of phase of 180° occurs; this is the *attenuation region. Here the wave impedance is reactive.*

Chains which posses these properties are called *filters*. Thus, for filter chains, if $\frac{|X_1|}{|X_2|} > 4$, we have the transmission region and if $0 \leqslant \frac{|X_1|}{|X_2|} \leqslant 4$ the attenuation region.

The condition $\frac{|X_1|}{|X_2|} = 4$ defines the *cut-off frequency of the filter*, which separates the transmission region from the attenuation region. The wave impedance of both Π-, and T-chains is resistive in the transmission region and reactive in the attenuation region in accordance with (7-43). Consequently, in the attenuation region a source connected to the filter *does not expend energy*. If the output of the filter is connected to a tube (or line) with an active characteristic resistance R, the reflection coefficient at the input to the filter, provided the filter is operating in the attenuation region where Z_0 is purely imaginary ($Z_0 = jY_0$), is

$$r = \frac{Z_0 - R}{Z_0 + R} = \frac{jY_0 - R}{jY_0 + R} = 1 \cdot e^{j2\varphi}, \text{ where } \tan\varphi = \frac{R}{Y_0}.$$

Thus $|r| = 1$, i.e. all the wave energy is reflected at the input. At the initial moment just after the filter is connected there is of course a certain flow of energy which gradually decreases to zero, after which a stationary state is established. Gradually attenuating standing waves are set up in the filter; the amplitude of the oscillations in each succeeding cell decreases by a factor of e^b, and the pressure and velocity (voltage and current) differ in phase by $\frac{\pi}{2}$. On going from one cell to another, the pressure (or velocity) phase abruptly changes by an amount π. The decrease in amplitude by the factor e^b in each cell characterizes the operation of the filter, but it does not characterize the damping process of the wave, since there is no wave process in the filter in this frequency region.

In the transmission region the wave impedance is purely resistive ($Z_0 = R_0$) and the reflection coefficient at the input to the filter

$$r = \frac{R_0 - R}{R_0 + R}$$

is less than unity. Part of the energy goes into the filter and is transmitted through it. If we make $R = R_0$, then $r = 0$ and all the energy of the incident wave passes through the filter.

The output impedance of the filter practically always has a certain active (resistive) component. Thus, it is impossible to realize exactly the reactive wave impedance at the output required to satisfy the conditions of operation of an infinite chain, and so the last mesh of a filter always operates into a resistance which is not equal to the wave impedance and, therefore, the quantity r differs from the calculated value. In practice, however, it is possible to make these deviations quite small.

Low pass filters. Suppose that the chain in Figure 59 consists of T-meshes with series inertances in the form of elements of short ($l < \lambda$) tubes of acoustic impedance

$$Z_1 = j\omega \frac{\rho\sigma l}{\sigma^2} = j\omega M_1$$

and parallel impedances in the form of side cavities of volume V with impedance

$$Z_2 = \frac{\rho c^2}{j\omega V} = -j \frac{E_2}{\omega}.$$

Consequently, we have:

$$X_1 = \omega M_1 \text{ and } X_2 = -\frac{E_2}{\omega}.$$

Condition (7-47) for the pass band has the form:

$$0 \leqslant \frac{\omega M_1}{\frac{E_2}{\omega}} \leqslant 4 \quad \text{or} \quad 0 \leqslant \omega^2 \leqslant 4\,\frac{E_2}{M_1},$$

whence the upper limiting frequency of the pass band is

$$\omega_b = 2\sqrt{\frac{E_2}{M_1}};\; f_b = 2\frac{1}{2\pi}\sqrt{\frac{E_2}{M_1}} = \frac{c}{\pi}\sqrt{\frac{\sigma}{lV}} = \\ = \frac{c}{\pi}\sqrt{\frac{K}{V}} = 2f_0, \tag{7-51}$$

where K is the conductance of a tube of length l and cross-section σ.

Thus the upper limiting frequency is equal to twice the frequency f_0 of a resonator with a neck conductance K and a volume V. At frequencies below the upper limiting frequency, we have a transmission region for frequencies from 0 to the limiting frequency f_b, and in this region the phase constant is found from expressions (7-46):

$$\cos a = 1 - \frac{|X_1|}{2|X_2|} = 1 - \frac{1}{2}\left(\frac{f}{f_0}\right)^2;$$

$$\sin\frac{a}{2} = \frac{f}{2f_0}.$$

For frequencies considerably below the cut-off frequency

$$a = 2 \arcsin\frac{f}{2f_0} \approx \frac{f}{f_0}.$$

The time taken for an acoustic wave to pass through one cell in this frequency band is

$$\tau = \frac{a}{\omega} \approx \frac{f}{f_0 2\pi f} = \frac{1}{2\pi f_0} = \frac{1}{\omega_0} = \sqrt{\frac{M_1}{E_2}}, \tag{7-52}$$

where ω_0 is the resonant angular frequency for the system

M_1, E_2. The phase velocity of the wave in the chain (i.e. the number of cells travelled by the wave per second is, for $f<f_b$

$$c=\frac{1}{\tau}=\frac{\omega}{a}\approx\sqrt{\frac{E_2}{M_1}}=\omega_0=\text{const.}$$

A chain of this type is of great practical value in obtaining a time delay independent of frequency. They have been developed in connection with both electrical and acoustic devices designed to produce a given time delay in certain processes and are called *delay lines*.

The value of the attenuation constant in the attenuation region for a low pass filter is found from equation (7-49):

$$\cosh b=\frac{1}{2}\frac{|X_1|}{|X_2|}-1;\ \cosh\frac{b}{2}=\sqrt{\frac{1+\cosh b}{2}}=\frac{1}{2}\frac{f}{f_0}=\frac{f}{f_b}. \quad (7\text{-}53)$$

Attenuation occurs only if $f>f_b$. It is easy to show that in the vicinity of the limiting frequency $b\approx\sqrt{8}\sqrt{\frac{\Delta f}{f_b}}$, where

$$\Delta f=f-f_b.$$

The wave impedance for Π- and T-links is found from formulae (7-43):

$$\left.\begin{aligned} Z_0^{\Pi}&=\sqrt{M_1E_2}\cdot\frac{1}{\sqrt{1-\frac{f^2}{f_b^2}}},\\ Z_0^{T}&=\sqrt{M_1E_2}\cdot\sqrt{1-\frac{f^2}{f_b^2}}.\end{aligned}\right\} \quad (7\text{-}54)$$

Thus, the wave impedance varies with frequency according to a definite law and, therefore, it is very difficult to select a value of Z_l at the output such that it is always equal to Z_0. Only in the region of low frequencies $(f\ll f_b)$ is the wave impedance independent of the frequency and purely active (resistive). It is easy to see from formula (7-54) that Z_0 is constant to within 13 per cent at frequencies $f < \frac{f_b}{2}$.

In real acoustic filters it is possible to construct a lumped series inertance only at low frequencies (for which $l < \frac{\lambda}{8}$). At higher frequencies the variation of Z_1 for a tube element is governed, strictly speaking, by the following law

$$Z_1 = j\frac{\rho c}{S} \tan kl.$$

If $l = \frac{\lambda}{4}$, $Z_1 = j\infty$; for larger values of l, the value Z_l becomes negative and imaginary. As a result it appears that a filter of this type would have several transmission and attenuation regions, rather than just one of each.

High pass filters. A tube with side apertures acts as a high pass filter (see Figure 60). In this case

$$X_1 = -\frac{E_1}{\omega};\ X_2 = \omega M_2,$$

where $E_1 = \frac{\rho c^2}{Sl}$ is the stiffness coefficient of the volume $V = Sl$, midway between two apertures, and ωM_2 is the inertance of the side tube ($M_2 = \frac{\rho}{K_2}$, where K_2 is the conductivity of the aperture). Condition (7-47) for the transmission band has the form:

$$0 \leqslant \frac{E_1}{\omega^2 M_2} \leqslant 4.$$

The cut-off frequency of the filter is:

$$f_b = \frac{1}{2}\frac{1}{2\pi}\sqrt{\frac{E_1}{M_2}} = \frac{1}{2}\frac{\omega_0}{2\pi},$$

where ω_0 is the angular frequency of a resonator of volume

V and neck conductance $\frac{\rho}{M_2}$. The phase constant a in the transmission region $f_b \leqslant f \leqslant \infty$ is found from expression (7-46):

$$\cos a = 1 - \frac{1}{2}\frac{|X_1|}{|X_2|} = 1 - \frac{1}{2}\left(\frac{f_0}{f}\right)^2,$$

$$\sin\frac{a}{2} = \sqrt{\frac{1-\cos a}{2}} = \frac{1}{2}\frac{f_0}{f} = \frac{f_b}{f}.$$

At frequencies $f \gg f_b$

$$a \approx 2\frac{f_b}{f}.$$

The time taken for a wave to pass through one cell if $f \gg f_b$ is

$$\tau \approx \frac{a}{\omega} = \frac{2\cdot\frac{1}{2}\sqrt{\frac{E_1}{M_2}}}{\omega^2} = \frac{\omega_0^2}{\omega^2},$$

i.e. it is not constant with frequency: the system possesses dispersion of phase velocity.

The attenuation constant in the band $0 \leqslant f \leqslant f_b$ is found by formula (7-49):

$$\cosh b = 2\left(\frac{f_b}{f}\right)^2 - 1; \qquad \cosh\frac{b}{2} = \frac{f_b}{f}.$$

Near the cut-off frequency

$$b \approx \sqrt{8}\sqrt{\frac{\Delta f}{f_b}}, \quad \text{where} \quad \Delta f = f - f_b.$$

At the cut-off frequency $b = 0$.

The wave impedance is obtained from formula (7-43):

$$Z_0^{\Pi} = \frac{\sqrt{E_1 M_2}}{\sqrt{1 - \frac{f_b^2}{f^2}}}; \qquad Z_0^T = \sqrt{E_1 M_2}\cdot\sqrt{1 - \frac{f_b^2}{f^2}}.$$

As in the case of a low pass filter, the approximate formulae are applicable at frequencies for which $l < \frac{\lambda}{8}$. In a real high pass filter there is not one but a series of transmission and absorption bands.

The practical realisation of a high pass filter presents considerable difficulties, since the side apertures lead to external space and sound is radiated out through them. Even though sound is very greatly attenuated in the main channel in the attenuation region, nevertheless it is partially transmitted by the side apertures. Consequently, it is necessary to isolate acoustically the tube of the filter from the external space.

CHAPTER VIII

THE NON-UNIFORM SPHERICAL RADIATOR

General Solution of the Wave Equation

It is assumed that the surface of a sphere of radius r_0 performs small oscillations transverse to the surface of the sphere and that these depend on the angular coordinates ϑ and ψ (the polar angle and azimuth) (Fig. 62), and on the time t:

$$q = q(\vartheta, \psi, t).$$

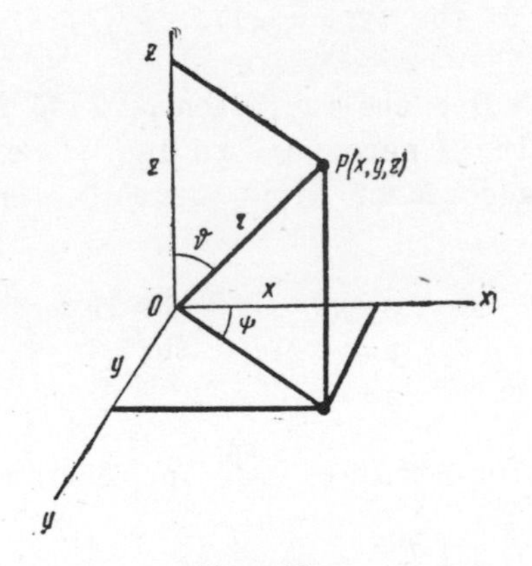

Fig. 62

If all points of the surface oscillate in the same phase, then:

$$q(\vartheta, \psi, t) = u(\vartheta, \psi) \cdot \varphi(t), \tag{8-1}$$

where $\varphi(t)$ expresses the dependence on time of the oscillatory velocities of all points on the sphere, and $u(\vartheta,\psi)$ describes the distribution of the amplitudes over the surface. It is assumed that the function $u(\vartheta,\psi)$ can take on positive or negative values, or be zero. Such a law of motion includes, among other things, systems of surface standing waves separated by nodal lines. For a harmonic law

$$q(\vartheta,\psi,t)=u(\vartheta,\psi)\cdot e^{j\omega t}. \tag{8-2}$$

A different form of oscillation can be obtained if we permit $u(\vartheta,\psi)$ to be complex. Thus, assuming that

$$u(\vartheta,\psi)=u(\vartheta)\cdot e^{-jm\psi},$$

we obtain waves of the following type on the surface of the sphere, travelling in the azimuthal direction,

$$q(\vartheta,\psi,t)=u(\vartheta)\,e^{j(\omega t-m\psi)}, \tag{8-3}$$

where the number m must obviously be integral, for otherwise the process at the point in question is not single-valued. The sum of two such progressive waves of equal amplitude travelling in opposite directions produces a standing wave of the type (8-1).

In order to solve the radiation problem for an oscillating sphere, it is necessary to introduce spherical coordinates in accordance with the relationships derived from Fig. 62:

$$x=r\cdot\sin\vartheta\cdot\cos\psi,$$
$$y=r\cdot\sin\vartheta\cdot\sin\psi,$$
$$z=r\cdot\cos\vartheta.$$

The wave equation $c^2\Delta\Phi=\frac{\partial^2\Phi}{\partial t^2}$ in spherical coordinates takes the form:

$$c^2\left[\frac{\partial^2\Phi}{\partial r^2}+\frac{2}{r}\frac{\partial\Phi}{\partial r}+\frac{1}{r^2\sin\vartheta}\cdot\frac{\partial}{\partial\vartheta}\left(\sin\vartheta\frac{\partial\Phi}{\partial\vartheta}\right)+\right.$$
$$\left.+\frac{1}{r^2\sin^2\vartheta}\frac{\partial^2\Phi}{\partial\psi^2}\right]=\frac{\partial^2\Phi}{\partial t^2}.$$

For a periodic wave process of angular frequency ω, it can be assumed that the velocity potential of the acoustic field is

$$\Phi(r,\vartheta,\psi,t)=\Psi(r,\vartheta,\psi)\cdot e^{j\omega t}.$$

Suppressing the time factor in the wave equation, we get:

$$\frac{\partial^2\Psi}{\partial r^2}+\frac{2}{r}\frac{\partial\Psi}{\partial r}+\frac{1}{r^2}\left[\frac{1}{\sin\vartheta}\cdot\frac{\partial}{\partial\vartheta}\left(\sin\vartheta\frac{\partial\Psi}{\partial\vartheta}\right)+\frac{1}{\sin^2\vartheta}\cdot\frac{\partial^2\Psi}{\partial\psi^2}\right]+k^2\Psi=0.$$

Suppose we write $\Delta_1\Psi$ for the expression in square brackets; we have, after multiplying by r^2:

$$r^2\frac{\partial^2\Psi}{\partial r^2}+2r\frac{\partial\Psi}{\partial r}+k^2r^2\Psi+\Delta_1\Psi=0. \tag{8-4}$$

Equation (8-4) can be solved using Fourier's method of separating the variables. Suppose we put:

$$\Psi(r,\vartheta,\psi)=R(r)\cdot Y(\vartheta,\psi). \tag{8-5}$$

Substituting this expression into (8-4),

$$\frac{\frac{\partial}{\partial r}\left(r^2\frac{\partial R(r)}{\partial r}\right)}{R(r)}+k^2r^2=-\frac{\Delta_1Y(\vartheta,\psi)}{Y(\vartheta,\psi)}.$$

The right- and left-hand sides of this equation can only equal a constant quantity λ. Two differential equations are obtained which are related by the common constant λ. The equation for the function $R(r)$, denoted simply by R, takes the form:

$$\frac{\frac{\partial}{\partial r}\left(r^2\frac{\partial R}{\partial r}\right)}{R}+k^2r^2=\lambda \quad\text{or}\quad \frac{d^2R}{dr^2}+\frac{2}{r}\frac{dR}{dr}+\left(k^2-\frac{\lambda}{r^2}\right)R=0 \tag{8-6}$$

(here the total derivative is substituted for the partial derivative, since the function R depends solely on the variable r). For the function $Y(\vartheta,\psi)$ we obtain the differential equation:

$$\Delta_1Y+\lambda Y=0,$$

or

$$\frac{1}{\sin\vartheta}\frac{\partial}{\partial\vartheta}\left(\sin\vartheta\frac{\partial Y}{\partial\vartheta}\right)+\frac{1}{\sin^2\vartheta}\frac{\partial^2 Y}{\partial\psi^2}+\lambda Y=0. \qquad (8\text{-}7)$$

The solution of equation (8-7) is known as a spherical harmonic function, and it is known that a unique, finite and continuous solution can be obtained only if*:

$$\lambda=m(m+1), \text{where } m=0, 1, 2, 3 \ldots$$

The solution of (8-7) for each m is called a *spherical harmonic of order* m of the first kind, often known as a *spherical surface harmonic:*

$$Y_m(\vartheta,\psi)=a_{m0}P_m(\cos\vartheta)+\sum_{\nu=1}^{\nu=m}(a_{m\nu}\cos\nu\psi+ + a'_{m\nu}\cdot\sin\nu\psi)\cdot P_m^{(\nu)}(\cos\vartheta), \qquad (8\text{-}8)$$

where

$$P_m(\cos\vartheta)=P_m(x)=\frac{1}{2^m m!}\frac{d}{dx}(x^2-1)^m= =\frac{1\cdot3\cdot5\ldots(2m-1)}{m!}\left[x^m+\frac{m(m-1)}{2(2m-1)}\cdot x^{m-2}+ +\frac{m(m-1)(m-2)(m-3)}{2.4.(2m-1)(2m-3)}\cdot x^{m-4}+\ldots\right] \qquad (8\text{-}9)$$

are the Legendre polynomials, which are functions of $x = \cos\vartheta$. They are also called *zonal spherical harmonics.*

Functions of the type

$$(a_{m\nu}\cos\nu\psi+a'_{m\nu}\sin\nu\psi)P_m^{(\nu)}(x)$$

are called *associated spherical harmonics of the first kind,* and depend on ψ as well as on ϑ. The *associated Legendre polynomials,* $P_m^{(\nu)}(\cos\vartheta)$ are defined by the expression:

$$P_m^{(\nu)}(x)=(1-x^2)^{\nu/2}\frac{d^\nu}{dx^\nu}[P_m(x)], \qquad (8\text{-}10)$$

---

* V.I. Smirnov, *Kurs vysshei matematiki (A Course of Advanced Mathematics)*, Moscow: Gostekhizdat 1956 (vol. III, ch.I).

the second factor being a polynomial of degree $(m-\nu)$.

For the first few orders we have the following expressions:

$$P_0(x)=1;\ P_1(x)=x;\ P_2(x)=\frac{1}{2}(3x^2-1);$$
$$P_3(x)=\frac{1}{2}(5x^3-3x);$$
$$P_0^{(m)}(x)=0;\ P_1^1(x)=(1-x^2)^{1/2}=\sin\vartheta;$$
$$P_2^{(1)}(x)=3(1-x^2)^{1/2}\cdot x=3\sin\vartheta\cos\vartheta; \tag{8-11}$$
$$P_2^{(2)}(x)=3(1-x^2)=3\cdot\sin^2\vartheta;$$
$$P_m^{(0)}(x)=P_m(x);$$
$$P_m^{(m)}(x)=1\cdot3\cdot5\ldots(2m-1)(1-x^2)^{m/2}=\bar{m}\cdot\sin^m\vartheta,$$

where $\bar{m}=1\cdot3\cdot5\ldots(2m-1)$.

A spherical harmonic of the form

$$\bar{P}_m(\vartheta,\psi)=\frac{Y_m(\vartheta,\psi)}{a_{m0}}=P_m(x)+$$
$$+\sum_{\nu=1}^{\nu=m}\left(\frac{a_{m\nu}}{a_{m0}}\cos\nu\psi+\frac{a'_{m\nu}}{a_{m0}}\sin\nu\psi\right)P_m^{(\nu)}(x) \tag{8-12}$$

will now be used for solving the wave equation. To solve equation (8-6), we put $R(r)=\frac{V(r)}{\sqrt{r}}$ and $\lambda=m(m+1)$; equation (8-6) then reduces to the Bessel equation:

$$\frac{d^2V}{dr^2}+\frac{1}{r}\frac{dV}{dr}+\left[k^2-\frac{\left(m+\frac{1}{2}\right)^2}{r^2}\right]V=0.$$

The solution of this equation is a linear combination of *Bessel* and *Neumann functions* of order $\left(m+\frac{1}{2}\right)$:

$$V_m(r)=A'_m\cdot J_{m+\frac{1}{2}}(kr)+B'_m\cdot N_{m+\frac{1}{2}}(kr). \tag{8-13}$$

Here A'_m and B'_m are arbitrary constants. The functions $J_{m+\frac{1}{2}}$ and $N_{m+\frac{1}{2}}$ have an oscillatory character.

In order to investigate the radiation process, it is more

convenient to avail ourselves of Hankel functions of the first and second kind, which are qualitatively similar to the functions $\frac{e^{jkr}}{\sqrt{r}}$ or $\frac{e^{-jkr}}{\sqrt{r}}$. They are expressible in terms of Bessel and Neumann functions:

$$H_p^{(1)}(kr) = J_p(kr) + jN_p(kr),$$
$$H_p^{(2)}(kr) = J_p(kr) - jN_p(kr).$$

The functions $H_p^{(1)}(kr)$ and $H_p^{(2)}(kr)$ diminish in magnitude, with increasing (kr) (if $kr \gg 1$ the decrease takes place according to the law $r^{-1/2}$) and they can be expressed as series with a finite number of terms (polynomials):

$$H^{(1)}_{m+\frac{1}{2}}(kr) = \sqrt{\frac{2}{\pi kr}} \cdot \frac{e^{j\left(kr - m\frac{\pi}{2} - \frac{\pi}{2}\right)}}{m!} \sum_{\nu=0}^{\nu=m} \binom{m}{\nu} \frac{(m+\nu)!}{2^\nu(-jkr)^\nu};$$

$$H^{(2)}_{m+\frac{1}{2}}(kr) = \sqrt{\frac{2}{\pi kr}} \cdot \frac{e^{-j\left(kr - m\frac{\pi}{2} - \frac{\pi}{2}\right)}}{m!} \sum_{\nu=0}^{\nu=m} \binom{m}{\nu} \frac{(m+\nu)!}{2^\nu(jkr)^\nu}. \tag{8-14}$$

The binomial coefficients have the following values:

$$\binom{m}{\nu} = \frac{m(m-1)\ \ldots\ (m-\nu+1)}{\nu!};$$
$$\binom{m}{0} = 1;\ \binom{m}{m} = 1;\ \binom{0}{0} = 1;\ 0! = 1.$$

In the following, we will introduce *spherical Bessel, Neumann and Hankel functions.*

These functions of order m are obtained by multiplying the fundamental functions of order $m + \frac{1}{2}$ by $\sqrt{\frac{\pi}{2kr}}$ Suppose we put $z = kr$. We then have

spherical Bessel function $j_m(z) = \sqrt{\frac{\pi}{2z}} \cdot J_{m+\frac{1}{2}}(z),$

(8-15)

spherical Neumann function $n_m(z) = \sqrt{\frac{\pi}{2z}} \cdot N_{m+\frac{1}{2}}(z),$

spherical Hankel function of the first kind

$$h_m^{(1)}(z)=\sqrt{\frac{\pi}{2z}}\cdot H_{m+\frac{1}{2}}^{(1)}(z),$$

spherical Hankel function of the second kind (8-15)

$$h_m^{(2)}(z)=\sqrt{\frac{\pi}{2z}}\cdot H_{m+\frac{1}{2}}^{(2)}(z).$$

The functions $j_m(z)$ and $n_m(z)$ of the first few orders can be calculated from the following formulae*:

$$\begin{aligned}
&j_0(z)=\frac{\sin z}{z};\quad n_0(z)=-\frac{\cos z}{z};\\
&j_1(z)=\frac{\sin z}{z^2}-\frac{\cos z}{z};\ n_1(z)=-\frac{\sin z}{z}-\frac{\cos z}{z^2};\\
&j_2(z)=\left(\frac{3}{z^3}-\frac{1}{z}\right)\cdot\sin z-\frac{3}{z^2}\cos z;\\
&n_2(z)=-\frac{3}{z^2}\sin z-\left(\frac{3}{z^3}-\frac{1}{z}\right)\cdot\cos z;
\end{aligned}\tag{8-16}$$

It is seen from formulae (8-14) and (8-15) that as $z\to\infty$ the spherical Hankel functions of the first and second kind are proportional to $\frac{e^{jz}}{z}$ and $\frac{e^{-jz}}{z}$. Thus, $h_0^{(2)}(z)$ coincides with the function for the radiation of a point source.

If we take into account the substitution $R(r)=\frac{V(r)}{\sqrt{r}}$, the solutions for the velocity potential can be written in either of two forms:

$$\begin{aligned}\Phi_m(r,\vartheta,\psi,t)=A_{m0}\cdot\overline{P}_m(\vartheta,\psi)\cdot j_m(kr)\,e^{j\omega t}+\\+B_{m0}\overline{P}_m(\vartheta,\psi)\cdot n_m(kr)\,e^{j\omega t}\end{aligned}\tag{8-17}$$

or

$$\begin{aligned}\Phi_m(r,\vartheta,\psi,t)=a_{m0}\,\overline{P}_m(\vartheta,\psi)\cdot h_m^{(2)}(kr)\cdot e^{j\omega t}+\\+b_{m0}\overline{P}_m(\vartheta,\psi)\cdot h_m^{(1)}(kr)\,e^{j\omega t}.\end{aligned}\tag{8-18}$$

---

* Numerical values of the spherical Bessel functions are given in *Tables of Spherical Bessel Functions*, New York: Columbia University Press, 1947 (a publication of the United States National Bureau of Standards).

The arbitrary constants A'_m and B'_m in the solution (8-13) for the function $R(r)$ can be discarded since the arbitrary constants A_{m0} and B_{m0} or a_{m0} and b_{m0} have been introduced. The sum of solutions of type (8-17) or (8-18) is the general solution of the wave equation.

The velocity potential can conveniently be expressed in the form (8-17) when investigating the natural oscillations of a spherical cavity, in which case it is necessary to put $B_{mo}=0$, since $n_m(0)=-\infty$ but the potential at the centre of the sphere must be finite in value. In order to calculate the natural frequencies of a spherical annulus, it is necessary to include the second term. When investigating radiation in free space, the second term (8-17) which contains the function $h_m^{(1)}(kr)$, has to be discarded since it corresponds to waves of the type $e^{(j\omega t+kr)}/r$, i.e. to waves which converge on the origin, which must be excluded on physical grounds.

The function $h_m^{(2)}(z)$ is complex. Suppose we put:

$$\begin{aligned} h_m^{(2)}(z) &= j_m(z) - jn_m(z) = G_m(z)\cdot e^{-j\varepsilon_m(z)} = \\ &= G_m(z)\left[\cos\varepsilon_m(z) - j\sin\varepsilon_m(z)\right]; \\ G_m(z) &= \sqrt{j_m^2(z) + n_m^2(z)}\,; \\ \sin\varepsilon_m(z) &= \frac{n_m(z)}{G_m(z)}; \quad \cos\varepsilon_m(z) = \frac{j_m(z)}{G_m(z)}. \end{aligned} \tag{8-19}$$

Taking into account expressions (8-14) and (8-15) for $h_m^{(2)}(z)$, we get:

$$h_m^{(2)}(z) = j\,\frac{e^{-jz}}{z^{m+1}}\,\overline{m}\left[1 + jz + \frac{2(m-1)}{2m-1}(jz)^2 + \ldots\right]. \tag{8-20}$$

The functions $j_m(z)$, $n_m(z)$ and $h_m^{(2)}(z)$ possess the following properties:

$$\begin{aligned} &\underset{z\to 0}{j_m(z)} \to \frac{z^m}{\overline{m}(2m+1)}, \qquad \underset{z\to 0}{n_m(z)} \to -\frac{\overline{m}}{z^{m+1}}, \\ &\underset{z\to 0}{h_m^{(2)}(z)} \to j\,\frac{\overline{m}}{z^{m+1}}; \end{aligned} \tag{8-21}$$

$$
\begin{aligned}
&j_m(z)_{z\to\infty} \to \frac{1}{z}\cos\left(z - \frac{m+1}{2}\pi\right),\\
&n_m(z)_{z\to\infty} \to \frac{1}{z}\sin\left(z - \frac{m+1}{2}\pi\right),\\
&h_m^{(2)}(z)_{z\to\infty} \to \frac{1}{z}e^{-j\left(z - \frac{m+1}{2}\pi\right)};
\end{aligned}
\tag{8-21}
$$

the general properties of functions $j(z)$ and $n(z)$ are

$$
\begin{aligned}
&j_{m-1}(z) + j_{m+1}(z) = \frac{2m+1}{z}\cdot j_m(z);\\
&\frac{d}{dz}j_m(z) = \frac{1}{2m+1}\left[mj_{m-1}(z) - (m+1)j_{m+1}(z)\right];\\
&\frac{d}{dz}\left[z^{m+1}j_m(z)\right] = z^{m+1}\cdot j_{m-1}(z);\\
&\frac{d}{dz}\left[z^{-m}j_m(z)\right] = -z^{-m}\cdot j_{m+1}(z);\\
&\int j_1(z)\,dz = -j_0(z); \quad \int j_0(z)\cdot z^2 dz = z^2 j_1(z);\\
&\int j_m^2(z)z^2dz = \frac{z^3}{2}\left[j_m^2(z) - j_{m-1}(z)\cdot j_{m+1}(z)\right]; \text{ if } m>0
\end{aligned}
\tag{8-21a}
$$

$$
\begin{aligned}
&n_{m-1}(z)\cdot j_m(z) - n_m(z)\cdot j_{m-1}(z) = \frac{1}{z^2};\\
&\int j_0^2(z)\,z^2dz = \frac{z^3}{2}\left[j_0^2(z) + n_0(z)j_1(z)\right];\\
&\int n_0^2(z)\,z^2dz = \frac{z^3}{2}\left[n_0^2(z) - j_0(z)\cdot n_1(z)\right].
\end{aligned}
\tag{8-21b}
$$

Brief tables of the functions $j_m(z)$ and $n_m(z)$ are given in the book by Morse*.

It follows from what has been said above that radiation processes are best investigated by writing the velocity potential in the form of a sum of solutions of type (8-18), in which case the constants $b_{m\nu}$ are assumed to be zero:

$$
\begin{aligned}
\Phi(r,\vartheta,\psi,t) &= \sum_{m=0}^{\infty} a_{m0}\cdot \overline{P}_m(\vartheta,\psi)\cdot G_m(z)\cdot e^{-j\varepsilon_m(z)}\cdot e^{j\omega t} =\\
&= \sum_{m=0}^{\infty} a_{m0}\cdot \overline{P}_m(\vartheta,\psi)\cdot h_m^{(2)}(z)\cdot e^{j\omega t}.
\end{aligned}
\tag{8-22}
$$

The coefficients of the expansion, $a_{m\nu}$ can be found if

* P.M. Morse, *Vibration and Sound*, New York: McGraw-Hill, 1948 (see p.446).

the normal velocity distribution over the surface of the sphere is known as a function of ϑ and ψ. It is a necessary condition that the radial velocity on the surface should equal the radial component of the velocity in the surrounding acoustic field, i.e.

$$u(\vartheta,\psi)\cdot e^{j\omega t} = -\left.\frac{\partial\Phi}{\partial r}\right|_{r=r_0} = = -k\sum_{m=0}^{\infty} a_{m0}\bar{P}_m(\vartheta,\psi)\frac{d}{dz}\left[h_m^{(2)}(z)\right]_{z=z_0} e^{j\omega t} \qquad (8\text{-}23)$$

Using formula (8-21a), we get:

$$\frac{dh_m^{(2)}(z)}{dz} = \frac{1}{2m+1}\{[mj_{m-1}-(m+1)j_{m+1}] - -j\left[mn_{m-1}-(m+1)n_{m+1}\right]\} = D_m(z)e^{-j\left[\delta_m(z)+\frac{\pi}{2}\right]}, \qquad (8\text{-}24)$$

where

$$D_m(z) = \frac{1}{2m+1}\times \times\sqrt{[mj_{m-1}-(m+1)j_{m+1}]^2+[mn_{m-1}-(m+1)n_{m+1}]^2}, \qquad (8\text{-}25)$$

$$\left.\begin{aligned} D_m(z)\cos\delta_m(z) &= \frac{1}{2m+1}[mn_{m-1}-(m+1)n_{m+1}], \\ -D_m(z)\sin\delta_m(z) &= \frac{1}{2m+1}[mj_{m-1}-(m+1)j_{m+1}]. \end{aligned}\right\} \qquad (8\text{-}26)$$

The quantities $D_m(z)$ and $\delta_m(z)$ are analogous to quantities introduced by Morse.*

* In many modern textbooks and papers on theoretical physics, including Morse's book *Vibration and Sound*, the function for the radiation of a point source is taken in the form $\frac{1}{r}e^{-j(\omega t-kr)}$ and the solution for the spherical case is accordingly expressed in terms of Hankel functions of the first kind $h_m^{(1)}(z)$. However, the majority of the older papers and works on acoustics (in particular Rayleigh's *Theory of Sound*) use the radiation function $\frac{1}{r}e^{j(\omega t-kr)}$ and Hankel functions of the second kind, and this method of description has been preferred for this reason. Nevertheless, in order to be able to use Morse's

continued on page 290

The values of the functions D_m and δ_m for the first two orders are:

$$D_0(z)=\frac{\sqrt{1+z^2}}{z^2};\quad \tan\delta_0(z)=\frac{\tan z-z}{z\tan z+1};$$
$$D_1(z)=\frac{\sqrt{4+z^4}}{z^3};\ \tan\delta_1(z)=\frac{2\tan z-z^2\tan z-2z}{2-z^2-2z\tan z}. \quad (8\text{-}27)$$

The maximum (limiting) values D_m and δ_m for large and small values of z are:

$$D_0(z)_{z\ll 1}\approx\frac{1}{z^2};\quad \delta_0(z)_{z\ll 1}\approx\frac{z^3}{3};\quad D_1(z)_{z\ll 1}\approx\frac{2}{z^3}$$
$$\delta_1(z)_{z\ll 1}\approx-\frac{z^3}{6};$$
$$D_m(z)_{z\ll m}\approx\frac{m(m+1)}{z^{m+2}},\ \delta_m(z)_{z\ll m}\approx-\frac{mz^{2m+1}}{m^2(2m+1)(m+1)}; \quad (8\text{-}28)$$
$$\underset{z\gg m}{D_m(z)}\approx\frac{1}{z},\qquad \underset{z\gg m}{\delta_m(z)}\approx z-\frac{m+1}{2}\pi .$$

Finally, the maximum values of the functions $G_m(z)$,

---

continued from page 289

valuable tables for functions $D_m(kr)$ and $\delta_m(kr)$, we have defined these functions in the form (8-24), which is slightly different from that given by Morse. The functions $D_m(z)$ and $\delta_m(z)$ are defined by Morse in the form:

$$\frac{dh_m^{(1)}(z)}{dz}=\frac{d}{dz}\left[j_m(z)+jn_m(z)\right]=D_m(z)e^{j\left[\delta_m(z)+\frac{\pi}{2}\right]}.$$

Unlike Morse, in expression (8-24) we have taken the corresponding complex conjugate expression $\left[\text{the function } \frac{dh^{(2)}{}_m(z)}{dz}\right]$.
Using this definition the functions $D_m(z)$ and $\delta_m(z)$ can be expressed in terms of $j_m(z)$ and $n_m(z)$ exactly as in the book by Morse and Morse's tables can be used unreservedly in all the following formulae.

$\varepsilon_m(z)$ and $h_m^{(2)}(z)$: are (see equation (8-19))

$$\left.\begin{aligned} &G_0(z)_{z\ll 1}=\frac{1}{z},\quad \varepsilon_0(z)_{z\ll 1}=z-\frac{\pi}{2};\quad G_1(z)_{z\ll 1}\approx\frac{1}{z^2},\\ &\varepsilon_1(z)_{z\ll 1}\approx\frac{z^3}{3}-\frac{\pi}{2};\\ &G_2(z)_{z\ll 2}\approx\frac{3}{z^3},\quad \varepsilon_2(z)_{z\ll 2}\approx\frac{z^5}{45}-\frac{\pi}{2};\\ &G_m(z)_{z\ll m}\approx\frac{\overline{m}}{z^{m+1}},\quad \varepsilon_m(z)_{z\ll m}\approx\frac{z^{2m+1}}{\overline{m}^2(m+1)}-\frac{\pi}{2}. \end{aligned}\right\}\quad (8\text{-}29)$$

$$h_m^{(2)}(z)_{z\ll m}\approx\frac{\overline{m}}{z^{m+1}}\,e^{-j\left[\frac{z^{2m+1}}{\overline{m}^2\cdot(2m+1)}-\frac{\pi}{2}\right]},$$

where $\overline{m}=1,3,5\ldots(2m-1)$ and $\overline{m}(0)=1$,

$$\left.\begin{aligned} &G_m(z)_{z\gg m}\approx\frac{1}{z};\ \varepsilon_m(z)_{z\gg m}\approx z-\frac{m+1}{2}\pi,\\ &h_m^{(2)}(z)_{z\gg m}\approx\frac{1}{z}e^{-j\left(z-\frac{m+1}{2}\pi\right)}. \end{aligned}\right\}\quad (8\text{-}30)$$

The exact values of the functions G_m and ε_m for the first orders m have the form:

$$\begin{aligned} &G_0(z)=\frac{1}{z};\ G_1(z)=\frac{\sqrt{1+z^2}}{z^2};\ G_2(z)=\frac{\sqrt{(3-z^2)^2+9z^2}}{z^3};\\ &\varepsilon_0(z)=z-\frac{\pi}{2};\ \varepsilon_1(z)=(z-\arctan z)-\frac{\pi}{2};\\ &\varepsilon_2(z)=\left(z-\arctan\frac{3z}{3-z^2}\right)-\frac{\pi}{2}\qquad (8\text{-}31)\\ &\tan\varepsilon_0(z)=-\cot z;\ \tan\left(\varepsilon_1+\frac{\pi}{2}\right)=\frac{\tan z-z}{z\tan z+1}=\tan\delta_0(z);\\ &\tan\left(\varepsilon_2+\frac{\pi}{2}\right)=\frac{(3-z^2)\tan z-3z}{3-z^2+3z\tan z}. \end{aligned}$$

Expanding the function $u(\vartheta,\psi)$ into a series of spherical harmonics and using expression (8-24), we write the boundary condition (8-23) in the form:

$$\sum_{m=0}^{\infty}\Big[u_{m0}P_m(\vartheta)+\sum_{\nu=1}^{m}(u_{m\nu}\cos\nu\psi+u'_{m\nu}\sin\nu\psi)\cdot P_m^{(\nu)}(\vartheta)\Big]e^{J\omega t}=$$

$$=-k\sum_{m=0}^{\infty}\Big[a_{m0}P_m(\vartheta)+\sum_{\nu=1}^{m}(a_{m\nu}\cos\nu\psi+a'_{m\nu}\sin\nu\psi)\,P_m^{(\nu)}(\vartheta)\Big]\times$$

$$\times D_m(z_0)\,e^{-j\left[\delta_m(z_0)+\frac{\pi}{2}\right]}\,e^{j\omega t}\quad, \qquad (8\text{-}32)$$

where $z_0=kr_0$.

In order to find the expansion coefficients a_{mo}, $a_{m\nu}$ and $a'_{m\nu}$, it is necessary to equate the terms with corresponding subscripts in the expansions on the right- and left-hand sides, respectively, of equation (8-32). The expansion coefficients of the function $u(\vartheta,\psi)$ are defined as integrals over the surface of a sphere S of unit radius*:

$$\left.\begin{aligned}u_{mo}&=\frac{2m+1}{4\pi}\iint_S u(\vartheta,\psi)P_m(\vartheta)dS,\\ u_{m\nu}&=\frac{2m+1}{2\pi}\frac{(m-\nu)!}{(m+\nu)!}\iint_S u(\vartheta,\psi)P_m^{(\nu)}(\vartheta)\cos\nu\psi\cdot dS,\\ u'_{m\nu}&=\frac{2m+1}{2\pi}\frac{(m-\nu)!}{(m+\nu)!}\iint_S u(\vartheta,\psi)P_m^{(\nu)}(\vartheta)\sin\nu\psi\cdot dS.\end{aligned}\right\}\qquad(8\text{-}33)$$

Surface oscillations which correspond to a spherical function with subscripts m and ν are called *oscillations of mode (m, ν)* or simply *the mode (m, ν)*. The amplitude of a standing wave of a zonal oscillation mode on the surface of a sphere is a maximum, equal to u_{mo}, at the poles. For sectorial modes *(m,m)*, the amplitude of the oscillations on the surface of the sphere will in accordance with

---

* V.I. Smirnov, *Kurs vysshei matematiki (A Course of Advanced Mathematics)*. Moscow, Gostekhizdat 1956 (vol.III, ch.I, sect. 201).

(8-12) depend on ϑ and ψ according to the law:

$$u(\vartheta, \psi) = (u_{mm} \cos m\psi + u'_{mm} \cdot \sin m\psi) \overline{m} \cdot \sin^m \vartheta.$$

The maximum amplitude occurs on the equator and is:

$$U_{mm} = \sqrt{u_{mm}^2 + (u'_{mm})^2} \cdot \overline{m}. \tag{8-34}$$

Equating coefficients of identical spherical harmonics in equation (8-32) defines the coefficients a_{mo}, $a_{m\nu}$ and $a'_{m\nu}$ of the velocity potential Φ_m in formula (8-22) in terms of the expansion coefficients of the surface velocity u_{m0}, $u_{m\nu}$ and $u'_{m\nu}$:

$$a_{m0} = \frac{u_{m0}}{kD_m(z_0)\, e^{-j\left[\delta_m(z_0) - \frac{\pi}{2}\right]}}. \tag{8-35}$$

Similar expressions are available for $a_{m\nu}$ and $a'_{m\nu}$. When the velocity $u(\vartheta,\psi)$ on the surface of the sphere is distributed symmetrically about the z axis and is independent of ψ, all the coefficients $a_{m\nu}$ and $a'_{m\nu}$ are zero and $P_m(\vartheta, \psi) = P_m(\vartheta)$. The velocity potential is in this case expressed solely in terms of zonal spherical harmonics in accordance with the fact that the oscillations of the sphere are expressed solely by zonal harmonics. If, in addition, the velocity distribution is symmetrical about the equatorial plane, the solution contains only terms having even subscripts m; if the distribution is not symmetric about the equator, the solution in general contains terms with both even and odd subscripts m.

The general solution of the wave equation for radiation takes the final form:

$$\Phi(r, \vartheta, \psi, t) = \sum_{m=0}^{\infty} \frac{u_{m0} \overline{P}_m(\vartheta, \psi) \cdot G_m(z)\, e^{-j\varepsilon_m(z)}}{kD_m(z_0)\, e^{-j\left[\delta_m(z_0) - \frac{\pi}{2}\right]}} \cdot e^{j\omega t}. \tag{8-36}$$

Using formula (8-30), it can be seen that at great distances the various terms characterizing radiation of different orders diminish in accordance with the same law (in inverse proportion to distance) and their amplitude and phase relationship remain unchanged. However, as can be seen from formulae (8-14) and (8-29), near the radiator terms of higher orders diminish the more quickly, the higher the order m. Thus, in the zone near the sphere, the amplitude and phase relationships of terms of different orders vary considerably.

Rayleigh* found an expression for the velocity potential of a spherical radiator in a slightly different form, and although it is less convenient to use, it was often included in many articles and books. We now consider Rayleigh's expressions and the link between his functions and the functions D_m and δ_m, given by Morse. The velocity potential is defined in the following form by Rayleigh:

$$\Phi_m(r,\vartheta,\psi,t)=\alpha_{m0}\bar{P}_m(\vartheta,\psi)\cdot\frac{e^{j(\omega t-kr)}}{r}f_m(jkr), \tag{8-37}$$

where

$$f(jkr)=\frac{1}{m!}\sum_{\nu=0}^{m}\binom{m}{\nu}\frac{(m+\nu)!}{2^{\nu}(jkr)^{\nu}}.$$

The polynomials $f(jkr)$ were first introduced by Stokes. There is no difficulty in calculating from these expressions the particle velocity in the acoustic field (for the solution of order m):

$$-\frac{\partial\Phi_m}{\partial r}(r,\vartheta,\psi,t)=-\alpha_{m0}\bar{P}_m(\vartheta,\psi)e^{j\frac{m\pi}{2}}\frac{\partial}{\partial r}\left[\frac{e^{-jkr}}{r}f_m(jkr)\right]\cdot e^{j\omega t}=$$
$$=\alpha_{m0}\bar{P}_m(\vartheta,\psi)e^{j\frac{m\pi}{2}}\frac{e^{-jkr}}{r}F_m(jkr)e^{j\omega t},$$

where

$$F_m(jkr)=\frac{1}{m!}\sum_{\nu=0}^{m}\binom{m}{\nu}\frac{(m+\nu)!}{2^{\nu}(jkr)^{\nu}}(1+\nu+jkr)=$$
$$=\frac{\bar{m}(m+1)}{(jkr)^m}\left[1+jkr+\frac{m^2(jkr)^2}{(m+1)(2m+1)}+\dots\right].$$

* Lord Rayleigh, *Theory of Sound*, New York: Dover Publications (see vol.II, sect. 324).

The first few Stokes and Rayleigh polynomials $f_m(y)$ and $F_m(y)$ have the form

$$f_0(y)=1,\ f_1(y)=1+\frac{1}{y};\ f_2(y)=1+\frac{3}{y}+\frac{3}{y^2};$$
$$f_3(y)=1+\frac{6}{y}+\frac{15}{y^2}+\frac{15}{y^3};$$
$$F_0(y)=y+1;\ F_1(y)=y+2+\frac{2}{y};\ F_2(y)=y+4+\frac{9}{y}+\frac{9}{y^2};$$
$$F_3(y)=y+7+\frac{27}{y}+\frac{60}{y^2}+\frac{60}{y^3}.$$

The velocity potential expansion coefficients α_{m0} in (8-37) are obtained in the same way as for (8-35):

$$\alpha_{m0}=\frac{u_{m0}\,e^{jkr_0}}{e^{j\frac{m\pi}{2}}F_m(jkr_0)}.$$

Similar expressions are obtained for $\alpha_{m\nu}$ and $\alpha'_{m\nu}$ if we substitute $u_{m\nu}$ and $u'_{m\nu}$ for u_{m0}. There is no difficulty in expressing the Rayleigh functions $F_m(jz_0)$ in terms of the functions $D_m(z_0)$ and $\delta_m(z_0)$:

$$\frac{F_m(jz_0)\,e^{-jz_0}\,e^{\frac{jm\pi}{2}}}{z_0^2}=D_m(z_0)\,e^{-j\delta_m(z_0)}.$$

This expression gives the values of the complex functions $F_m(jz_0)$ in terms of the tabulated functions D_m and δ_m. Using formulae (8-19) and (8-37), we also find:

$$\frac{fm(jz)\,e^{-jz}\cdot e^{j\frac{(m+1)\pi}{2}}}{z}=G_m(z)\,e^{-j\varepsilon_m(z)}.$$

Lower Order Solutions of the Wave Equation

We will now consider the simplest radiators, those corresponding to the values $m=0,1,2$.

Zero order radiator (m = 0) If in formula (8-36) all the constants $u_{m\nu}$, except u_{00}, are zero then only the zero order term remains in the series expansion of the velocity potential in spherical harmonics:

$$\Phi_0(r,t) = \frac{u_{00} G_0(z) \cdot e^{-j\varepsilon_0(z)}}{jk D_0(z_0) e^{-j\delta_0(z_0)}} \cdot e^{j\omega t}.$$

The constant u_{00}, in accordance with (8-33), is the mean normal surface velocity.

Using formulae (8-16), (8-28) and (8-31), it is found that

$$\Phi_0(r,t) = \frac{u_{00} \frac{e^{-jz}}{z} \; je^{j\omega t}}{jk \frac{1+jz_0}{z_0^2} \cdot e^{-jz_0}} = \left(\frac{4\pi r_0^2 u_{00}}{1+jkr_0}\right) \frac{e^{j[\omega t - k(r-r_0)]}}{4\pi r} =$$

$$= \frac{A}{4\pi r} e^{j(\omega t - kr)}. \tag{8-38}$$

The quantity A represents the strength of a point radiator:

$$A = \frac{4\pi r_0^2 u_{00}}{1+jkr_0} e^{jkr_0}.$$

It should be borne in mind that the expression for the potential contains the strength A and not the volume velocity $\dot{X}_0 = 4\pi r_0^2 \cdot u_{00}$. The value of A is only approximately equal to the volume velocity in the case of long waves $(kr_0 \ll 1)$. For short waves, A can be much larger than $\dot{X}_0$ and may differ from it in phase.

If the velocity distribution over the sphere is completely defined by the function $P_m(\vartheta), (m \neq 0)$, then, in accordance with formulae (8-33), $u_{00} = 0$, i.e. there is no zero order radiation, but since $u_{m0} \neq 0$ there is radiation characterized by the spherical function $P_m(\vartheta)$.

First order radiator (m = 1). Considering formulae (8-11) and (8-12), we assume that only the constants a_{10}, a_{11} and a'_{11} are non-zero, and then from expression (8-22) we get:

$$\Phi_1(r, \vartheta, \psi, t) = [a_{10}\cos\vartheta + (a_{11}\cos\psi + a'_{11}\sin\psi)\sin\vartheta]\, G_1(z)\, e^{-j\varepsilon_1(z)} e^{j\omega t}. \quad (8\text{-}39)$$

Using equations (8-16), (8-19) and (8-31), we find:

$$G_1(z)\, e^{-j\varepsilon_1(z)} = j\,\frac{1+jkr}{k^2 r^2}\, e^{j(\omega t - kr)}.$$

The first term in expression (8-39) depends only on the polar angle ϑ:

$$\Phi_{10}(r, \vartheta, t) = j\frac{a_{10}}{k^2}\cos\vartheta\,(1+jkr)\,\frac{e^{j(\omega t - kr)}}{r^2}. \quad (8\text{-}40)$$

There is an expression similar to this for the potential of an acoustic dipole (see Chapter IV), the axis of which lies in the direction $\vartheta = 0$, and in this case the quantity $\frac{a_{10}}{k^2}$ corresponds to the moment of the dipole. If the velocity distribution on the surface is governed by an arbitrary law, the constants a_{10}, a_{11} and a'_{11} can be found by formulae (8-33) and (8-35).

It will now be shown that the second term of equation (8-39)

$$\Phi_{11}(r, \vartheta, \psi, t) = j\,\frac{a_{11}\cos\psi + a'_{11}\sin\psi}{k^2}\,\sin\vartheta\,(1+jkr)\,\frac{e^{j(\omega t - kr)}}{r^2} \quad (8\text{-}41)$$

represents the radiation of a dipole whose axis is shifted 90° relative to the axis of the first dipole. The expression $(a_{11}\cos\psi + a'_{11}\sin\psi)$ can be written in the form:

$$a_{11}\cos\psi + a'_{11}\sin\psi = \sqrt{a_{11}^2 + (a'_{11})^2}\left[\frac{a_{11}}{\sqrt{a_{11}^2 + (a'_{11})^2}}\cos\psi + \frac{a'_{11}}{\sqrt{a_{11}^2 + (a'_{11})^2}}\sin\psi\right] = A_1\cos(\psi - \psi_1),$$

where $\tan\psi_1 = \frac{a'_{11}}{a_{11}}$. The part of expression (8-41) which depends on the angle is then

$$\cos(\psi - \psi_1) \cdot \sin\vartheta.$$

A new system of polar coordinates is now required and this is obtained by turning the z axis through 90° in the plane of the azimuth ψ_1 (Fig. 63). In the new system the polar coordinates of each point P are ϑ' and ψ'. Using the cosine formula, it is found from the spherical triangle ABP (Fig. 64) that

$$\cos a = \cos b \cdot \cos c + \\ + \sin b \cdot \sin c \cdot \cos\alpha.$$

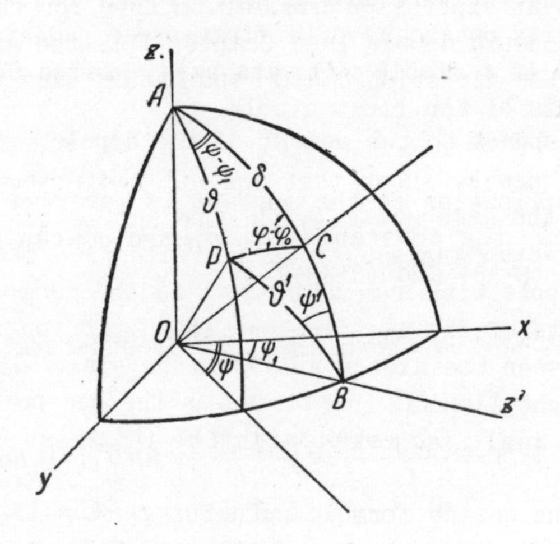

Fig. 63

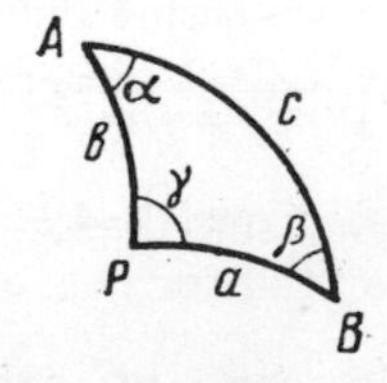

Fig. 64

Putting

$$a=\vartheta',\ b=\vartheta,\ c=90^\circ,$$
$$\alpha=\psi-\psi_1,\ \beta=\psi',$$

we get:

$$\cos\vartheta'=\cos(\psi-\psi_1)\sin\vartheta.$$

The expression for the velocity potential in the new system of coordinates takes the form:

$$\Phi_{11}(r,\vartheta',t)=j\frac{A_1}{k^2}\cdot\cos\vartheta'(1+jkr)\frac{e^{j(\omega t-kr)}}{r^2}. \qquad (8\text{-}42)$$

Since this expression is identical with (8-40), it is clear that the second term in the general expression (8-39) for the velocity potential of a first-order radiator gives the radiation of a dipole with its axis shifted 90° relative to the axis of the first dipole.

It will now be shown that the net radiation of two dipoles in the same phase (with constant a_1 and a'_1 and axes inclined at an angle 90°) is equivalent to the radiation of one dipole with a moment equal to the geometric sum of the moments of the two dipoles, the direction of its axis lying between the axes Z and Z' in the plane ZOZ'. We take the straight line OC in Fig. 63 as the new polar axis and call the angle OC makes with the OZ axis δ.

Using the cosine formula and putting $PC=\theta$, $AC=\delta$, and $\sphericalangle ACP=\varphi-\varphi_0$, we have from the spherical triangles APC and BPC:

$$\cos\vartheta=[\cos\delta\cdot\cos\theta+\sin\delta\sin\theta\cos(\varphi-\varphi_0)],$$
$$\cos\vartheta'=\{\sin\delta\cos\theta+\cos\delta\sin\theta\cos[\pi-(\varphi-\varphi_0)]\}.$$

Using an expression of type (8-42) for the second term in expression (8-39), we find for the entire spherical harmonic:

$$a_1[\cos\delta\cdot\cos\theta+\sin\delta\sin\theta\cos(\varphi-\varphi_0)]+$$
$$+a_1'[\sin\delta\cos\theta-\cos\delta\sin\theta\cos(\varphi-\varphi_0)]=(a_1\cos\delta+$$
$$+a_1'\sin\delta)\cos\theta+(a_1\sin\delta-a_1'\cos\delta)\sin\theta\cos(\varphi-\varphi_0). \quad (8\text{-}43)$$

If it is required that $(a_1\sin\delta-a_1'\cos\delta)$ be zero, the velocity potential becomes independent of the azimuthal angle $(\varphi-\varphi_0)$ relative to the polar axis OC, i.e. it is expressed by an equation like (8-40) and thus represents the potential of a dipole with its axis along OC. In this case the angle of the new axis OC to OZ is found from the expression:

$$\tan\delta=\frac{a_1'}{a_1}. \quad (8\text{-}44)$$

The expression for the spherical harmonic (8-43) can now be put into the form

$$\sqrt{a_1^2+(a_1')^2}\cos(\delta-\alpha)\cos\theta=\sqrt{a_1^2+(a_1')^2}\cos\theta,$$

since

$$\alpha=\operatorname{arc}\tan\frac{a_1'}{a_1}=\delta.$$

It is easy to see that the total velocity potential is that of a dipole with a moment

$$A_1=\frac{\sqrt{a_1^2+(a_1')^2}}{k^2},$$

the axis of which is inclined to the OZ axis at an angle δ defined by expression (8-44).

Second order radiator ($m = 2$). Suppose we put $m = 2$ in the general formula (8-22) and avail ourselves of expressions (8-11), (8-12) and (8-31). We then get for the velocity potential of a second order radiator:

$$\Phi_2(r,\vartheta,\psi,t)=\Big[a_{20}\frac{3\cos^2\vartheta-1}{2}+$$

$$+3(a_{21}\cos\psi+a'_{21}\sin\psi)\cos\vartheta\sin\vartheta+3(a_{22}\cos 2\psi+ \\ +a'_{22}\sin 2\psi)\sin^2\vartheta\Big]\Big[\frac{3}{kr}+j\Big(1+\frac{3}{k^2r^2}\Big)\Big]\frac{e^{j(\omega t-kr)}}{r}. \quad (8\text{-}45)$$

The first term in the expression for the spherical harmonic $P_2(\vartheta,\psi)$, which depends solely on ϑ (a zonal second order harmonic), vanishes if

$$\cos\vartheta=\pm\frac{1}{\sqrt{3}}\ (\vartheta=55^\circ \text{ and } \vartheta=125^\circ).$$

This implies that there is no sound radiation in any direction on the surface of a cone of vertex angle equal to 55°. The surface displacement of a second order zonal radiator is illustrated in Fig. 65a, with maximum positive (dotted line) and negative (dots and dashes) displacements indicated. The regions near the poles (the two polar caps) oscillate in phase; the equatorial zone from $\vartheta=55^\circ$ to $\vartheta=125^\circ$ oscillates in inverse phase to the polar regions; the amplitude at the equator is half that at the poles. In one half period the streamlines in the zone near the sphere, where $kr\ll 1$, have the form of fountains which leave the polar caps and go into the equatorial zone(Fig. 65b), whilst in the next half period the direction is reversed. A typical real example of a zonal radiator is a droplet or bubble of gas in a fluid oscillating in accordance with the law $P_2(\cos\vartheta)$. In this case the sphere alternately takes the approximate form of an extended ellipsoid of rotation, and of a flattened ellipsoid of rotation (Fig. 65a). The oscillations of a sphere of this type are called *zonal second order modes of oscillation.*

The third term in expression (8-45) contains a spherical harmonic of the type

$$Y_{22}(\vartheta,\psi)=(a_{22}\cos 2\psi+a'_{22}\sin 2\psi)\sin^2\vartheta= \\ =A_{22}\cos(2\psi-\psi_{22})\sin^2\vartheta, \quad (8\text{-}46)$$

$$\text{where } A_{22}=\sqrt{a_{22}^2+(a'_{22})^2} \text{ and } \tan\psi_{22}=\frac{a'_{22}}{a_{22}}.$$

The angle ψ_{22} can be taken as the initial angle of reference and we can put $\psi_{22}=0$. Thus, a radiator of this type is characterized by a relationship between the velocity potential and the angular parameters of the form:

$$Y_{22}(\vartheta, \psi) = A_{22}\cos 2\psi \cdot \sin^2\vartheta.$$

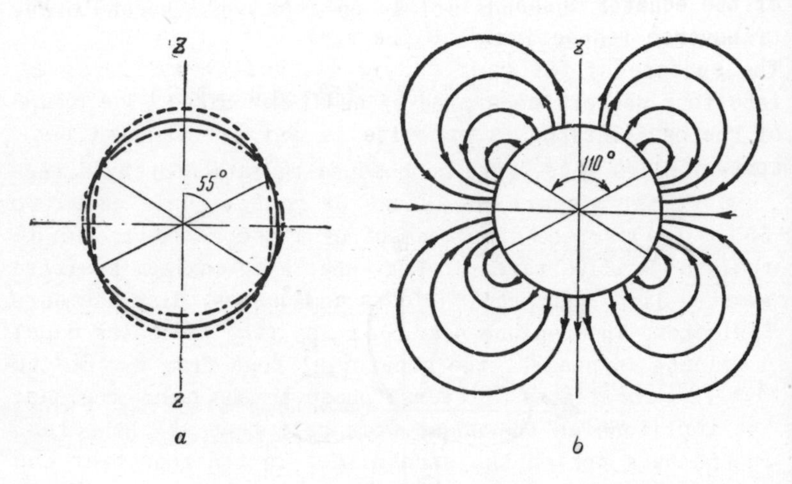

Fig. 65

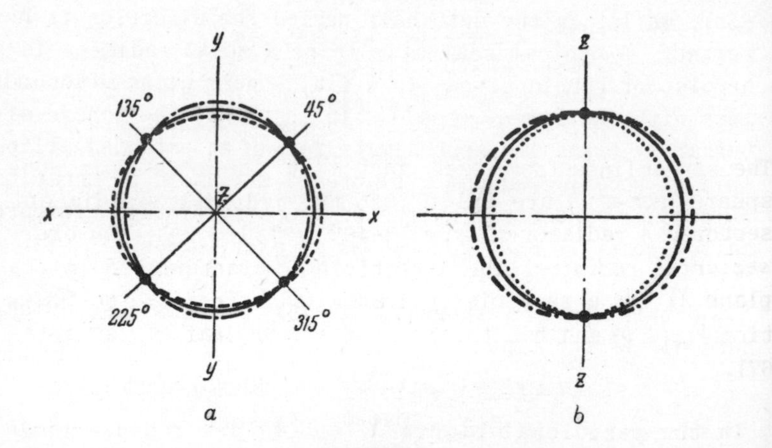

Fig. 66

It is obvious that $Y_{22}(\vartheta, \psi)$ vanishes at the four azimuthal angles $\psi = 45°$, 135, 225, and 315°. In the meridional planes defined by these angles $\Phi_{22} = 0$. The radial velocity and acoustic pressure are zero along these directions and there is no radiation of sound. The distortion of the surface of the oscillating sphere in the plane of the equator is shown in Fig. 66a, and that in the planes transverse respectively to the axes X and Y in Fig. 66b. The surface of the radiator is divided by nodal curves into four sectors separated by nodal meridians. The phase of the oscillations is opposite in any two adjacent sectors.

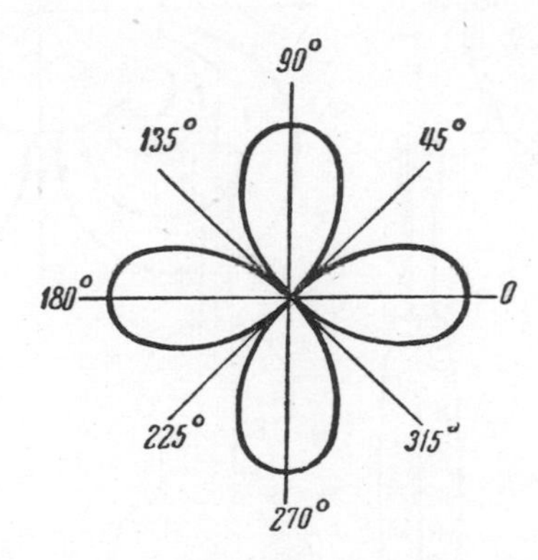

Fig. 67

The streamlines from each sector in the zone near the sphere $(kr \ll 1)$ are split into two and go into adjacent sectors. A radiator of type (8-46) is called *a second order sectorial radiator*. The directivity characteristic in the plane XY for a sectorial radiator is defined by the function $Y_{22}(\vartheta, \psi)$ and has the form of a four-leaf clover (Fig. 67).

In the meridional planes XZ and YZ the radiation is maximum near the equator $\left(\vartheta = \frac{\pi}{2}\right)$ and zero in the polar directions $(\vartheta = 0;\ \vartheta = \pi)$.

Sectorial modes of oscillation can be produced by rigid spherical shells, droplets and air bubbles in a liquid. Sectorial modes are also possible in vibrations of bells and cylinders. Sectorial oscillating systems in general have an even number of sectors (4, 6, 8, ... $2n$), the four sector type (second order oscillations) being a special case. Backhaus' investigations showed that at low frequencies, up to 200 c/s, the body of a violin oscillates in a way more or less reminiscent of the second order sectorial mode, the nodal lines lying along the middle of the front and rear sounding boards and along the middle of the side walls (Fig. 68).

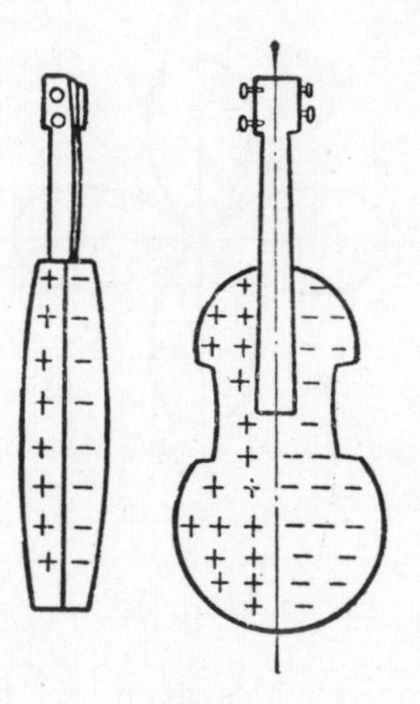

Fig. 68

The second term in expression (8-45) contains a spherical function of the type

$$Y_{21}(\vartheta,\psi) = (a_{21}\cos\psi + a'_{21}\sin\psi)\sin\vartheta\cos\vartheta =$$
$$= A_{21}\cos(\psi - \psi_{21})\sin\vartheta\cos\vartheta.$$

Without loss of generality, it can be assumed that $\psi_{21} = 0$. This type of radiator is known as a *tesseral second order radiator*. It is easy to show that a radiator of this type

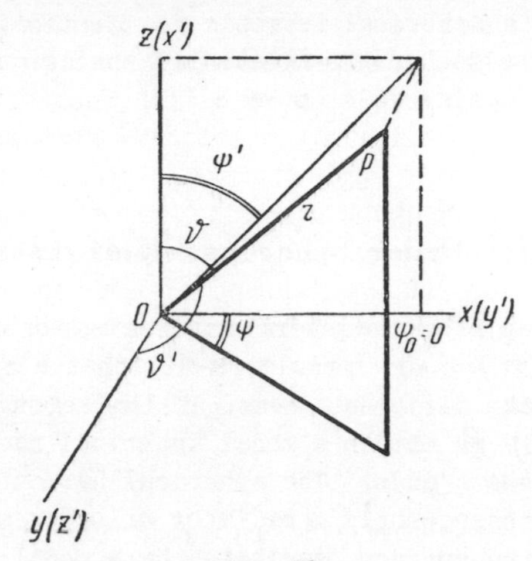

Fig. 69

is identical with a sectorial radiator whose axis has been turned through 90° in such a way that the new axis Z' occupies the position of the old axis Y (Fig. 69). The X' axis then occupies the position of the old Z axis, and the Y' axis, that of the old X axis. Putting ϑ' for the new polar angle and ψ' for the new azimuth, we express the Cartesian coordinates of the point P in terms of the old and new polar angles:

$$x = r \cdot \sin\vartheta \cos\psi = r \sin\vartheta' \cos\psi',$$
$$y = r \cdot \sin\vartheta \sin\psi = r \cos\vartheta',$$
$$z = r \cdot \cos\vartheta = r \sin\vartheta' \cos\psi'.$$

It is found from these expressions that:

$$\sin\vartheta \cdot \cos\psi = \sin\vartheta' \cos\psi',$$
$$\cos\vartheta = \sin\vartheta' \cos\psi'.$$

Putting $\psi_{21} = 0$ and substituting the expressions for the new angular coordinates in terms of the old into the expression for $Y_{21}(\vartheta, \psi)$ we get:

$$Y_{21}(\vartheta,\psi) = A_{21} \sin\vartheta' \sin\psi' \sin\vartheta' \cos\psi' =$$
$$= \frac{A_{21}}{2} \sin 2\psi' \sin^2\vartheta' = \frac{A_{21}}{2} \cos\left(2\psi' - \frac{\pi}{2}\right) \sin^2\vartheta'.$$

The form of this spherical harmonic is identical with that in (8-46) for a sectorial radiator if the azimuthal angle of reference ψ_{22} is taken to be $\pi/2$.

Higher Order Spherical Radiators

It can be seen from the general expression for the spherical function $Y_m(\vartheta, \psi)$ (formula (8-8)) that a radiator of order m can take different forms. If the second subscript is zero ($\nu = 0$), we obtain a zonal spherical radiator symmetric about the z axis. The spherical harmonic $P_m(\vartheta)$ has m roots; consequently, a radiator of order m will have $m+1$ zones on the surface, separated by m nodal circles in planes parallel to the equator. The oscillations in any two adjacent zones are always opposite in phase. If m is odd, one of the nodal circles must necessarily be the circle $\vartheta = \pi/2$, i.e. the equator.

If $\nu = m$ we have a sectorial radiator with $2m$ meridional nodal curves (traces on the sphere of m meridional planes). The surface is divided into $2m$ sectors, and the oscillation in each sector is opposite in phase to that in the sector on either side. It is clear that a factor of the type $(a_{m\nu} \cos \nu\psi + a'_{m\nu} \sin \nu\psi)$ can be written in the form

$$A_{m\nu} \cdot \cos(\nu\psi - \psi_{m\nu}).$$

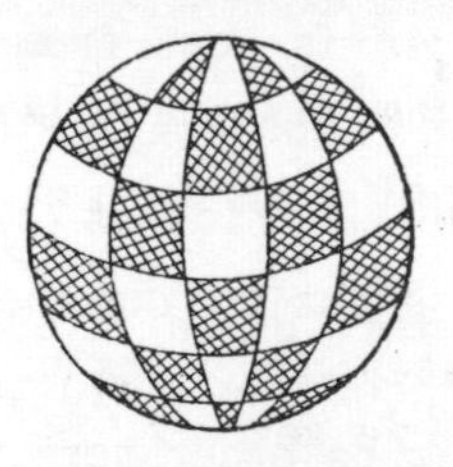

Fig. 70

In the general case of a radiator of mode (m,ν) there

are $m-\nu$ nodal circles parallel to the equator and 2ν meridional nodal curves, i.e. ν meridional planes. The surface of the oscillating sphere thus is divided into a number of spherical quadrangles or triangles which are separated by nodal curves (Fig. 70). It is of interest to point out that if $m>2$ the tesseral radiators can no longer be obtained by rotating a sectorial radiator through 90°. This transformation is only possible for a second order radiator in which case one of the nodal meridians on rotation through 90°, is converted into a nodal circle, coinciding with the equator, so that a "tesseral" oscillation mode is obtained having one nodal meridian.

The Distant Field of a Complex Spherical Radiator

We now inquire into the nature of the distant or radiation field of a spherical radiator which is made up of radiators of different orders having equal or gradually diminishing amplitudes u_{m0}. In expression (8-36) for the velocity potential it is, as we have seen, necessary to put

$$G_m(z) \underset{z \to \infty}{\longrightarrow} \frac{1}{z}; \quad \varepsilon_m(z) \underset{z \to \infty}{\longrightarrow} z - \frac{m+1}{2}\pi.$$

The quantities $\frac{1}{D_m(z_0)}$ appear in the individual terms of the sum. If $z_0 \ll 1$, it is seen from formula (8-21) that the term will be maximum in which z_0 is of least degree; this is the term with the coefficient $\frac{1}{D_0(z_0)} \sim z_0^2$ (a term of zero order), of the form given in equation (8-38). Thus for long waves, the acoustic field far from the radiator is dominated by the zero order term which depends on the mean volume velocity of the oscillations over the surface of the sphere. Coefficients $\frac{1}{D_m(z_0)}$ of higher orders $m=1$, $2, 3, \ldots$, which are proportional respectively to $z_0^3, z_0^4, \ldots, z^{m+2}$, are small in comparison with the zero order term. If $u_{00}=0$, the main role in the radiation will be played by the next term in order. This conclusion makes it possible to estimate the acoustic field of a non-uniform radiator at great distances; even with identical velocity amplitudes u_{m0} on the surface of the sphere the major role is played by radiation of the lowest order m, no matter how complicated the motion of the surface of the sphere actually is. This conclusion applies of course only when z_0 is small.

If the oscillations of an actual spherical shell are caused by a periodic force of frequency ω, standing waves are formed on the surface of the shell, and these waves can be analysed into spherical harmonics of different orders. The length of these standing waves λ' is always less than the length of the circumference $(\lambda' < 2\pi r_0)$, or equal to it. The parameter z_0 can be written in the form:

$$z_0 = kr_0 = \frac{\omega r_0}{c'} \cdot \frac{c'}{c} = \frac{2\pi r_0}{\lambda'} \cdot \frac{c'}{c},$$

where c' is the speed of bending waves in the shell. In metallic shells which are not too thin, c' is usually large and is often approximately equal to the speed c in the surrounding medium or is even larger than c. In such a case it may well be that the condition $z_0 \ll 1$ cannot be satisfied for spherical shells oscillating in a gas or fluid, and the preponderance of zero order radiation cannot occur; the radiation acquires a directional character. A good illustration of these considerations is the formula for the speed of bending waves in a plane plate:

$$c' = \sqrt{\frac{2\pi}{\sqrt{12}}} \cdot \sqrt{af\sqrt{\frac{E}{\rho'}}}; \qquad (8\text{-}47)$$

where a is the thickness of the plate, f the frequency, E

Young's modulus, and ρ' the density of the material of the plate*. The speed of the wave in a shell of spherical shape is given by a more complicated expression, and is considerably larger than that calculated by formula (8-47). For a steel plate, formula (8-47) gives $c' = 1\cdot 64 \times 10^5$ cm/sec if $a = 1$ cm and $f = 3 \times 10^4$ c/s if $f = 100$ c/s, $c' \approx 10^4$ cm/sec. Thus, at low acoustic frequencies it may well be that $c' < c$ (e.g. if the fluid is water) and thus it is sometimes possible for the condition $z_0 \ll 1$ to be fulfilled for a plate or a cylindrical shell.

Natural Oscillations Inside a Spherical Cavity

In this case the velocity potential is best written in the form (8-17) (by putting $B_n = 0$, since $n_m(0) = -\infty$ but the potential must be of finite value at the centre of the sphere)

$$\Phi_m(r,\vartheta,\psi,t) = A_{m0}\bar{P}_m(\vartheta,\psi)\, j_m(z)\, e^{j\omega t}. \qquad (8\text{-}48)$$

The radial component of velocity on the internal surface of a rigid sphere must be zero, so when $z = z_0$,

$$q_m(r_0) = -k\left.\frac{\partial\Phi_m}{\partial z}\right|_{r=r_0} = -kA_{m0}\bar{P}_m(\vartheta,\psi)\cdot\left.\frac{d}{dz}j_m(z)\right|_{r=r_0} = 0.$$

The condition $\frac{dj_m(z)}{dz} = 0$ defines the frequency of the mth order natural oscillation. Using formula (8-21a) we find the equation:

$$m j_{m-1}(z_0) - (m+1)\, j_{m+1}(z_0) = 0 \qquad (8\text{-}49)$$

or using (8-15),

$$mJ_{m-\frac{1}{2}}(z_0) = (m+1)\, J_{m+\frac{3}{2}}(z_0). \qquad (8\text{-}49a)$$

From tables of Bessel functions of half-integral order, we can find the roots of this equation. In view of ex-

* Formula (8-47) also expresses with sufficient accuracy the speed of bending waves in the direction transverse to the axis of a cylindrical shell.

pression (8-26), the condition for the natural frequencies can also be represented in the form:

$$(2m+1)\,D_m(z_0)\sin\delta_m(z_0)=0$$

or since

$$D_m(z_0)\neq 0,\text{ then }\sin\delta_m(z_0)=0,$$

whence

$$\delta_m(z_0)=n\pi.$$

Thus, from tables of the functions $\delta_m(z)$ the values $z_0=\frac{\omega r_0}{c}$ corresponding to the natural frequencies of the cavity oscillations can be found directly. The first roots can be found approximately from the tables for δ_m in the book by Morse. More exact values of the roots z_0 can be found from equation (8-49).

Assuming $m = 0$ in formula (8-49) for the natural oscillations of zero order, we get the equation $j_1(z)=0$ or

$$\frac{\sin z_0}{z_0^2}-\frac{\cos z_0}{z_0}=0,\qquad\text{whence}\qquad \tan z_0=z_0. \tag{8-50}$$

The first three roots of this transcendental equation are:

$$z_{01}=4{\cdot}493,\qquad z_{02}=7{\cdot}725,\qquad z_{03}=10{\cdot}904.$$

Each of these roots corresponds to a natural oscillation mode (0, n). For a root of the type z_{0n} we always have (n–1) roots less than z_{0n}, so that at the same frequency equation (8-50) is satisfied at values $r<r_0$. Thus the condition that the radial velocity vanishes is satisfied not only on the spherical shell itself, but also on (n–1) internal nodal spheres, i.e. there are n nodal spheres.

For example, if $z_{02}=7{\cdot}725=\frac{\omega_{02}r_0}{c}$ we satisfy equations (8-50), but at the same frequency ω_{02} equation (8-50) is also satisfied if $z_{01}=\frac{\omega_{02}\cdot r_1}{c}=4{\cdot}493$, that is, on a sphere of smaller radius r_1; the radius of the internal nodal sphere is

$$r_1=\frac{z_{01}}{z_{02}}r_0=0{\cdot}581\,r_0.$$

For the root z_{03} two nodal spheres are obtained with radii:

$$r_1'=\frac{z_{01}}{z_{03}}\cdot r_0=0{\cdot}413\,r_0 \text{ and } r_1''=\frac{z_{02}}{z_{03}}r_0=0{\cdot}708\,r_0.$$

The subscript n indicates the number of nodal spheres including the spherical shell itself, and it is also equal to the number of spherical annuli separated by the nodal spherical surfaces.

For natural oscillation modes of type (1, n) we obtain the equation for the natural frequencies from expression (8-49) by putting m = 1:

$$2z_1\,j_2(z_1)=j_0(z_1),$$

from which by formula (8-16) we find:

$$\tan z_1=\frac{2z_1}{2-z_1^2}\,. \tag{8-51}$$

The first three roots of this equation have the values:

$$z_{11}=2{\cdot}082,\ z_{12}=5{\cdot}940,\ z_{13}=9{\cdot}206.$$

The first root of equation (8-50) for radial oscillations corresponds to a wavelength $\lambda_{01}=0{\cdot}7(2r_0)$, whilst the first root of (8-51) gives $\lambda_{11}=1{\cdot}59(2r_0)$. This oscillation mode represents motion from one hemisphere into the other across the equatorial plane $\vartheta=\frac{\pi}{2}$, the plane being an antinode of velocity and a pressure node, since

$$P_1\left(\frac{\pi}{2}\right)=\cos\frac{\pi}{2}=0.$$

Oscillations of this kind are rather like those in a tube which is closed at both ends, where, as is known, $\lambda = 2l$. In the case of the sphere (assuming $l = 2r_0$) we have for the smallest wavelength $\lambda_{11} = 1.59l$. This can be explained by considering a short tube of length l with rounded hemispherical ends. In such a tube the effective elasticity is increased (owing to the decrease in volume of the end parts) whilst the effective mass, primarily dependent on the mass of fluid in the zone of maximum velocities, is almost unchanged. Consequently, the natural frequency must be increased.

The condition (8-49) provides the values of all the natural frequencies $\omega_{nm} = \frac{z_{mn} \cdot c}{r_0}$ and makes it possible to find the radii of the internal nodal spheres. It should be borne in mind that oscillations of order m can correspond to any type of spherical harmonic (8-8):

$$a_{m0}\bar{P}_m(\vartheta,\psi) = a_{m0} \cdot P_m(\vartheta) + \sum_{\nu=1}^{m} (a_{m\nu} \cos \nu\psi + a'_{m\nu} \sin \nu\psi) P_m^{(\nu)}(\vartheta).$$

Individual cells can therefore be formed inside the spherical cavity which are bounded not only by the spherical nodal surfaces (being as it were rigid boundaries of these cells), but also by nodal cones and nodal meridional planes. The number of meridional nodal planes is equal to ν, and the number of nodal cones to $(m - \nu)$, (here one pair of cones always degenerates into an axial line, $\vartheta = 0$, $\vartheta = \pi$).

The structure of the cells into which the sphere is divided in the presence of mth order oscillations can also be determined from the condition of maximum oscillatory velocity, which corresponds to zero acoustic pressure, i.e. zero velocity potential. This condition will be satisfied for zonal modes if

$$P_m(\cos\vartheta) = 0 \quad \text{or} \quad j_m(k_{mn}r_n) = 0. \tag{8-52}$$

In accordance with formula (8-9), $P_m(x)$ is a polynominal

of degree m and argument $x = \cos\vartheta$. Polynomials of this type have m real roots, which are equal in pairs and have different signs. Thus, surfaces of zero pressure are pairs of cones whose vertices touch at the centre and which have a common axis; accordingly the cells are bounded by such conical surfaces of constant polar angle. As regards the radius, the boundaries are defined from the condition $j_m(k_{mn}r_n) = 0$, where r_n assumes a number of discrete values less than r_0.

The condition of zero pressure at the various boundaries of the cells has the following form for oscillatory modes depending on the associated Legendre polynomials:

$$\left.\begin{aligned} j_m(k_{mn}r_n) = 0, \quad \text{or} \quad P_m^{(\nu)}(\vartheta) = 0, \\ \text{or} \qquad a_{m\nu}\cos\nu\psi + a'_{m\nu}\sin\nu\psi = 0. \end{aligned}\right\} \tag{8-52a}$$

The third condition defines the location of ν meridional planes on which the pressure is zero. Since, in accordance with (8-10)

$$P_m^{(\nu)}(\vartheta) = \sin(\vartheta)\frac{d^\nu P_m(x)}{dx^\nu},$$

we always have the solution $\vartheta = 0, \pi$; thus, the axis is always a line of zero pressure. The ν order derivatives of $P_m(x)$ are polynomials of degree $(m - \nu)$ in x. The condition $\frac{d^\nu P_m}{dx^\nu} = 0$ provides an equation of degree $(m - \nu)$ in x, which has $(m - \nu)$ roots which define $(m - \nu)$ cones of zero pressure. As in the case of zonal modes, these cones touch at the centre. Thus, for modes depending on associated Legendre polynomials, the bounding surfaces of the individual oscillation cells are spheres (the number of which varies between 1 and m), meridional planes (ν in number), and cones (of number $m - \nu$) all being surfaces of zero pressure. If $(m - \nu)$ is even, one pair of cones degenerates into the equatorial plane.

The condition (8-49) gives all the natural frequencies ω_{mn} corresponding to the values of the subscripts m and n. However, the nature of the oscillations for the given ω_{mn}, can obviously be quite different depending on the value of ν (i.e. depending on the number of nodal planes). Thus, it is necessary to define the oscillation mode of a spherical cavity by three subscripts $m, n,$ and ν. The roots which have been found for equations (8-50) and (8-51) for $m = 0$ and $m = 1$ correspond to the modes $(0, n, 0)$ and $(1, n, 0)$. The total number of different geometric configurations for given n and m is equal to the number of constants in equation (8-8), i.e. $(2m + 1)$. The configurations corresponding to the constants $a_{m\nu}$ and $a'_{m\nu}$, differ only by a 90° rotation about the z axis. Therefore, there will only be $(m+1)$ essentially different configurations. The natural frequencies of a spherical cavity have been calculated by Ferris* up to high orders for various values of n and m. Table 8 shows values $z_{mn} = \frac{2\pi f_{mn}}{c} r_0$.

It should be pointed out that zones on the surface of a spherical radiator can be identified, just as in (8-52), by equating to zero the individual terms in the spherical function $\overline{P}_m(\vartheta,\psi)$ (see (8-52) and (8-52a)). These conditions imply that the radial component of velocity vanishes on certain curves on the sphere (see (8-23)). If $m = 1$, we obtain for a spherical radiator, from the condition $P_1(\vartheta) = 0$, two zones on the surface, separated by a nodal circle (the equator). A spherical resonator in the mode (1, 0, 0) has only a nodal cone which has degenerated into a line (the polar axis), apart from the nodal surface $r = r_0$. No velocities transverse to the axis are present and the whole sphere is a single integral resonant cell in which there is flow from one polar region to the other and back. If we take the condition $P_1(\vartheta) = 0$, as the criterion of division, the equator is a surface of zero pressure and divides the sphere into two cells.

* H. Ferris, *J. Acoust. Soc. Amer.* 24, 57, 1952.

If $m = 2$ and $\nu = 0$, the radiator has three zones, namely, from 0 to 55°, from 55°, to 125°, and from 125° to 180°. For the natural oscillations of a cavity, in the zonal mode (2,0,0), we have the condition $P_2(\vartheta) = 0$; it defines a cone with an angle 55° at the vertex over the surface of which $p = 0$; the velocities are maximum on this surface along the normal to the cone. During an oscillation the medium moves from the polar regions $0 < \vartheta < 55°$ and $125° < \vartheta < 180°$ into the equatorial region $55° < \vartheta < 125°$ and back. The particles move tangentially along the line $\vartheta = 0, \pi$ and over the plane $\vartheta = \frac{\pi}{2}$.

TABLE 8

m \ n	1	2	3	4	5	6	7
0	4·49341	7·72523	10·9042	14·0663	17·2207	20·3714	23·5194
1	2·08158	5·94036	9·20586	12·4046	15·5793	18·7428	21·8997
2	3·34209	7·28990	10·6140	13·8463	17·0431	20·2219	23·3960
3	4·51408	8·58376	11·9729	15·2446	18·4682	21·6667	24·8503
4	5·64670	9·84043	13·2956	16·6094	19·8625	23·0829	24·8503
5	6·75643	11·0703	14·5906	17·9473	21·2312	24·4749	
6	7·85107	12·2794	15·8633	19·2623	22·5781		
7	8·93489	13·4721	17·1176	20·5596	23·9069		
8	10·0102	14·6513	18·3565	21·8401			
9	11·0791	15·8193	19·5819	23·1067			
10	12·1423	16·9776	20·7660	24·3608			
11	13·2024	18·1276	22·0000				
12	14·2580	19·2704	23·1950				
13	15·3108	20·4065	24·3821				
14	16·3604	21·5372					
15	17·4079	22·6625					
16	18·4527	23·7832					
17	19·4964	24·8995					
18	20·5379						
19	21·5779						
20	22·6165						
21	23·6534						
22	24·6899						

The Energy Flow in the Field of a Spherical Radiator

The intensity vector J, representing the flow of energy across a unit area, is defined as the mean product of the pressure p and the particle velocity q of the medium over a period and is calculated from the formula:

$$J=\frac{1}{2}\ \mathrm{Re}(pq^*),\ \text{ or }\ J=\frac{1}{2}\cdot\frac{1}{4}(pq^*+p^*q).$$

The energy flow can be calculated in any direction and defined by the component of velocity q in the direction under consideration. In order to calculate the energy flow in the field of a spherical radiator, we take the velocity potential in the form:

$$\Phi=\sum_{m=0}^{\infty} a_{m0}\bar{P}_m(\vartheta,\psi)\,G_m(z)\,e^{-j\varepsilon_m(z)}\,e^{j\omega t}.$$

The acoustic pressure at a point of the field is

$$p=\rho\frac{\partial\Phi}{\partial t}=e^{j\frac{\pi}{2}}\,\omega\rho\sum_{m=0}^{\infty} a_{m0}\cdot\bar{P}_m(\vartheta,\psi)\cdot G_m(z)\,e^{-j\varepsilon_m(z)}\,e^{j\omega t}.$$

The radial component of velocity q_r from expression (8-24) is:

$$q_r=-k\frac{\partial\Phi}{\partial z}=e^{j\frac{\pi}{2}}\sum_{m=0}^{\infty} a_{m0}\cdot\bar{P}_m(\vartheta,\psi)\,D_m(z)\,e^{-j\delta_m(z)}\,e^{j\omega t}.$$

The component of velocity in the latitudinal direction is

$$q_\vartheta=-\frac{1}{r}\frac{\partial\Phi}{\partial\vartheta}=-k\sum_{m=0}^{\infty} a_{m0}\frac{\partial\bar{P}_m}{\partial\vartheta}\frac{G_m(z)}{z}e^{-j\varepsilon_m(z)}\,e^{j\omega t},$$

and the component of velocity in the azimuthal direction

$$q_\psi=-\frac{1}{r\sin\vartheta}\frac{\partial\Phi}{\partial\psi}=-k\sum_{m=0}^{\infty}\frac{a_{m0}}{\sin\vartheta}\frac{\partial\bar{P}_m}{\partial\psi}\frac{G_m(z)}{z}\ e^{-j\varepsilon_m(z)}\cdot e^{j\omega t}.$$

These formulae enable us to write the components of the intensity vector J in the radial, latitudinal and azimuthal directions, namely J_r, J_ϑ, and J_ψ. Using the expression (8-35) we get:

$$J_r = \frac{1}{2}\rho c \sum_{m,n=0}^{\infty} u_{m0} u_{n0} \bar{P}_m \bar{P}_n \frac{G_m(z) D_n(z)}{D_m(z_0) D_n(z_0)} \times$$
$$\times \cos[\varepsilon_m(z) - \delta_n(z) - \delta_n(z_0) + \delta_n(z_0)], \qquad (8\text{-}53)$$

where the summation is performed over all possible values of the subscripts m and n from zero to infinity. The latitudinal and azimuthal components of the intensity vector have the form:

$$J_\vartheta = \frac{\rho c}{2} \sum_{m,n=0}^{\infty} u_{m0} u_{n0} \bar{P}_m \frac{\partial \bar{P}_n}{\partial \vartheta} \frac{G_m(z) G_n(z)}{z \cdot D_m(z_0) D_n(z_0)} \times$$
$$\times \cos\left[\frac{\pi}{2} - \varepsilon_m(z) + \varepsilon_n(z) + \delta_m(z_0) - \delta_n(z_0)\right]; \qquad (8\text{-}54)$$

$$J_\psi = \frac{\rho c}{2} \sum_{m,n=0}^{\infty} u_{m0} u_{n0} \frac{\bar{P}_m}{\sin\vartheta} \frac{\partial P_n}{\partial \psi} \frac{G_m(z) G_n(z)}{z D_m(z_0) D_n(z_0)} \times$$
$$\times \cos\left[\frac{\pi}{2} - \varepsilon_m(z) + \varepsilon_n(z) + \delta_m(z_0) - \delta_n(z_0)\right]. \qquad (8\text{-}55)$$

If the radiating sphere oscillates in such a way that its motion can be expressed solely by a spherical harmonic of order m, it is necessary to take $m = n$ in the expressions for the energy flow. The sums in the expressions for J_ϑ and J_ψ then transform into one term, which contains the factor $\cos\frac{\pi}{2} = 0$. Thus, for a radiator solely of one order

$$J_\vartheta = J_\psi = 0. \qquad (8\text{-}55a)$$

Since the expression for J_r contains the factor $\cos[\varepsilon_m(z) - \delta_m(z)] \neq 0$, it follows that for radiation solely of one order

$$J_r = \frac{1}{2}\rho c \sum_{m=0}^{\infty} u_{m0}^2 \bar{P}_m^2 \frac{G_m(z) D_m(z)}{D_m^2(z_0)} \cos[\varepsilon_m(z) - \delta_m(z)] \neq 0.$$

If $m \neq n$, then generally speaking none of the terms in the sums (8-53), (8-54) and (8-55) vanish, and the following important conclusions can be drawn:

1. A simple spherical radiator with a surface which oscillates according to a law expressed by a spherical harmonic solely of one order m, produces a flow of energy at any point which is solely in the radial direction, and the tangential components of the energy flow will be zero;

2. A non-uniform spherical radiator with a surface which oscillates according to a law expressed by the sum of two or a larger number of spherical harmonics of various orders, produces a flow of energy in the tangential directions as well as the radial direction. In accordance with (8-28) and (8-30), we get for J_r, J_ϑ and J_ψ at large distances ($z \to \infty$) : for,

$$J_r = \frac{1}{2}\frac{\rho c}{z^2}\sum_{m,n=0}^{\infty}\frac{u_{m0}\cdot u_{n0}\cdot \overline{P}_m\cdot \overline{P}_n}{D_m(z_0)\,D_n(z_0)}\cdot\cos\left[\delta_m(z_0)-\delta_n(z_0)+\frac{m-n}{2}\pi\right],$$

$$J_\vartheta = \frac{1}{2}\frac{\rho c}{z^3}\sum_{m,n=0}^{\infty}\frac{u_{m0}\cdot u_{n0}\cdot \overline{P}_m\frac{\partial \overline{P}_n}{\partial\vartheta}}{D_m(z_0)\cdot D_n(z_0)}\sin\left[\delta_m(z_0)-\delta_n(z_0)+\frac{m-n}{2}\pi\right],$$

$$J_\psi = \frac{1}{2}\frac{\rho c}{z^3}\sum_{m,n=0}^{\infty}\frac{u_{m0}\,u_{n0}\cdot \overline{P}_m\frac{\partial \overline{P}_n}{\partial\psi}}{\sin\vartheta D_m(z_0)\cdot D_n(z_0)}\sin\left[\delta_m(z_0)-\delta_n(z_0)+\frac{m-n}{2}\pi\right]. \quad (8\text{-}56)$$

At great distances the tangential energy flows are considerably less than the radial according to the factor $1/z^3$ instead of $1/z^2$. In the zone near the sphere, where $z \ll 1$, the tangential flow can be of the same order of magnitude as the radial flow and it may even be greater.

We now estimate the total (global) radiated power of a non-uniform radiator oscillating solely in zonal spherical modes, for which $P_m(\vartheta,\psi)=P_m(\vartheta)$ is independent of

ψ. The total radiated power is found by integrating J_r over the surface of a sphere of very large radius:

$$\Pi = \int_0^{2\pi} d\psi \int_0^{\pi} J_r r^2 \sin\vartheta \, d\vartheta = -2\pi r^2 \int_0^{\pi} J_r(\vartheta)\, d(\cos\vartheta). \quad (8\text{-}57)$$

In term by term integration all the terms containing $P_m(\vartheta)\cdot P_n(\vartheta)$ drop out if $m \neq n$, since

$$\int_0^{\pi} P_m(\cos\vartheta)\cdot P_n(\cos\vartheta)\cdot d(\cos\vartheta) = 0, \qquad (m \neq n),$$

$$\int_0^{\pi} P_m^2(\cos\vartheta)\cdot d(\cos\vartheta) = -\frac{2}{2m+1}, \qquad (m = n).$$

As a result we get:

$$\Pi = \frac{2\pi\rho c}{k^2} \sum_{m=0}^{\infty} \frac{u_{m0}^2}{(2m+1)\cdot D_m^2(z_0)}. \quad (8\text{-}58)$$

Using expressions (8-27) which give $D_0(z_0)$ and $D_1(z_0)$, we get for the intensity and the total radiated power of a source of order 0:

$$J_0 = \frac{1}{2}\rho c \frac{z_0^4}{1+z_0^2}\cdot\frac{u_{00}^2}{z_0^2} = \frac{1}{2}\left[\rho c \frac{k^2\cdot r_0^2}{1+k^2 r_0^2}\cdot\frac{r_0^2}{r^2}\right]\cdot u_{00}^2.$$

$$\text{If } kr_0 \ll 1 \qquad J_0 = \frac{1}{2}\left[\frac{\rho\omega^2 S^2}{4\pi c}\cdot\frac{r_0^2}{r^2}\right]\cdot u_{00}^2, \quad (8\text{-}59)$$

$$\Pi_0 = \frac{2\pi\rho c}{k^2}\frac{z_0^4}{1+z_0^2}u_{00}^2 = \frac{1}{2}\rho c\frac{z_0^2}{1+z_0^2}(4\pi r_0^2)u_{00}^2 =$$

$$= \frac{1}{2}\frac{\rho\omega^2 S^2}{4\pi c}\cdot\frac{1}{1+z_0^2}u_{00}^2 = \frac{1}{2}R_0\cdot u_{00}^2,$$

where R_0 is the radiation resistance, $S = 4\pi r_0^2$; and

$$R_0 = (4\pi r_0^2)\rho c\cdot\frac{z_0^2}{1+z_0^2} = \frac{\rho\omega^2 S^2}{4\pi c}\cdot\frac{1}{1+z_0^2}. \quad (8\text{-}60)$$

Likewise, we find for a source of order 1;

$$J_1 = \frac{1}{2}\left[\rho c\frac{z_0^6}{4+z_0^4}\cdot\frac{1}{z^2}\cos^2\vartheta\right]u_{10}^2, \quad (8\text{-}61)$$

$$\Pi_1 = \frac{2\pi\rho c}{k^2} \cdot \frac{z_0^6}{3(4+z_0^4)} \cdot u_{10}^2 = \frac{1}{2} \frac{\rho\omega^4 S^3 u_{10}^2}{48\pi^2 c^3 (4+z_0^4)} = \frac{1}{2} R_1 \cdot u_{10}^2, \quad (8\text{-}62)$$

where

$$R_1 = \frac{1}{3} S\rho c \frac{z_0^4}{4+z_0^4} = \frac{\rho\omega^4 S^3}{48\pi^2 c^3 (4+z_0^4)}.$$

When calculating the radiation of energy for a sectorial radiator of order 2, it is necessary to remember that the coefficient u_{22} in the series expansion in spherical harmonics is equal to $U_{22}/3$ (see formula (8-34)), where U_{22} is the velocity amplitude at the antinode of the sectorial zone, i.e. on the equator $\left(\vartheta = \frac{\pi}{2}\right)$; in (8-34)$u'_{22}$ is assumed equal to zero.

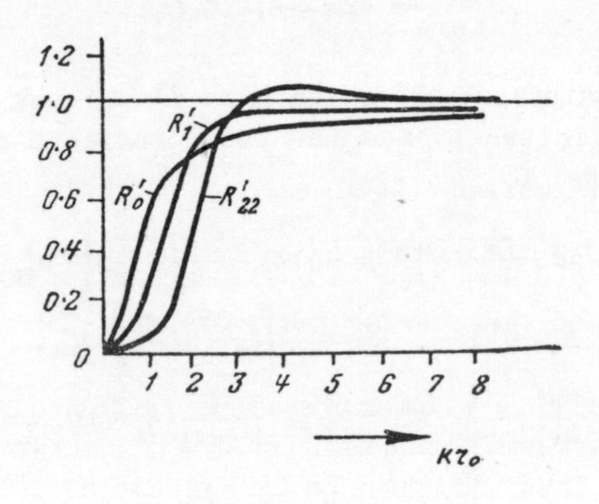

Fig. 71

There is no difficulty in calculating the radiation resistance of a second order sectorial radiator if expressions can be found for the radial velocity $q_r = -\frac{\partial\Phi}{\partial r}$ and for the acoustic pressure. We form an expression for the intensity vector $J_r(\vartheta, \psi) = \frac{1}{2}\operatorname{Re}(pq_r^*)$, and then find the total radiation across a sphere of radius *r*:

$$\Pi = 2\pi \int_0^{2\pi} d\psi \int_0^{\pi} J(\vartheta, \psi) \cdot r^2 \cdot \sin\vartheta \, d\vartheta = \frac{1}{2} R_{22} u_{22}^2 .$$

For the radiation resistance, we have

$$R_{22} = \frac{4}{15} S\rho c \frac{k^6 r_0^6}{k^6 r_0^6 - 2k^4 r_0^4 + 9k^2 r_0^2 + 81} .$$

In order to facilitate a comparison of the dependence on frequency of the various radiation resistances, curves have been plotted in Fig. 71 for the following dimensionless quantities:

$$R_0' = \frac{R_0}{S\rho c}, \qquad R_1' = \frac{R_1}{\frac{1}{3} S\rho c} \text{ and } R_{22}' = \frac{R_{22}}{\frac{4}{15} S\rho c},$$

which tend to unity at high frequencies. A second order sectorial radiator is even less effective than zero or first order radiators at low frequencies, since the radiation is proportional to $(kr_0)^6$. It is interesting that there is a shallow maximum in the curve for R_{22} at $kr_0 \approx 4$ and at this maximum the dimensionless radiation resistance $\frac{R_{22}}{S\rho c} \cdot \frac{15}{4}$ is greater than unity. There are no such maxima for zero and first order radiators.

In accordance with expressions (8-28), the quantities $1/D_m(z_0)$ are small and of order z_0^{m+2} in expression (8-58) if $z_0 \ll 1$. Thus, if the surface velocities are of the same order of magnitude in the various modes, the radiated energy is dominated by the zero order term.

As an example of the energy relationship in the field of a non-uniform spherical radiator, we consider a radiator with a surface on which there are only velocity components of zero, u_{00}, and first, u_{10}, orders, and assume that they are in phase; such a radiator may be conveniently referred to as a radiator of order (0+1)*. If $u_{00}=u_{10}$, such a radiator is a sphere with one pole fixed, and the other free to oscillate with velocity amplitude $2u_{00}$, whilst the points along the equator oscillate with the velocity amplitude u_{00} (Fig. 72).

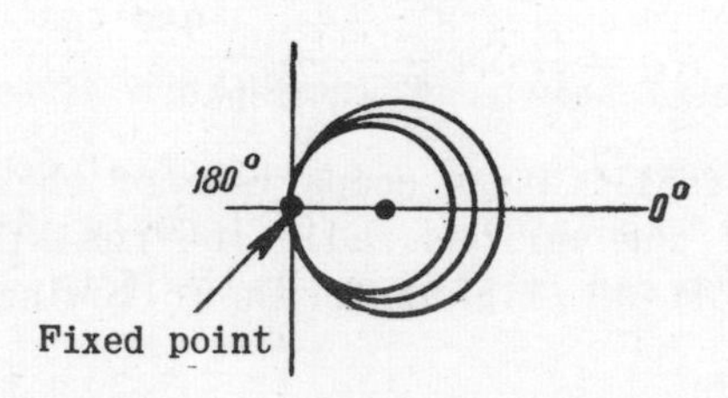

Fig. 72

The radial component of the sound intensity can be calculated from formula (8-53) and put into the form:

$$(J_r)_{0+1}=\frac{1}{2}\rho c\Big\{u_{00}^2\frac{G_0(z)\cdot D_0(z)}{D_0^2(z_0)}\cdot\cos[\varepsilon_0(z)-\delta_0(z)]+$$
$$+u_{10}^2\frac{G_1(z)D_1(z)}{D_1^2(z_0)}\cdot\cos[\varepsilon_1(z)-\delta_1(z)]\cdot\cos\vartheta+$$
$$+u_{00}u_{10}\frac{G_0(z)D_1(z)}{D_0(z_0)D_1(z_0)}\cos[\varepsilon_0(z)-\delta_1(z)-\delta_0(z_0)+\delta_1(z_0)]\cos\vartheta+$$
$$+u_{10}u_{00}\frac{G_1(z)D_0(z)}{D_1(z_0)D_0(z_0)}\cdot\cos[\varepsilon_1(z)-\delta_0(z)-\delta_1(z_0)+\delta_0(z_0)]\cos\vartheta.$$

The quantities appearing here can be calculated by formulae (8-27) and (8-31). After transformation we get:

$$(J_r)_{0+1}=\frac{1}{2}\rho c\frac{z_0^4}{z^2}\Big[\frac{u_{00}^2}{1+z_0^2}+\frac{u_{10}^2\cdot\cos^2\vartheta\cdot z_0^2}{4+z_0^4}+$$
$$+u_{00}u_{10}\cos\vartheta\frac{2zz_0(2+z_0^2)+(2z^2-1)z_0^4}{(1+z_0^2)(4+z_0^4)z^2}. \qquad (8\text{-}63)$$

At $z=z_0$ on the surface of the sphere:

$$(J_r)_{0+1}=\frac{1}{2}\rho cz_0^2\Big[u_{00}^2\frac{1}{1+z_0^2}+u_{10}^2\cdot\cos^2\vartheta\frac{z_0^2}{4+z_0^4}+$$
$$+u_{00}\cdot u_{10}\cdot\cos\vartheta\frac{4+z_0^2+2z_0^4}{(1+z_0^2)(4+z_0^4)}\Big].$$

* S.N. Rschevkin, *Zhur. tekh. phys.* 19, 1380, 1949.

The first two terms in (8-63) give the flow of energy corresponding respectively to radiators of order 0 and 1, as can easily be seen by comparison with expressions (8-59) and (8-61). The presence of a third term proportional to $\cos\vartheta$ shows that the intensity of sound in the region of the "front" hemisphere (from 0 to $\frac{\pi}{2}$) is always greater than the sum of the intensities (J_0+J_1) and that the intensity in the region of the "rear" hemisphere (from $\frac{\pi}{2}$ to π) is always less than J_0+J_1. The tangential component of the intensity is calculated from the formula (8-54) and after transformation can be written in the form:

$$(J_\vartheta)_{0+1}=\frac{1}{2}\rho c\, u_{00}u_{10}\cdot\sin\vartheta\frac{z_0^5\left[\left(1-\frac{z_0}{z}\right)z_0^2+2\right]}{z^3(1+z_0^2)(4+z_0^4)}= \quad (8\text{-}64)$$

$$=\frac{1}{2}\rho c\, u_{00}u_{10}\sin\vartheta\left[\frac{(2+z_0^2)z_0^5}{(1+z_0^2)(4+z_0^4)z^3}-\frac{z_0^6}{(1+z_0^2)(4+z_0^4)z^4}\right].$$

On the surface of the sphere $(z=z_0)$ we get:

$$(J_\vartheta)_{0+1}=\frac{1}{2}\rho c\, u_{00}u_{10}\sin\vartheta\left[\frac{2z_0^2}{(1+z_0^2)(4+z_0^4)}\right]. \quad (8\text{-}65)$$

The tangential energy flow in the whole space surrounding the sphere (i.e. for $z>z_0$), as can be seen from (8-64), is always positive, i.e. it goes in the positive direc- of the angle ϑ from the front pole, which oscillates with the total amplitude $u_{00}+u_{10}$, to the rear pole, which oscillates with the amplitude $(u_{00}-u_{10})$. A large amount of the energy which is radiated from the "front" hemisphere flows across the equatorial plane $\left(\vartheta=\frac{\pi}{2}\right)$ into the "rear" half-space. If $u_{00}=u_{10}$ and $z_0\ll 1$ (long waves)

$$(J_\vartheta)_{0+1}\approx\frac{1}{2}\rho c\; u_{00}^2\sin\vartheta\,\frac{z_0^2}{2}=\frac{1}{2}\cdot\frac{\rho\omega^2S^2}{8\pi c}\sin\vartheta\cdot u_{00}^2.$$

On $\vartheta=\frac{\pi}{2}$ the density of the tangential energy flow at the surface is half the density of the radial flow for a zero order radiator, as can be seen from (8-59). For short waves $(z_0\gg 1)$ the square bracket in formula (8-65) is equal to $2/z_0^4$ and therefore $(J_\vartheta)_{0+1}$ is very small.

If $u_{00}=u_{10}$ and $z\to\infty$, expression (8-63) can be represented in the form

$$(J_r)_{0+1}=J_0\left[1+\frac{z_0(1+z_0^2)}{4+z_0^4}\cos^2\vartheta+\frac{2z_0^4\cos\vartheta}{4+z_0^4}\right], \tag{8-66}$$

where

$$J_0=\frac{1}{2}\rho c\ \frac{z_0^4}{1+z_0^2}\ \frac{1}{z^2}u_{00}^2$$

is the intensity of a radiator of order 0 with a velocity amplitude u_{00} (independent of ϑ). The square bracket in expression (8-66), if plotted in polar coordinates, gives what is known as the directivity characteristic for the sound intensity of a radiator of order $(0+1)$.

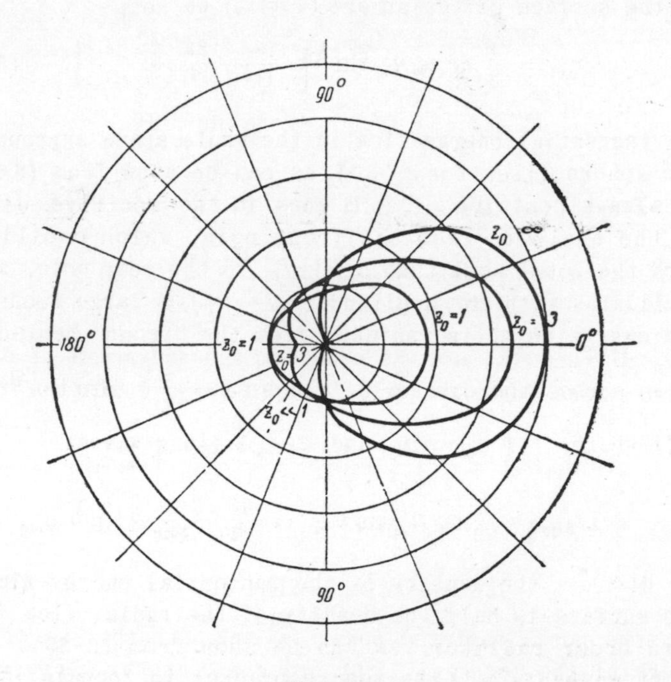

Fig. 73

If $z_0 \ll 1$, the radiator becomes non-directional; the directivity characteristic is a sphere of unit radius. If $z_0 \gg 1$

$$(J_r)_{0+1} = J_0 (1 + \cos \vartheta)^2,$$

i.e. the characteristic has the form of a cardioid. Figure 73 shows the directivity characteristics for various values of z_0.

It is essential to investigate the energy balance for a radiator of order (0+1) and in order to understand this better we will calculate the total power radiated from the surface of the front hemisphere (Π') and that from the rear hemisphere (Π''), for which purpose it is necessary to integrate $(J_r)_{0+1}$ over the surface of the sphere;

$$\Pi'(r_0) = \int_0^{\frac{\pi}{2}} (J_r)_{0+1} \cdot 2\pi r_0^2 \cdot \sin\vartheta \cdot d\vartheta,$$

$$\Pi''(r_0) = \int_{\frac{\pi}{2}}^{\pi} (J_r)_{0+1} \cdot 2\pi r_0^2 \cdot \sin\vartheta \cdot d\vartheta.$$

The calculation gives:

$$\Pi'(r_0) = \frac{\Pi_0}{2} + \frac{\Pi_1}{2} + \Pi_{12}(r_0),$$

$$\Pi''(r_0) = \frac{\Pi_0}{2} + \frac{\Pi_1}{2} - \Pi_{12}(r_0),$$

where Π_0 and Π_1 are the powers of the radiators of order 0 and 1 (see formulae (8-59) and (8-62)), whilst

$$\Pi_{12}(r_0) = \frac{1}{2} \left[\frac{S\rho c}{4} \frac{z_0^2 (4 + z_0^2 + 2z_0^4)}{(1 + z_0^2)(4 + z_0^4)} \right] u_{00} u_{10},$$

where $S = 4\pi r_0^2$. On the surface of the sphere we have:

$$\Pi'(r_0) + \Pi''(r_0) = \Pi_0 + \Pi_1, \tag{8-67}$$

i.e. the total radiated power is equal to the sum of the powers of the zero and first order radiators. If $u_{00} = u_{10}$

and $z_0 \ll 1$, $\Pi_1 \ll \Pi_0$ and $\Pi_{12} \approx \frac{\Pi_0}{4}$; consequently:

$$\Pi'(r_0) \approx \frac{\Pi_0}{2} + \frac{\Pi_0}{4} = \frac{3}{4}\Pi_0; \qquad \Pi''(r_0) \approx \frac{\Pi_0}{2} - \frac{\Pi_0}{4} = \frac{\Pi_0}{4},$$

i.e. three times more energy is radiated from the front hemisphere than from the rear.

At infinity, using (8-56), we find the power radiated across the front and rear hemispheres; they will not be equal either:

$$\Pi'(\infty) = \int_0^{\frac{\pi}{2}} (J_r)_{0+1} \cdot 2\pi r^2 \cdot \sin\vartheta \cdot d\vartheta = \frac{\Pi_0}{2} + \frac{\Pi_1}{2} + \Pi_{12}(\infty),$$

$$\Pi''(\infty) = \int_{\frac{\pi}{2}}^{\pi} (J_r)_{0+1} 2\pi r^2 \cdot \sin\vartheta \cdot d\vartheta = \frac{\Pi_0}{2} + \frac{\Pi_1}{2} - \Pi_{12}(\infty),$$

where

$$\Pi_{12}(\infty) = \frac{1}{2}\left[\frac{S\rho c}{4} \frac{2z_0^6}{(1+z_0^2)(4+z_0^4)}\right] u_{00} u_{10}.$$

At infinity

$$\Pi'(\infty) + \Pi''(\infty) = \Pi_0 + \Pi_1$$

which should be compared with expression (8-67).

The difference in the energy flows across the front and rear hemispheres on the surface of the sphere and at infinity is

$$\Pi_{12}(r_0) - \Pi_{12}(\infty) = \frac{1}{2}\left[\frac{S\rho c}{4} \frac{4z_0^2 + z_0^4}{(1+z_0^2)(4+z_0^4)}\right] u_{00} \cdot u_{10}.$$

The total energy flow in the tangential direction across the equatorial plane $(\vartheta = \frac{\pi}{2})$

$$\Pi_\vartheta = \int_{r_0}^{\infty} (J_\vartheta)_{0+1} \cdot 2\pi r \cdot dr = \frac{1}{2}\left[\frac{S\rho c}{4} \frac{4z_0^2 + z_0^4}{(1+z_0^2)(4+z_0^4)}\right] u_{00} u_{10}$$

is equal to $\Pi_{12}(r_0) - \Pi_{12}(\infty)$. Consequently, there is diffraction of the sound, i.e. the sound energy flows across the equatorial plane from the front region of large energy density into the rear region of lower energy density. In the case of long waves $\Pi_{12}(\infty) \sim z_0^6$, i.e. it becomes very small. This implies that the complete balancing out of the acoustic flow in all directions has already taken place in the zone near the sphere.

The Total Attached Energy and the Total Attached Mass of a Spherical Radiator

It was shown in Chapter IV in our analysis of the total effective mass of a zero and first order radiator that the "additional" or "attached" masses are equal, respectively, to $M_0 = 3M$ and $M_1 = \frac{M}{2}$ for very long waves $(z_0 \ll 1)$, where $M = \frac{4}{3}\pi r_0^3 \rho$ is the mass of the medium displaced by a sphere of radius r_0. With much shorter waves the attached mass gradually decreases and as $z_0 \to \infty$ it tends to zero. In the calculations we will ignore terms which contain the quantity z of a degree greater than the first in view of the fact that "additional" or "attached" energy is formed owing to the kinetic energy of the reactive component of velocity, which diminishes sharply with distance. Strictly speaking this is permissible only in the zone where $z \ll 1 \left(r \ll \frac{\lambda}{2\pi}\right)$, but since the additional energy of interest is that obtaining in the limit of very long waves, it follows that the expression $z \ll 1$ is applicable over a very large area.

Using (8-18), we write the following approximate equation for the velocity potential of a radiator of order m

$$\Phi_m(r,\vartheta,\psi,t) \approx ja_{m0} \cdot P_m(\vartheta,\psi) \frac{m}{z^{m+1}} (1 + jz) e^{j(\omega t - z)}. \quad (8\text{-}68)$$

Zonal radiator. Firstly we consider the case of zonal

oscillations, $P_m(\vartheta, \psi) = P_m(\vartheta)$. The acoustic pressure is

$$p \approx -a_{m0}\rho\omega P_m(\vartheta)\frac{\overline{m}}{z^{m+1}}(1+jz)e^{j(\omega t - z)}.$$

The radial velocity is

$$q_r = -\frac{\partial\Phi}{\partial r} = q_a + q_i,$$

where

$$q_a \approx -ka_{m0}P_m(\vartheta)\frac{\overline{m}(m+1)}{z^{m+1}}e^{j(\omega t - z)} \qquad (8\text{-}69)$$

is the active velocity which is in phase with the pressure (apart from terms of order z), and

$$q_i \approx jka_{m0}P_m(\vartheta)\frac{\overline{m}(m+1)}{z^{m+2}}\left(1+\frac{z^2}{m+1}\right)e^{j(\omega t - z)} \qquad (8\text{-}70)$$

is the reactive velocity, which lags behind the pressure in phase by $\frac{\pi}{2}$. The term $\frac{z^2}{m+1}$ in expression (8-70) is small and can be ignored in the zone near the radiator.

It can be seen from expressions (8-69) and (8-70) that if $z \ll 1$, then $q_i \gg q_a$, i.e. the velocity field in the zone near the sphere is dominated by the reactive component of velocity. The tangential component of the particle velocity in the zone near the radiator in the direction of the angle ϑ is obtained from (3-68):

$$q_\vartheta = -k\frac{\partial\Phi_m}{z\partial\vartheta} = -jka_{m0}\frac{dP_m}{d\vartheta}\frac{\overline{m}}{z^{m+2}}e^{j(\omega t - z)}. \qquad (8\text{-}71)$$

Thus, q_ϑ is in antiphase with q_i and is also a reactive velocity. Suppose we put u_i and u_ϑ, for the amplitudes of the quantities q_i and q_ϑ:

$$u^2 = u_i^2 + u_\vartheta^2 \approx \left(\frac{ka_{m0}\overline{m}}{z^{m+2}}\right)^2\left[P_m^2(\vartheta)(m+1)^2 + \left(\frac{dP_m}{d\vartheta}\right)^2\right],$$

which can alternatively be written in the form:

$$u^2 = u_{m0}^2\left[P_m^2 + \frac{\left(\frac{dP_m}{d\vartheta}\right)^2}{(m+1)^2}\right]\left(\frac{r_0}{r}\right)^{2m+4},$$

where

$$u_{m0} = \frac{ka_{m0}\overline{m}\,(m+1)}{z^{m+2}}. \qquad (8\text{-}72)$$

As can be seen from (8-69), (8-70) and (8-71), the velocity amplitude is dominated by the reactive component if $z \ll 1$. The quantity u_{m0} represents the maximum velocity amplitude on the surface of the sphere, which occurs at $\vartheta = 0, \pi$. The mean value of the square of the velocity u, the velocity varying with time according to a sinusoidal law, is at each point in space proportional to $\frac{u_{m0}^2}{2}$. In order to find the total kinetic energy, we can restrict ourselves to the zone near the sphere, assume that the velocities are in phase, and add the mean kinetic energies of the individual elements of the field surrounding the sphere, in which case only the reactive component of velocity is taken into account. For an element of the volume we have

$$dV = 2\pi r^2 \sin\vartheta dr \cdot d\vartheta.$$

The mean kinetic energy in the entire field over a period is defined by the following integral:

$$\overline{T}_m = \frac{1}{2}\iiint\limits_V \rho\frac{u^2}{2}dV \approx \frac{1}{2}\rho u_{m0}^2\int\limits_{r_0}^{\infty}\frac{r_0^{2m+4}\cdot 2\pi r^2}{r^{2m+4}}dr\int\limits_0^{\pi}\left[P_m^2 + \left(\frac{\frac{\partial P_m}{\partial\vartheta}}{m+1}\right)^2\sin\vartheta\right]d\vartheta.$$

Strictly speaking, it is impossible to integrate up to infinity with respect to r, since it was assumed that $kr \ll 1$ (so that terms of higher orders can be ignored). There is no difficulty in seeing that if we take all the terms in series (8-20) into account we can remove the limitation $kr \ll 1$, and obtain a correction factor for the integral which tends to unity if $kr_0 \ll 1$. The kinetic energy in the volume between r_0 and $r_0 + \frac{\lambda}{2\pi}$ is $\overline{T}_m [1 - z_0^{2m+1}]$, i.e. if $kr_0 \ll 1$, the main part of the kinetic energy is in the zone from r_0 to $r_0 + \frac{\lambda}{2\pi}$.

It is known from the theory of spherical harmonics that

$$\int_0^\pi P_m^2(\vartheta) \cdot \sin\vartheta d\vartheta = \frac{2}{2m+1},$$

$$\int_0^\pi \left(\frac{dP_m}{d\vartheta}\right)^2 \sin\vartheta \cdot d\vartheta = \frac{2m(m+1)}{2m+1}.$$

For the mean kinetic energy of the reactive component of velocity in the entire field, we get:

$$\overline{T}_m = \frac{1}{2}\rho \frac{u_{m0}^2}{2} \frac{4\pi r_0^{2m+4}}{m+1} \int_{r_0}^\infty \frac{dr}{r^{2m+2}} =$$

$$= \frac{1}{2} \frac{4\pi r_0^3 \rho}{(m+1)(2m+1)} \cdot \frac{u_{m0}^2}{2} = \frac{1}{2} M_m \cdot \frac{u_{m0}^2}{2} = \frac{1}{2} M_m \cdot u_{m\,\mathrm{eff}}^2, \tag{8-73}$$

where

$$M_m = \frac{3\left(\frac{4}{3}\pi r_0^3 \rho\right)}{(m+1)(2m+1)} = \frac{3M}{(m+1)(2m+1)}. \tag{8-73a}$$

The quantity M_m can be called the *attached mass of a zonal radiator of order m*. The quantity M represents the mass of the medium displaced by the sphere. Formula (8-73 a) gives the following values for the attached masses of radiators of order 0, 1, 2 and 3:

$$M_0 = 3M \text{ (pulsating sphere)},$$

$$M_1 = \frac{M}{2} \text{ (oscillating sphere)},$$

$$M_2 = \frac{M}{5},$$

$$M_3 = \frac{3}{28}M.$$

Sectorial radiator. We will now calculate the additional energy and mass for radiators of the sectorial type. For a sectorial radiator of order m, it is necessary to take only one term in the associated spherical harmonic in formula (8-12):

$$P_m^{(m)}(\vartheta) = 1.3.5\ldots(2m-1)\sin^m\vartheta = \overline{m}\cdot\sin^m\vartheta.$$

The velocity potential, if $z \ll 1$ can be represented in the following form, in view of expressions (8-9), (8-11) and (8-20):

$$\Phi_{mm}(r,\vartheta,\psi,t) = ja_{mm}\cdot\cos m(\psi-\psi_0)\cdot\sin^m\vartheta\frac{(1+jz)\,e^{-jz}}{z^{m+1}}\,e^{j\omega t}.$$

The reactive component of the velocity along the radius can be found from this expression:

$$q_i \approx jka_{mm}\cdot\cos m(\psi-\psi_0)\cdot\sin^m\vartheta\,\frac{m+1}{z^{m+2}}\cdot e^{j(\omega t - z)},$$

along the polar angle (meridian):

$$q_\vartheta \approx -jka_{mm}\cdot\cos m(\psi-\psi_0)\sin^{m-1}\vartheta\cdot\cos\vartheta\,\frac{m}{z^{m+2}}\,e^{j(\omega t - z)}$$

and along the azimuth:

$$q_\psi = -jka_{mm}\sin m(\psi-\psi_0)\sin^{m-1}\vartheta\,\frac{m}{z^{m+2}}e^{j(\omega t - z)}.$$

The square of the amplitude of the total reactive velocity is

$$u^2 = \frac{k^2a^2_{mm}}{z^{2m+4}}\Big[(m+1)^2\cos^2 m(\psi-\psi_0)\sin^{2m}\vartheta + m^2\cos^2 m(\psi-\psi_0)\times$$
$$\times\sin^{2(m-1)}\vartheta\cdot\cos^2\vartheta + m^2\sin^2 m(\psi-\psi_0)\sin^{2(m-1)}\vartheta\Big] =$$
$$= u^2_{mm}\left(\frac{r_0}{r}\right)^{2m+4}\Big[\cos^2 m(\psi-\psi_0)\sin^{2m}\vartheta +$$

$$+\left(\frac{m}{m+1}\right)^2 \cos^2\vartheta\cdot\cos^2 m(\psi-\psi_0)\cdot\sin^{2(m-1)}\vartheta+$$
$$+\left(\frac{m}{m+1}\right)^2 \sin^2 m(\psi-\psi_0)\sin^{2(m-1)}\vartheta\Big]=$$
$$=u_{mm}^2\left(\frac{r_0}{r}\right)^{2m+4}\left[\frac{2m+1}{(m+1)^2}\cos^2 m(\psi-\psi_0)\sin^{2m}\vartheta+\right. \tag{8-74}$$
$$\left.+\left(\frac{m}{m+1}\right)^2\sin^{2(m-1)}\vartheta\right],$$

where

$$u_{mm}=\frac{ka_{mm}(m+1)}{z_0{}^{m+2}}$$

is the maximum amplitude on the surface of the sphere occurring at $\vartheta=\frac{\pi}{2}$ and $\psi=\psi_0$, as can be seen from formula (8-74). After simple transformations we find for the mean (over a period) kinetic energy of the entire field:

$$\overline{T}_{mm}=\frac{1}{2}\rho\int_{r_0}^{\infty}\frac{u^2}{2}dV=$$

$$=\frac{1}{2}\rho\,\frac{u_{mm}^2}{2}r_0^{2m+4}\left[\frac{2m+1}{(m+1)^2}\int_0^{\pi}\sin^{2m+1}\vartheta d\vartheta\int_0^{2\pi}\cos^2 m(\psi-\psi_0)\,d\psi+\right.$$
$$\left.+\left(\frac{m}{m+1}\right)^2\cdot 2\pi\int_0^{\pi}\sin^{2m-1}\vartheta d\vartheta\right]\cdot\int_{r_0}^{\infty}\frac{dr}{r^{2m+2}}$$

Using tables of integrals* we find:

$$\int_0^{\pi}\sin^{2m-1}\vartheta d\vartheta=2\frac{2.\,4.\,6\ldots(2m-2)}{1.\,3.\,5\ldots(2m-1)}=2^m\frac{(m-1)!}{\overline{m}},$$

and we finally get:

$$\overline{T}_{mm}=\frac{1}{2}\left(\frac{4}{3}\pi r_0^3\rho\right)\frac{3.\,2^m.\,m!}{2(2m+1)(m+1)\overline{m}}\,\frac{u_{mm}^2}{2}=\frac{1}{2}M_{mm}u_{m\,\text{eff}}^2. \tag{8-74a}$$

* N.M. Ryzhik, *(Tables of Integrals, Sums, Series and Products, (Tablitsy integralov, summ, rjadovi proizvedeni)* 1951 Gostekhizdat, (p. 175, formula 3-421).

where

$$u_{m\,\mathrm{eff}}^2 = \frac{1}{2} u_{mm}^2 .$$

The quantity

$$M_{mm} = \frac{3.\,2^m.\,m!}{2(2m+1)(m+1)\overline{m}} \left(\frac{4}{3}\pi r_0^3 \rho\right) = \frac{3.\,2^{m-1}\,m!}{(2m+1)(m+1)\overline{m}} M$$

is the *attached or additional mass of a sectorial radiator.* For $m = 1, 2, 3, 4$ we get:

$$M_{11} = \frac{M}{2} \text{ (oscillating sphere)},$$

$$M_{22} = \frac{4}{15} M,$$

$$M_{33} = \frac{6}{35} M,$$

$$M_{44} = \frac{192}{525} M.$$

The value M_{11} for a sectorial radiator of order 1 is equal to the additional mass of a zonal radiator of order 1, i.e. to that of an oscillating sphere, which is quite understandable, since a sectorial radiator of order 1 is a zonal radiator with its axis rotated through 90°.

A Point Source on the Surface of a Sphere

We represent a point source of sound on the surface of a sphere by a small circular surface ΔS, having a velocity u_0 situated at the north pole ($\vartheta = 0$). The volume velocity produced by the source is $A_0 = u_0 \Delta S$. The constants in the series expansion of the velocity potential (8-22) can be calculated from formula (8-33):

$$\overline{u}_{m0} = \frac{2m+1}{4\pi} \iint_S P_m(\vartheta)\, u(\vartheta)\, dS_1 ,$$

$$u_{m\nu} = u'_{m\nu} = 0.$$

The surface element dS_1 is that of a sphere of unit radius. In view of the smallness of the circular element ΔS we assume in the integration that $u(\vartheta)=u_0$ over the entire are ΔS and that it is zero on the rest of the area of the sphere. Then, bearing in mind that $P_m(0)=1$,

$$\iint_S P_m(\vartheta)\,u(\vartheta)\,dS_1=\frac{u_0}{r_0^2}\iint_S dS=\frac{A_0}{r_0^2},$$

we get

$$u_{m0}=\frac{2m+1}{4\pi r_0^2}A_0.$$

Substituting these values u_{mo} in formula (8-56) for the intensity when $kr=z\gg 1$ we get:

$$J_r(r,\vartheta)=\frac{1}{2}\frac{\rho c A_0^2}{16\pi^2 r_0^4}\left\{\frac{1}{z^2}\sum_{m,n=0}^{\infty}\frac{P_mP_n(2m+1)(2n+1)}{D_m(z_0)D_n(z_0)}\cos\left[\delta_m(z_0)-\delta_n(z_0)+\right.\right.$$

$$\left.\left.+\frac{m-n}{2}\pi\right]\right\}=\frac{1}{2}\frac{\rho\omega^2A_0^2}{4\pi c\cdot 4\pi r^2}\left\{\frac{1}{z_0^4}\sum_{m,n=0}^{\infty}\frac{P_mP_n(2m+1)(2n+1)}{D_m(z_0)D_n(z_0)}\times\right. \quad (8\text{-}75)$$

$$\left.\times\cos\left[\delta_m(z_0)-\delta_n(z_0)+\frac{m-n}{2}\pi\right]\right\}=J_oF(z_0,\vartheta).$$

Here $J_o=\frac{1}{2}\cdot\frac{\rho\omega^2A_0^2}{4\pi c\cdot 4\pi r^2}$ is the intensity (at the distance r) of a non-directional source of order 0 with a strength A_0, and $F(z_0,\vartheta)$ is the directivity characteristic of the point source on the sphere. Figure 74 shows directivity characteristics of such a source at various values of z_0; the quantity $F(z_o,\vartheta)\cdot z_0^2$ is marked off along the ordinate. It is easy to show that if $z_o\ll 1$ the quantity $F(z_0,\vartheta)$ tends to unity, i.e. the characteristic is changed into a sphere, and the intensity tends to the value of the intensity J_0 of a free source of order 0. Thus, a sphere which is small in comparison with the wavelength does not affect the radiation of a point source.

The acoustic pressure at great distances $(z\gg 1)$ can be

represented in the following form:

$$\underset{z\to\infty}{p \to} j\,\frac{A_0\rho c e^{j(\omega t-kr)}}{4\pi r_0^2\cdot kr}\sum_{m=0}^{\infty}\frac{j^m P_m(\vartheta)(2m+1)}{D_m(z_0)\,e^{-j\delta_m(z_0)}}. \quad (8\text{-}76)$$

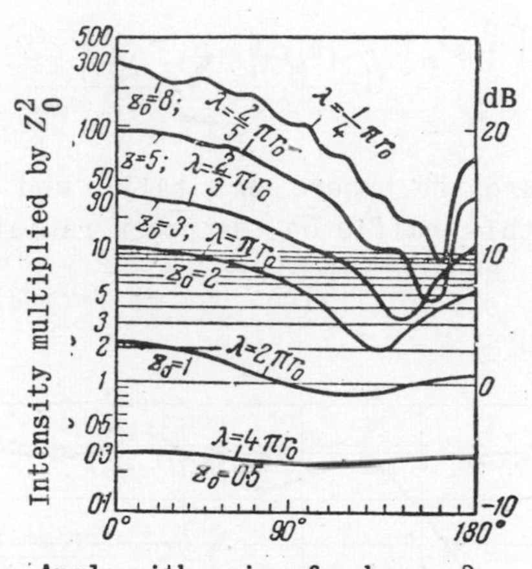

Fig. 74

The Radiation of a Dipole Source, the Poles of which are situated at the Poles of a Solid Sphere

The total power radiated by a source which is symmetrical about the axis can be calculated by formula (8-58). Assuming that point sources are situated at the poles ($\vartheta=0$ and $\vartheta=\pi$) having strength $+A_0$ and $-A_0$, respectively, we obtain non-zero values of the integral over the surface by formula (8-33) only if $\vartheta=0$ and $\vartheta=\pi$. Since for odd m we have $P_m(0)=1$ and $P_m(\pi)=-1$, we finally get:

$$u_{m0}\Big|_{m=1,3,5\ldots} = \frac{2m+1}{4\pi r_0^2} A_0 - \left[\frac{2m+1}{4\pi r_0^2}\left(-A_0\right)\right] = \frac{2m+1}{4\pi r_0^2} 2A_0.$$

For even $m, P_m(0) = P_m(\pi) = 1$ and therefore $u_{m0} = 0$. Consequently

$$\Pi = \frac{\rho c A_0^2}{2\pi k^2 r_0^4} \sum_{m=1,3,5,\ldots}^{\infty} \frac{2m+1}{D_m^2(z_0)}. \tag{8-77}$$

We now regard the sphere as a baffle and enquire into the effect of this baffle on the power radiation on just one side of the equatorial plane.

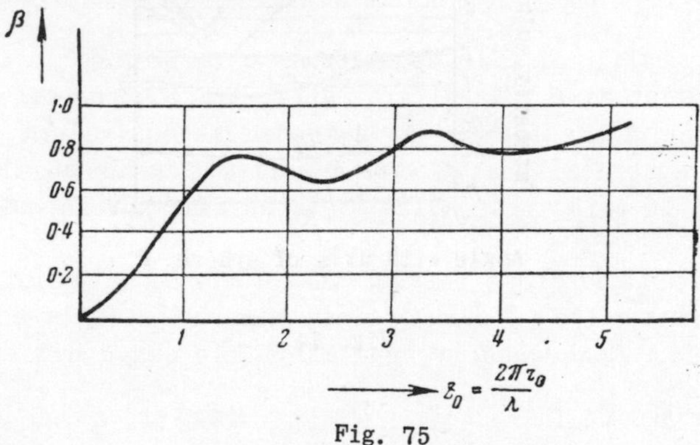

Fig. 75

We compare the quantity $\frac{\Pi}{2}$ with the power radiated by a point source situated on an infinite baffle:

$$\Pi_0 = \frac{1}{2} \frac{\rho\omega^2 A_0^2}{2\pi c}.$$

The quantity $\frac{\Pi}{2}$ can be represented in the form:

$$\frac{\Pi}{2} = \beta\Pi_0, \text{where } \beta = \frac{1}{z_0^4} \sum_{m=1,3,5,\ldots}^{\infty} \frac{2m+1}{D_m^2(z_0)}. \tag{8-77a}$$

Figure 75 shows the variation of the quantity β as a function of z_0. In order to calculate β up to $z_0 = 5$, it is sufficient to take the first three terms of the sum. It will be seen from the diagram that if $z_0 = \frac{2\pi r_0}{\lambda} = 1$, we then get $\beta \approx 0{\cdot}6$, and that there is very little further increase in β. It is obvious that a spherical baffle of radius larger than $r_0 = \frac{\lambda}{2\pi}$, hardly increases the power radiation of the dipole at all. If $z_0 \leqslant 1$, in accordance with (8-28) we get

$$\beta \approx \sum_{m=1,3,5,\ldots}^{\infty} \frac{(2m+1)\, z_0^{2m}}{m^2 (m+1)^2} \approx \frac{3}{8} z_0^2,$$

i.e. an increase in the radius of the baffle has a great effect if z_0 is small.

The baffle of a loudspeaker is usually made in the form of a flat disc. As a first approximation the effect of a baffle in the form of a flat disc is equivalent to that of a spherical baffle with a semi-circumferential length equal to twice the radius R of the flat screen, $\pi r_0 = 2R$.

It can therefore be seen that there is no point in increasing z_0 to a figure greater than unity for a spherical baffle. Consequently, a flat baffle can expediently be increased to the quantity $R = \frac{\lambda}{4}$. However, even this condition gives a very large minimum diameter of the baffle at the frequency 100 c/s, namely $2R = 1{\cdot}7$m.

A Spherical Radiator with a Progressive Wave*

We define the radial velocity u of a progressive wave in the azimuthal direction (ψ) on the surface of a sphere

---

* S.N. Rschevkin, *Vest. Moscow State University*, No.8, 3, 1954.

as follows:

$$u = u_m \cdot \sin^n \vartheta e^{j(\omega t - m\psi)}, \tag{8-78}$$

where u_m is the velocity amplitude on the equator, ϑ the polar angle, ω the angular frequency, t the time and m and n are integers. Solving this problem in the usual way we get for the velocity potential of the acoustic field:

$$\Phi = \frac{u_{mm} P_m^{(m)}(\vartheta) G_m(z) e^{-j\varepsilon_m(z)}}{jkD_m(z_0) e^{-j\delta_m(z_0)}} e^{j(\omega t - m\psi)}. \tag{8-79}$$

It is seen from this expression that waves which progress in the azimuthal direction are set up in the region surrounding the sphere.

The coefficient u_{mm} is calculated by integration over the surface of the sphere:

$$u_{mm} = \frac{2m+1}{2\pi \cdot (2m)!} u_m \int_0^{2\pi} \cos^2 m\psi \int_0^{\pi} P_m^{(m)}(\vartheta) \sin^n \vartheta \sin \vartheta d\vartheta =$$
$$= \frac{(2m+1)\overline{m}}{2 \cdot (2m)!} u_m \int_0^{\pi} \sin^{m+n+1} \vartheta d\vartheta = \frac{(2m+1)\overline{m} u_m}{2 \cdot (2m)!} i_{mn}, \tag{8-80}$$

where

$$i_{mn} = \begin{cases} 2 \dfrac{2.4.6 \ldots (m+n)}{1.3.5 \ldots (m+n+1)} & \text{if } (m+n)\text{ - even,} \\ \pi \dfrac{1.3.5 \ldots (m+n)}{2.4.6 \ldots (m+n+1)} & \text{if } (m+n)\text{ - odd.} \end{cases} \tag{8-80a}$$

Assuming that the amplitude diminishes from the equator to the poles according to the law $\sin^m \vartheta$, i.e. assuming as a special case that $m = n$, we get:

$$i_{mm} = 2 \frac{2.4.6 \ldots 2m}{1.3.5 \ldots (2m+1)} = \frac{2(2m)!}{\overline{m}^2 (2m+1)}.$$

Then

$$u_{mm} = \frac{u_m}{\overline{m}}. \tag{8-80b}$$

If $m \gg 1$, the following approximations are obtained by use of Stirling's formula:

$$i_{mm} \approx \sqrt{\frac{\pi}{m}} \quad \text{if } n=m$$

$$\text{and } i_{m1} \approx \sqrt{\frac{2\pi}{m}} = \sqrt{2}\, i_{mm} \quad \text{if } n=1.$$

If $n = m$ and is large then, due to the surface velocity being proportional to $\sin^n\vartheta$, the progressive waves are very small in amplitude in the polar regions; they increase rapidly in the region near the equator, and finally take on almost constant values. In this case the radiation is concentrated in a circular equatorial belt (in directions near $\vartheta = \frac{\pi}{2}$). Such a radiator can be more or less realized in practice by a rapidly rotating spherical belt having sinusoidal furrows (m in number on the entire circumference), the rotating belt being an equatorial zone of an otherwise fixed sphere. We will consider the theory of such a radiator in somewhat greater detail since it is possible to construct this type of radiator experimentally.

The velocity potential (8-79), takes the following form in view of (8-11) and (8-80b), if $n = m$:

$$\Phi = \frac{u_m \sin^m\vartheta\, G_m(z)\, e^{-j\delta_m(z)}}{jkD_m(z_0)\, e^{-j\delta_m(z_0)}} \cdot e^{j(\omega t - m\psi)}.$$

At large values of r far from the radiator, in accordance with formulae (8-28) and (8-29), we get:

$$\Phi = \frac{u_m \sin^m\vartheta\, e^{jm\frac{\pi}{2}}}{k^2 D_m(z_0)\, e^{-j\delta_m(z_0)}} \cdot \frac{e^{j(\omega t - kr - m\psi)}}{r}.$$

The intensity vector in the radial direction is

$$J_r = \rho c \frac{u_m^2}{2} \frac{\sin^{2m}\vartheta}{D_m^2(z_0)\, k^2 r^2}, \qquad (8\text{-}81)$$

and the acoustic pressure amplitude

$$p_m = \rho c u_m \frac{\sin^m \vartheta}{D_m(z_0)\, kr}. \tag{8-82}$$

The intensity vector in the azimuthal direction ψ is:

$$J_\psi = \rho c \frac{u_m^2}{2} \frac{m \sin^{2m-1}\vartheta}{D_m^2(z_0)} \cdot \frac{G^2(kr)}{kr} \approx \frac{m \sin^{2m-1}\vartheta}{D_m^2(z_0)} \cdot \frac{1}{k^3 r^3}\Bigg|_{r\to\infty}. \tag{8-83}$$

Thus, there is a radial and an azimuthal flow of energy for radiators with progressive waves. The azimuthal flow sharply diminishes with distance, so that it is concentrated in a ring around the sphere and, consequently, is not related to the energy loss on radiation.

A radiator with a progressive wave in any azimuthal direction produces a sound intensity independent of the azimuthal angle ψ. This is a characteristic feature of a radiator with a progressive wave. A radiator of the sectorial type for which the velocity on the surface is defined by the expression $u = u_m \sin^m \vartheta \cdot \cos m\psi e^{j\omega t}$, produces a directivity characteristic with $2m$ lobes dependent on the azimuth; it can be regarded as the superposition of two radiators with progressive waves having equal amplitudes but opposite directions. For example, the acoustic field of two co-axial propellers rotating in opposite directions is of this nature.

Suppose we compare the total energy flows in the radial (Π_r) and azimuthal (Π_ψ) directions:

$$\Pi_r = \int_0^{2\pi} 2\pi r^2 \cdot \sin\vartheta \cdot J_r d\vartheta = \frac{1}{2} \frac{2\pi\rho c u_m^2}{k^2 D_m^2(z_0)} \cdot \frac{2(2m)!}{\overline{m}^2(2m+1)} =$$
$$= S\rho c \frac{u_m^2}{2} \frac{1}{z_0^2 D_m^2(z_0)} \frac{(2m)!}{\overline{m}^2(2m+1)}, \tag{8-84}$$
$$\Pi_\psi = \int_{r_0}^{\infty} r dr \int_0^{\pi} J_\psi d\vartheta = \frac{1}{2} \frac{2\pi\rho c u_m^2}{k^2 D_m^2(z_0)} \cdot \frac{1}{z_0} \cdot \frac{(2m)!}{\overline{m}^2}.$$

Thus,

$$\frac{\Pi_\psi}{\Pi_r} = \frac{m + \frac{1}{2}}{z_0}.$$

If the condition $m \gg z_0$ is fulfilled (long waves), the azimuthal flow of energy can be considerably greater than the radial flow. The addition of two opposite azimuthal flows of equal magnitude corresponds to a spherical radiator, with a standing wave of the sectorial type on its surface. As has been shown (see (8-55a)) the azimuthal flow of energy is zero for a radiator of this type, but in the zone near the sphere there arises an "additional energy" formed by the addition of two opposite azimuthal waves. It is the inertial energy of the acoustic field and can be characterized by introducing the concept of an "attached mass" M_{mm}, possessing the kinetic energy

$$T_{mm} = \frac{1}{2} M_{mm} \frac{u_m^2}{2} \text{ (see (8-74))}.$$

For long waves the total radiated power is

$$\Pi_{r_{z_0 \ll m}} \approx S\rho c \frac{u_m^2}{2} \cdot \frac{z_0^{2m+2}}{\overline{m}^2 (m+1)^2} i_{mm}, \tag{8-85}$$

and the sound intensity

$$J_{r_{z_0 \ll m}} \approx \rho c \frac{u_m^2}{2} \frac{\sin^{2m}\vartheta \cdot z_0^{2m+4}}{\overline{m}^2 (m+1)^2} \cdot \frac{1}{k^2 r^2}. \tag{8-86}$$

If $z_0 \gg m$, then $D_m \approx \frac{1}{z_0}$ and for $r = r_0$ we get from equation (8-81)

$$J_{r_{z_0 \gg m}} \approx \rho c \frac{u_m^2}{2} \sin^{2m}\vartheta. \tag{8-87}$$

Thus, in the plane of the equator $J_r \approx \rho c \frac{u_m^2}{2}$ and the radiation is maximum; in magnitude it corresponds to the radiation from a unit area of a plane of infinite dimensions with velocity amplitude u_m. In accordance with expressions (8-84), if $z_0 \gg m$

$$\Pi_{r_{z_0 \gg m}} \approx S\rho c \frac{u_m^2}{2} \cdot \frac{1}{2} \left[\frac{2\,(2m)!}{m^2\,(2m+1)} \right] = S\rho c \frac{u_m^2}{2} \frac{i_{mm}}{2}.$$

The total power radiated by a sphere is less than that radiated by an equivalent area S of an infinite piston, because the intensity diminishes in directions other than the equatorial direction, becoming zero at $\vartheta = 0$ and $\vartheta = \pi$

Values of the factor $\frac{1}{2} i_{mm}$ are given in Table 9.

TABLE 9

m	2	4	8	10
$\frac{1}{2} i_{mm}$	0.53	0.41	0.30	0.28

Radiation of sound by progressive waves in the azimuthal direction can be realized by the kinematically equivalent system of a radiator in the form of a rigid sphere with sinusoidal furrows (Fig. 76), rotating rapidly about its axis. If N is the number of revolutions of the sphere per second and m the number of furrows around the circumference, the frequency of the radiated sound will then be $f = Nm$, and

$$z_0 = \frac{\omega}{c} r_0 = \frac{2\pi N r_0 m}{c} = m \cdot \frac{c'}{c}, \tag{8-88}$$

where

$$c' = 2\pi N r_0$$

is the peripheral speed of the sphere at the equator. In this case the condition $z_0 \ll m$ is equivalent to the condition:

$$c' \ll c.$$

Thus, formula (8-85) and (8-86) are valid at peripheral speeds (or at speeds of bending waves in a spherical shell), considerably less than the velocity of sound. It follows from equations (8-85) and (8-86) that the efficiency of radiation if $c' < c$ is markedly dependent on the size of the ratio c'/c. If $c' \gg c$, the radiation tends to the limit-value which is independent of c'/c in accordance with (8-87).

It is of interest to calculate the radiation by the exact formula (8-81) for an actual case of a sphere with sinusoidal furrows rotating in air.

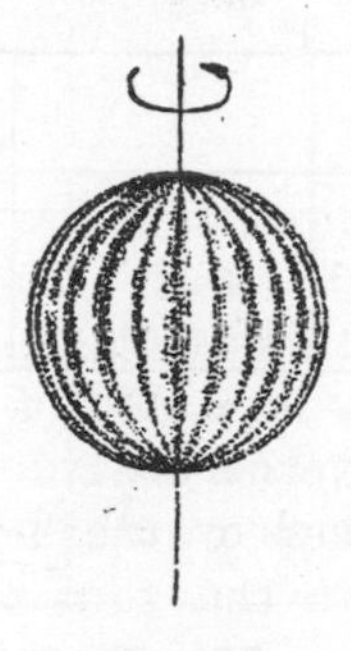

Fig. 76

Suppose the radius of the sphere is $r_0 = 15$ cm, and the amplitude of the furrows $a_m = 0{\cdot}2$ cm. Using tables for the functions $D_m(z_0)$, we get quantities which define the acoustic field as shown in Table 10.

It is of interest to point out that the radiated power increases rather more rapidly with the number of revolutions if $m = 8$ than if $m = 2$.

At frequencies $N > 200$ rev/sec, a radiator with two furrows around the circumference is considerably more effective than a radiator with eight furrows. It should be pointed out that the first radiator produces only a quarter of the frequency in the same number of revolutions. Equal intensities are obtained for $m = 2$ and $m = 8$ at a peripheral speed $c' \approx 0{\cdot}6c$, but at correspondingly different frequencies. The results of theoretical analysis show that considerable sound intensities can be obtained in air at peripheral speeds approximately equal to the speed of sound.

TABLE 10

z_0	No. rev/sec $N = \frac{z_0 c}{2\pi m r_0}$	$\frac{c'}{c}$	Frequency $f = mN$	$\Pi_r \left(\frac{erg}{sec}\right)$	Intensity $J_r \left(\frac{erg}{cm^2\ sec}\right)$	Intensity level β (db)	Acoustic pressure (eff. bar)
					at $\vartheta = \frac{\pi}{2}$ and r = 100 cm		
m = 2							
0·4	73	0·2	146	$0{\cdot}5 \times 10^7$	0·775	89	5·6
0·8	146	0·4	292	$1{\cdot}23 \times 10^7$	$1{\cdot}88 \times 10^2$	113	88
1·2	219	0·6	438	$2{\cdot}90 \times 10^8$	$4{\cdot}50 \times 10^3$	126	430
1·6	292	0·8	584	$2{\cdot}53 \times 10^9$	$3{\cdot}87 \times 10^4$	136	1260
2·4	438	1·2	876	$6{\cdot}33 \times 10^{10}$	$9{\cdot}70 \times 10^5$	150	6400
m = 8							
2·2	100	0·275	800	60	$1{\cdot}61 \times 10^3$	62	0·258
3·0	136	0·375	1090	$2{\cdot}38 \times 10^4$	0·64	88	5·13
4·0	182	0·50	1450	$5{\cdot}20 \times 10^6$	$1{\cdot}38 \times 10^2$	111	75·3
5·0	227	0·625	1820	$2{\cdot}80 \times 10^8$	$7{\cdot}50 \times 10^3$	129	553

A similar analysis for the radiation of sound in water shows that the efficiency of radiation for the same number of revolutions of the radiator is extremely low since the ratio c'/c is considerably less and, consequently, z_0 is small. In order to increase the intensity such large rotational speeds are required that it is impossible to obtain them in practice.

All the foregoing calculations are based on the linear

theory of the acoustic field and do not take into account the viscosity of the medium. There is no doubt about the applicability of the calculation to cases where progressive bending waves are excited in a cylindrical shell or plate (by a suitable mechanism), since the radial and tangential velocities of the shell remain slightly less than the velocity of sound. However, if progressive waves are obtained by rotating a sphere with furrows, there equally is no doubt about the important part played by the effects of viscosity at large peripheral speeds when c' is comparable with c; the boundary layer of the medium is carried around by the furrows and as a result the rotating ridges are as it were enveloped by an adhering layer and become smoother than they would otherwise be. Hence, it can be assumed that the amplitude of the radial oscillations is reduced and the efficiency of radiation is less than that calculated theoretically without including viscosity. On the other hand, it is known from aerodynamics that at tangential velocities near the velocity of sound each uneveness on the surface causes the emergence of a shock wave. It is obvious that the furrows on the surface of a rotating sphere must act in the same way and a considerable radiated sound intensity is to be expected.

The acoustic field of a spherical zone lying between $\frac{\pi}{2} - \varphi$ and $\frac{\pi}{2} + \varphi$ on which are progressive surface waves in the azimuthal direction ψ, in accordance with (8-78), the sphere having fixed polar segments, can be calculated roughly by formula (8-79), where in place of u_{mm} in expression (8-80) we put

$$u'_{mm} = \frac{(2m+1)\overline{m}\, u_m}{2\cdot(2m)!} \int\limits_{\frac{\pi}{2}-\varphi}^{\frac{\pi}{2}+\varphi} \sin^{m+n+1}\vartheta\, d\vartheta.$$

If $n = m$, then the coefficient u'_{mm} is expressed in the following way:

$$u'_{mm} = \frac{2^m m!}{(2m)!} \sin\varphi \left[1 + \frac{1}{2}\cos^2\varphi + \frac{1.3}{2^2.1.2.}\cos^4\varphi + \ldots + \frac{m}{2^m m!}\cos^{2m}\varphi \right].$$

For a radiator with a radius $r_0 = 15$ cm and a zone of width $2\varphi = 0{\cdot}2$, if $m = 8$

$$u'_{mm} = 0{\cdot}604 \frac{u_m}{m}$$

instead $u_{mm} = \frac{u_m}{m}$ for a full sphere.

If $m = 2$

$$u_{mm} = 0{\cdot}364 \frac{u_m}{m}.$$

Since expression (8-79) for the velocity potential contains the factor $P_m^{(m)}(\vartheta) = \bar{m} \sin^m \vartheta$ and the amplitude coefficient u_{mm}, the acoustic pressure for a zone (other things being equal) will be less than for a complete sphere in the ratio of 0·604 (if $m = 8$) and 0.364 (if $m = 2$). Thus, the radiation of a spherical zone bounded by two polar hemispherical screens is not greatly different from the radiation of a complete sphere, and the difference is the less, the greater the parameter m, which characterizes the law ($\sin^m \vartheta$) governing the decrease in amplitude of the waves from the equator to the poles.

It is of interest to draw an analogy between the field of radiators with progressive waves and the "rotational sound" of a propeller. Gutin* solved the problem of finding the acoustic field of a propeller and showed that the "rotational sound" is related to the reaction of the propeller on the surrounding medium and depends on the thrust of the screw P and its moment of rotation M. He also calculated the additional sound radiation due to the periodic displacement of the medium by the rotating body. For the

* L.Ya. Gutin, *Zhur. tekh. phys.* 6, 899, 1936; *Zhur. tekh. phys.* 12, 76, 1942.

amplitude of the nth harmonic of the acoustic pressure at a distance r and at an angle ϑ to the axis of the screw, Gutin obtained an expression for this latter part of the rotational noise which in our notation takes the form:

$$p_{mn} = \frac{\omega^2 \rho V}{2\pi r} J_{mn}(kR_0 \sin\vartheta), \tag{8-89}$$

where m is the number of blades on the propeller, $\omega = kc = 2\pi Nnm$ the angular frequency of the sound, N the number of revolutions of the propeller per second, V the volume of all the propeller blades, and R_0 a certain mean radius approximately equal to 0·75 of the blade tip radius.

Introducing the peripheral speed which corresponds to the radius R_0,

$$c' = 2\pi NR_0,$$

we get

$$kR_0 = \frac{c'}{c} mn \text{ and } \omega = \frac{2\pi NR_0 mn}{R_0 c} = \left(\frac{c'}{c}\right)\frac{cmn}{R_0}.$$

For the fundamental ($n = 1$)

$$p_{m1} = \frac{\rho Vc^2 m^2}{2\pi rR_0^2}\left(\frac{c'}{c}\right) J_m\left(\frac{c'}{c} m \sin\vartheta\right).$$

For long waves $kR_0 \ll 1$ and $\frac{c'}{c} \ll 1$, so it is possible as a first approximation to assume that

$$J_m(x) \approx \left(\frac{x}{2}\right)^m \cdot \frac{1}{m!}.$$

Using Stirling's formula, we get:

$$p_{m1} \approx \frac{\rho c^2 V \sin^m\vartheta}{2\pi rR_0^2}\left(\frac{c'}{c}\right)^{m+2} \cdot \left(\frac{m^{m+2}}{2^m m!}\right) \approx$$
$$\approx \frac{\rho c^2 V \sin^m\vartheta}{2\pi rR_0^2}\left(\frac{ec'}{2c}\right)^{m+2} \cdot \frac{4m^2}{e^2\sqrt{2\pi m}}. \tag{8-89a}$$

This expression provides a good approximation if $m > 3$. We will compare the pressure p_{m1} with the corresponding quantity (in the case of long waves) for a rotating sphere with m sinusoidal furrows on the surface (formula (8-82)):

$$p_m = \frac{\rho c u_m \sin^m \vartheta}{D_m(z_0)\, kr} \approx \frac{\rho c^2 \sin^m \vartheta \cdot z_0^{m+2} u_m}{\omega r (m+1) \overline{m}}.$$

Since the amplitude of the furrow $a_m = A_m \sin^m \vartheta$, where A_m is the amplitude of the furrow at the equator, and the cross-sectional area of a furrow is $a_m \cdot \frac{2\pi r_0}{m}$, the volume displaced by one furrow is:

$$V_1 = \int_0^\pi \frac{2\pi r_0^2 A_m}{m} \sin^m \vartheta\, d\vartheta = \frac{2\pi r_0^2 A_m}{m} \int_0^\pi \sin^m \vartheta\, d\vartheta.$$

The integral is calculated in the same way as in formulae (8-80) and if $m > 3$ it is approximately $\sqrt{\frac{2\pi}{m}}$. Denoting this integral by i_m, the total volume of the medium displaced by the furrows is:

$$V = mV_1 = 2\pi r_0^2 A_m i_m.$$

Introducing the quantity V in the expression for the velocity amplitude u_m, we get

$$u_m = \omega A_m = \frac{\omega V}{2\pi r_0^2 i_m}.$$

Since

$$z_0 = \frac{2\pi N r_0 m}{c} \left(\frac{c'}{c}\right) m,$$

where c' is the peripheral velocity of the waves at the equator, it follows that the expression for the acoustic pressure takes the following form at large values of m if use is made of Stirling's formula:

$$p_m \approx \frac{\rho c^2 V \sin^m \vartheta}{2\pi r \cdot r_0^2} \left(\frac{c^1}{c}\right)^{m+2} \cdot m^{m+2} \cdot \left(\frac{1}{(m+1)\, \overline{m} i_m}\right) \approx \qquad (8\text{-}90)$$

$$\approx \frac{\rho c^2 V \sin^m \vartheta}{2\pi r \cdot r_0^2} \left(\frac{ec'}{2c}\right)^{m+2} \cdot \left(\frac{4m^2}{e^2 \sqrt{2\pi m}\, \sqrt{2}}\right).$$

Expressions (8-89a) and (8-90) are almost identical relationships between the pressure and the magnitude of the displaced volume V, the angle ϑ, the distance r, the radius of the rotating body R_0 or r_0, and the ratio of the peripheral wave speed c' to the sound velocity c in the surrounding medium. The dependence on the number of blades (or furrows) m is identical in the limiting forms of both expressions; the differences in the other factors in formulae (8-89a) and (8-90) are not significant. We have

$$\frac{p_m}{p_{m1}}=\left(\frac{1}{(m+1)\,m\,i_m}\right):\left(\frac{1}{2^m\,m!}\right)=\frac{2^{2m}\,(m!)^2}{(m+1)(2m!)\,i_m}.$$

If $m>3$, this expression is approximately equal to $\frac{1}{\sqrt{2}}$. If $m=2$ and $m=3$, this ratio, as calculated by the exact formula, is approximately of the same value. Thus, the acoustic pressure in the case of a rotational radiator, as calculated by Gutin's formula for "rotational sound" is of the same order as the acoustic pressure in the field of a spherical radiator with a progressive wave.

In view of the insignificant difference between the results obtained by these two quite different methods, it is clear that the acoustic field of such systems in the case of long waves is fundamentally determined by the volume of the rotating blades (or furrows), their number, their distance from the axis, and the rotational speed, independently of the shape of the rotating bodies.

CHAPTER IX

SCATTERING OF SOUND AT A SPHERE

The Scattering of Sound at a Rigid Fixed Sphere

The acoustic field at a rigid fixed surface can be calculated by assuming that the incident wave generates a new scattered (diffracted) wave at the surface, the sum of the two waves (the incident and the scattered) being a field having zero normal velocity on the surface. Diffraction is usually taken to mean the bending of rays in the zone of a geometric shadow, and scattering to mean the dispersal by a body of an incident wave from a remote source. In this chapter a general method is considered which describes the whole pattern of both scattered and diffracted waves without necessarily distinguishing between them.

Suppose that a plane incident wave is propagated in the negative x direction and that a rigid sphere of radius r_0 is placed at the origin (Fig. 77). The acoustic pressure of this incident wave is

$$p_i = p_0 e^{jkx} e^{j\omega t}.$$

At point P, we have $x = r\cos\vartheta = r\mu$, where $\mu = \cos\vartheta$. Putting z for kr, we get

$$p_i = p_0 e^{jkr\cos\vartheta} \cdot e^{j\omega t} = p_0 e^{jz\mu} \cdot e^{j\omega t}.$$

The plane wave is expanded into a series of spherical

waves:

$$e^{jz\mu} = \sum_{m=0}^{m=\infty} A_m P_m(\mu), \tag{9-1}$$

where $P_m(\mu)$ is a spherical harmonic (Legendre polynominal) of degree m. Both sides of the equation are then multiplied by $P_n(\mu)$ and we integrate the right- and left-hand sides with respect to μ from -1 to +1:

$$\int_{-1}^{+1} P_n(\mu) e^{j\mu z} d\mu = \sum_{m=0}^{\infty} A_m \int_{-1}^{+1} P_m(\mu) \cdot P_n(\mu)\, d\mu.$$

It is known from the theory of spherical harmonics* that

$$\int_{-1}^{+1} P_n(\mu) P_m(\mu)\, d\mu = \begin{cases} 0 & \text{if } m \neq n, \\ \dfrac{2}{2m+1} & \text{if } m = n. \end{cases}$$

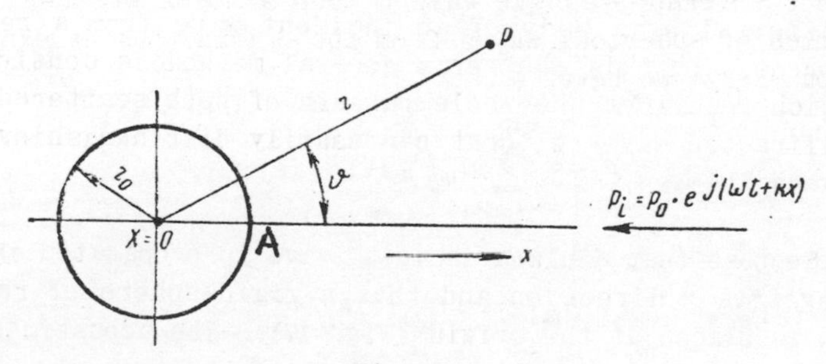

Fig. 77

Consequently

$$A_m = \frac{2m+1}{2} \int_{-1}^{+1} P_n(\mu) e^{jz\mu} d\mu.$$

* V.I. Smirnov, *A Course of Advanced Mathematics*, Moscow: Gostekhizdat (Vol. III, Ch. IV)..

It can be proved* that the integral appearing in A_m is expressible in terms of zero order Bessel functions of argument z

$$\int_{-1}^{+1} P_n(\mu)\, e^{jz\mu} d\mu = 2j^m \sqrt{\frac{\pi}{2z}}\, J_{m+\frac{1}{2}}(z).$$

Introducing spherical Bessel functions $j_m(z)$ (see Chapter VIII), we get:

$$A_m = \frac{2m+1}{2} \cdot 2j^m \sqrt{\frac{\pi}{2z}}\, J_{m+\frac{1}{2}}\, z = (2m+1)\, j^m j_m(z). \quad (9\text{-}2)$$

Thus, a plane wave incident on a sphere can be expressed as a series of spherical waves, the origin being the centre of the sphere:

$$p_i = p_0 e^{j\omega t} \sum_{m=0}^{\infty} j^m (2m+1)\, P_m(\vartheta)\, j_m(z). \quad (9\text{-}3)$$

The scattered pressure wave p_s can also be written as a series of spherical waves from the origin. Using expression (8-22) we have:

$$p_s = \sum_{m=0}^{\infty} a_m P_m(\vartheta)\, h_m(z)\, e^{j\omega t}, \quad (9\text{-}4)$$

where

$$h_m(z) = G_m(z) e^{-j\varepsilon_m(z)}$$

is a spherical Hankel function of the second kind.

Since the particle velocity in the radial direction is given by the expression

$$q_n \Big|_{r=r_0} = -\frac{1}{j\omega\rho} \frac{\partial p}{\partial r} \Big|_{r=r_0} = -\frac{k}{j\omega\rho} \frac{\partial p}{\partial z} \Big|_{r=r_0},$$

* Lord Rayleigh, *Theory of Sound,* New York, Dover Publications, 1945 (see vol. II, Sect. 330).

it follows that the boundary condition at the rigid sphere takes the form

$$(q_{in}+q_{sn})\Big|_{r=r_0}=-\frac{k}{j\omega\rho}\left[\frac{\partial p_i}{\partial z}+\frac{\partial p_s}{\partial z}\right]_{r=r_0}=0.$$

In accordance with formulae (8-21), (8-23) and (8-24), we have:

$$\frac{d}{dz}\Big[j_m(z)\Big]=\frac{1}{2m+1}\Big[mj_{m-1}(z)-(m+1)\,j_{m+1}(z)\Big]=$$
$$=-D_m(z)\sin\delta_m(z)$$

and

$$\frac{dh_m(z)}{dz}=-jD_m(z)\,e^{-j\delta_m(z)}.$$

Using these expressions and cancelling the non-zero factor $\frac{k}{j\omega\rho}$, we find that the boundary condition simplifies to

$$p_0\sum_{m=0}^{\infty}j^m(2m+1)\,P_m(\vartheta)\,D_m(z_0)\sin\delta_m(z_0)+$$
$$+\sum_{m=0}^{\infty}a_mP_m(\vartheta)(-j)\,D_m(z_0)\,e^{-j\delta_m(z)}=0.$$

The mth term must vanish independently of the other terms; we thus find

$$a_m=jp_0j^m(2m+1)\sin\delta_m(z_0)\,e^{j\delta_m(z_0)}. \qquad (9\text{-}5)$$

Substituting a_m into equation (9-3) gives the final expression for the pressure p_s of the scattered wave,

$$p_s=p_0e^{j\omega t}\sum_{m=0}^{\infty}j^{m+1}(2m+1)P_m(\vartheta)\sin\delta_m(z_0)\,e^{j\delta_m(z_0)}\cdot h_m(z). \qquad (9\text{-}6)$$

This expression can be used to find the scattered acoustic field for any $z_0=\frac{2\pi r_0}{\lambda}$. But if $z_0>1$ the series begins to converge slowly and if $z_0>5$ the calculation becomes extremely cumbersome.

The particle velocity in the radial direction is:

$$q_{sn} = -\frac{k}{j\omega\rho}\frac{\partial p_s}{\partial z} = \frac{p_0}{\rho c}\sum_{m=0}^{\infty} j^{m+1}(2m+1)\times \qquad (9\text{-}6a)$$
$$\times P_m \sin\delta_m(z_0)\, e^{j\delta_m(z_0)} D_m(z)\, e^{-j\delta_m(z)}.$$

Since if $z \gg 1$

$$G_m(z) \approx \frac{1}{z};\ D_m(z) \approx \frac{1}{z};\ h_m(z) \approx \frac{e^{-j\left(z - \frac{m+1}{2}\pi\right)}}{z};$$
$$\delta_m(z) \approx z - \frac{m+1}{2}\pi,$$

it follows that the radial component of the intensity vector of the scattered wave is:

$$J_s = \frac{1}{2} Re(p_s q^*_{sn})\Big|_{z\gg 1} =$$
$$= Re\left[\frac{p_0^2}{2\rho c}\sum_{m,n=0}^{\infty} e^{j\frac{m+1}{2}\pi}\cdot e^{-j\frac{n+1}{2}\pi} P_m\cdot P_n\cdot(2m+1)\times\right.$$
$$\times (2n+1)\, e^{j\delta_m(z_0) - j\delta_n(z_0)} \sin\delta_m(z_0)\sin\delta_n(z_0)\frac{e^{-j\left(z-\frac{m+1}{2}\pi\right)}}{z}$$
$$\times\frac{e^{j\left(z-\frac{n+1}{2}\pi\right)}}{z} = \frac{p_0^2}{2\rho c}\cdot\frac{1}{z^2}\sum_{m,n=0}^{\infty}(2m+1)(2n+1)P_m P_n \sin\delta_m(z_0)\times$$
$$\times \sin\delta_n(z_0)\cos[\delta_m(z_0) - \delta_n(z_0) + (m-n)\pi]. \qquad (9\text{-}7)$$

Instead of adding $(m-n)\pi$ to the cosine of the argument, we can introduce the factor $(-1)^{m-n}$.

If the wave is incident in the positive x direction*, it is necessary to expand e^{-jkx} into a series of spherical functions. A similar expression containing $j_m(-z) = j^m j_m(z)$ is then obtained in place of (9-2). The expression for p_i contains j^{-m} instead of j^m, the coefficient a_m contains j^{-m} instead of j^m and $j^{-(m+1)}$ appears in p_s in place

* P.M. Morse, *Vibration and Sound*, New York: McGraw-Hill, (see sect. 29). 1948.

of j^{m+1}. The radial intensity then takes a form similar to that in (9-7) except that the term $(m-n)\pi$ is discarded from the cosine bracket.

A simpler expression is thus obtained for J_s if the angle ϑ is measured from the direction of the incident wave.

Figure 78 (from Morse's book) shows polar characteristics of the scattered intensity from a sphere for various values of the argument $z_0 = \frac{2\pi r_0}{\lambda}$.

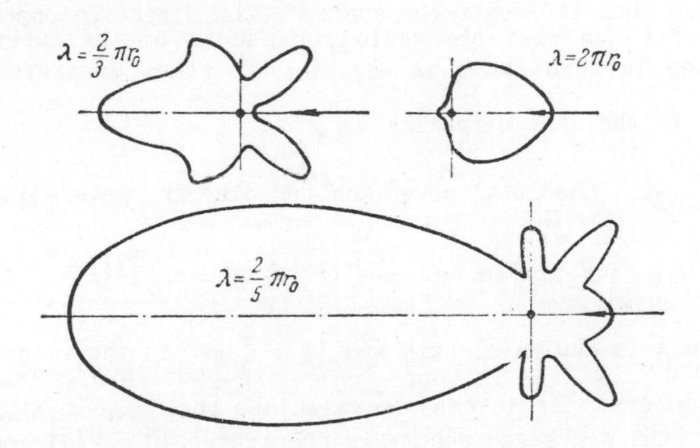

Fig. 78

We now consider expression (9-7) in the case of long waves ($z_0 \ll 1$):

$$D_0(z_0) \approx \frac{1}{z_0^2};\; D_1(z_0) \approx \frac{2}{z_0^3};\; D_2 \approx \frac{9}{z_0^4},$$
$$\delta_0(z_0) \approx \frac{z_0^3}{3};\; \delta_1(z_0) \approx -\frac{z_0^3}{6};\; \delta_2(z_0) \approx -\frac{2z_0^5}{135}. \tag{9-8}$$

The appropriate terms contain z_0^6 for combinations (m,n) of (0,0), (0,1), (1,0) and (1,1). They contain z_0^8, for (0,2), (2,0), (1,2) and (2,1), but if $m = n = 2$ they contain z_0^{10}. Thus series (9-7) is dominated by the first four terms for which m and n are equal to 0 or 1, since the rest will be less by at least two orders of magnitude:

$$J_s \Big|_{\substack{z_0 \ll 1 \\ z \gg 1}} \approx \frac{p_0^2}{2\rho c}\left\{\left(\frac{z_0^3}{3}\right)\left(\frac{z_0^3}{3}\right) + 1.3.\left(\frac{z_0^3}{3}\right)\left(-\frac{z_0^3}{6}\right)\cos\left[\frac{z_0^3}{3}+\frac{z_0^3}{6}-\pi\right]\cos\vartheta + \right.$$

$$+3.1\left(-\frac{z_0^3}{6}\right)\left(\frac{z_0^3}{3}\right)\cos\left[-\frac{z_0^3}{3}-\frac{z_0^3}{6}+\pi\right]\cos\vartheta +$$

$$\left. +3.3\left(\frac{z_0^3}{6}\right)\left(\frac{z_0^3}{6}\right)\cos^2\vartheta\right\} = \frac{J_0}{z^2}\frac{z_0^6}{9}\left[1+3\cos\vartheta+\frac{9}{4}\cos^2\vartheta\right] =$$

$$= J_0\frac{(\pi r_0^2)\, z_0^4}{9\pi^2 r^2}\left(1+\frac{3}{2}\cos\vartheta\right)^2, \tag{9-9}$$

where $J_0 = \frac{p_0^2}{2\rho c}$ is the intensity of the incident plane wave.* Thus the scattered energy in the direction opposite to the incident wave is $\left(\frac{5}{2}\Big/\frac{1}{2}\right)^2 = 25$ times greater than that in the same direction.

If $z_0 \ll 1$, the total power scattered by the sphere is

$$\Pi_s \approx \int_0^\pi J_s\, 2\pi r^2 \sin\vartheta d\vartheta = \frac{7}{9}(\pi r_0^2 J_0) z_0^4 = \frac{7\pi^3 V_0^2}{\lambda^4} J_0, \tag{9-10}$$

where λ is the wavelength and $V_0 = \frac{4}{3}\pi r_0^3$ is the volume of the sphere. It is easy to calculate that $^{13}/_{14}$ (or 93%) of the total scattered energy is propagated in the direction opposite to the incident wave (at angles 0 to 90°) and that only $^{1}/_{14}$ (or 7%) is propagated in the forward direction. In the general case (without restricting the calculation by the magnitude of z_0), integration of expression (9-7) gives:

$$\Pi_s = \frac{4\pi J_0}{z_0^2}\sum_{m=0}^{\infty}(2m+1)\sin^2\delta_m(z_0). \tag{9-10a}$$

---

* The formulae in Morse's book contain the factor $\left(1-\frac{3}{2}\cos\vartheta\right)^2$ instead of $\left(1+\frac{3}{2}\cos\vartheta\right)^2$ since the angles ϑ are measured from the line to the source from the origin.

The scattering when $z_0 \ll 1$ is called Rayleigh scattering and was first considered by Rayleigh in explaining the blue colour of the sky.

Suppose it is required to find the scattering cross-section (γ) of a sphere. Equating the quantity Π_s to the energy flow $J_0 S$ of a plane wave across a circle of area S, it is found that

$$\gamma \approx \frac{S}{\pi r_0^2} = \frac{7}{9}(kr_0)^4,$$

i.e. for long waves the cross-section γ is only a small fraction of that of the sphere πr_0^2.

Using (9-6), we get for the acoustic pressure p_s of the scattered wave at great distances ($z \gg 1$)

$$p_s \approx -p_0 e^{j(\omega t - kr)} \cdot \frac{(kr_0)^3}{3kr}\left(1 + \frac{3}{2}\cos\vartheta\right) =$$

$$= -p_0 e^{j(\omega t - kr)}\left(\frac{\pi V_0}{r\lambda^2}\right)\left(1 + \frac{3}{2}\cos\vartheta\right). \qquad (9\text{-}11)$$

It follows from formulae (9-9) and (9-11) that for long waves the scattered wave is equivalent to the radiation of two radiators, namely a zero order radiator and a first order radiator (a dipole), the radiation of the second being 1·5 times greater in amplitude. This can be interpreted as follows. A rigid fixed sphere will impede the motion of a fluid. The volume occupied by this sphere can neither pulsate or oscillate (in the wave direction) as if no sphere were present. But the sphere hence must react on the surrounding medium in a manner equivalent to a motion of the spherical volume equal in amplitude but opposite in phase to the incident wave. This reaction is the cause of the zero-plus-first order source to which reference was made above.

It may be hard to see why first and zero order radiation are almost equally important since the velocity amplitude of a plane wave incident on the surface of a sphere, proportional to $(2m+1)\,D_m(z_0)\sin\delta_m(z_0)$, for each order, is greater for first order radiation than for zero order radiation. In fact, substituting the values D_m and δ_m, from equation (9-6a) for $m = 0, 1$ and 2, we find that the surface velocity amplitudes are proportional to:

$$\text{for } m=0;\ q_{i0} \sim \frac{1}{z_0^2}\,\frac{z_0^3}{3} = \frac{z_0}{3},$$

$$\text{for } m=1;\ q_{i1} \sim 3\,\frac{2}{z_0^3}\cdot\frac{z_0^3}{6} = 1,$$

$$\text{for } m=2;\ q_{i2} \sim 5\,\frac{9}{z_0^4}\,\frac{2z_0^5}{135} = \frac{2}{3}\,z_0.$$

Hence it is clear that the oscillatory motion (m-1) is the most pronounced in the incident wave. The intensity of the scattered wave is defined as the product of the radiation resistance by the square of the velocity amplitude. Using expressions (8-60) and (8-62) for the radiation resistance, we find that the radiated power is of the order of:

$$\text{for } m=0;\ \Pi_0 = \frac{1}{2} R_0 q_{i0}^2 \sim z_0^2 \cdot z_0^2 = z_0^4,$$

$$\text{for } m=1;\ \Pi_1 = \frac{1}{2} R_1 q_{i1}^2 \sim z_0^4 \cdot 1 = z_0^4,$$

$$\text{for } m=2;\ \Pi_2 = \frac{1}{2} R_{22} q_{i2}^2 \sim z_0^6 \cdot z_0^2 = z_0^8.$$

The zero and first order radiated powers are thus the same despite the larger ($3/z_0$ times greater) surface velocity amplitude in first order radiation.

If $z_0 \gg 1$, the directivity characteristic of the scattered radiation is of a complicated shape with many maxima and minima. The scattered sound intensity is greatest in the direction of the incident wave ($\vartheta = \pi$). Yet in this direction it is known that there is a shadow; this apparent contradiction will be clarified below. It can be seen from the scattering characteristics in Fig. 78 that the maximum grows with increasing z_0 and becomes more and more peaked.

Expression (9-7) ceases to have any practical value if

z_0 is large. Morse* has put forward the following asymptotic approximation for the intensity of sound scattered by a sphere when $z_0 \gg 1$,

$$J_s \approx J_0 \frac{r_0^2}{4r^2} \left\{1 + \cot^2\left(\frac{\pi - \vartheta}{2}\right) J_1^2 \left[z_0 \sin(\pi - \vartheta)\right]\right\}. \quad (9\text{-}12)$$

In the direction opposite to the incident wave $|\vartheta = 0|$, the intensity $J_{s0} \approx J_0 \frac{r_0^2}{4r^2}$, and in the other direction of the incident wave $(\vartheta = \pi)$ $J_{s\pi} \sim J_0 \frac{r_0^2}{4r^2}$ $(1 + z_0^2)$, which is much larger than J_{s0} if $z_0 \gg 1$. If the angle satisfies the condition

$$z_0 \sin(\pi - \vartheta) = z_0 \sin\vartheta = 1{\cdot}84,$$

then $J_1(z_0 \sin\vartheta) = 0$ and the second term in the curly brackets in (9-12) is zero. Thus, we have a sharply defined beam with its maximum at the angle $\vartheta = \pi$ and an angular width $\sin\vartheta \approx \vartheta = \frac{1{\cdot}84}{2\pi} \cdot \frac{\lambda}{r_0} = 0{\cdot}61 \frac{\lambda}{r_0}$.

If

$$z_0 \sin(\pi - \vartheta) = z_0 \sin\vartheta = 5{\cdot}33$$

the function J_1 has a maximum of 0·34 and the value of the additional term in (9-12) is:

$$(0{\cdot}34)^2 : \left(\frac{0{\cdot}85}{2}\right)^2 \left(\frac{\lambda}{r_0}\right)^2 = 0{\cdot}64 \frac{r_0^2}{\lambda^2} = 0{\cdot}016 z_0^2 .$$

The maximum intensity off the axis (at the angle $\vartheta = \pi - 0{\cdot}85 \frac{\lambda}{r_0}$) is $(0{\cdot}016)^{-1}$ = 63 times less than that at the angle $\vartheta = \pi$. The subsequent maxima will be still less. It should however be borne in mind that formula (9-7) and

* P.M. Morse, *Vibration and Sound,* New York: McGraw-Hill (see sect. 29) 1948.

all those derived from it, including (9-12), are applicable only if $z \gg 1$, which corresponds to the zone of Fraunhofer diffraction. The interference pattern in the zone of Fresnel diffraction, where the distance from the centre of the sphere is less than $\frac{r_0^2}{\lambda}$, cannot be described by these formulae.

For very short waves an approximation has to be obtained from geometric acoustics. The scattered wave can be regarded as being split into two parts, namely, that part which is scattered in all directions from the centre of the sphere, and a narrow shadow-forming beam in the $\vartheta = \pi$ direction which is restricted to the cross-sectional area πr_0^2 of the sphere. The intensity in the shadow-forming wave is equal to that in the incident wave, but the two waves are opposite in phase so that the shadow is produced by the mutual cancellation of these two waves. The second term in equation (9-12) represents this shadow-forming wave.

The total scattered energy for very short waves is

$$\Pi_s = 2(\pi r_0^2) J_0.$$

One half of this energy is in the shadow-forming wave, and the other half in the true scattered wave. Incidentally, the integral of the first term in (9-12) just gives $\pi r_0^2 J_0$, exactly equal to the integral of the second term. A detailed analysis of the scattering of sound in the case of short waves would involve great mathematical difficulties.

Reciprocity Theorem

In 1860 Helmholtz* proved a very important theorem known

* H. von Helmholtz, *Vorlesungen über die mathematischen Prinzipien der Akustik*, Leipzig, 1898.

as the reciprocity theorem:

"In an air-filled region having bounding surfaces $S_1, S_2, S_3, \ldots$, the region containing only one point source at A, the velocity potential of sound waves is the same in magnitude and phase at another point B as it would have been at A had the source been located at B".

In particular it follows from the reciprocity theorem that a point source at the pole of a sphere (Fig. 77) produces the same sound pressure at a certain distance $r = x \cos \vartheta$ from the centre of the sphere (point P) as a point source with the same volume velocity at a point A on the surface of the sphere an angular distance ϑ from the radius drawn to point P from the centre of the sphere. This makes it possible to find the distribution of the pressure on the surface of a rigid fixed sphere from the solution of the problem of the acoustic field of a point source at the pole of a sphere (see Chapter VIII). The sound pressure at a distant point with the coordinate $r = x$ is given by expression (8-76):

$$p\,|_{x \to \infty} \approx j \frac{A_0 \rho c \cdot e^{j(\omega t - kx)}}{4\pi r_0^2 \cdot kx} \sum_{m=0}^{\infty} \frac{j^m P_m(\vartheta)(2m+1)}{D_m(z_0)\, e^{-j\delta_m(z_0)}}, \qquad (9\text{-}13)$$

where A_0 is the strength of the source.

It is known from the theory of zero order radiators (see Chapter IV) that the sound pressure at the point $x = 0$ due to a distant source with strength A_0 at the point x in the positive direction is:

$$p_0 = j\omega\rho \frac{A_0}{4\pi x} e^{jkx}.$$

This quantity has to be substituted into formula (9-6), it being remembered that the pressure p_0 is created by a distant source.

Suppose we require the total sound pressure on the surface of the sphere. It follows from (9-3) and (9-6) that

$$(p_i + p_s)_{r=r_0} = p_0 e^{j\omega t} \sum_{m=0}^{\infty} j^m (2m+1) P_m(\vartheta) [j_m(z_0) + + j \sin \delta_m (z_0) e^{j\delta_m(z_0)} h_m(z_0)]. \quad (9\text{-}14)$$

Using (8-26) we get

$$\sin\delta_m = -\frac{mj_{m-1} - (m+1) j_{m+1}}{(2m+1) D_m} = -\frac{1}{D_m}\frac{dj_m}{dz} = -\frac{j'_m}{D_m};$$

$$h_m = j_m - jn_m; \quad \frac{dh_m}{dz} = j'_m - jn'_m = D_m e^{-j\left(\delta_m - \frac{\pi}{2}\right)}.$$

The expression in square brackets in (9-14) is then transformed into:

$$j_m + j\frac{(j_m - jn_m)\, j'_m}{j'_m - jn'_m} = -j\frac{j_m n'_m - n_m j'_m}{j'_m - jn'_m}.$$

Using formula (8-21a) for the derivatives j'_m and n'_m we get:

$$j_m n'_m - n_m j'_m = \frac{1}{2m+1}[m(j_m n_{m-1} - n_m j_{m-1}) + (m+1)(j_{m+1} n_m - - n_{m+1} j_m)].$$

Since in accordance with (8-21)

$$j_m n_{m-1} - n_m j_{m-1} = \frac{1}{z^2},$$

it follows that

$$j_m n'_m - n_m j'_m = \frac{1}{2m+1}\left[m\frac{1}{z^2} + (m+1)\frac{1}{z^2}\right] = \frac{1}{z^2}.$$

After these transformations, the bracketed expression in formula (9-14) simplifies to

$$-j\frac{\frac{1}{z_0^2}}{j'_m - jn'_m} = \frac{1}{z_0^2 D_m(z_0)\, e^{-j\delta_m(z_0)}}.$$

Then

$$(p_i + p_s)_{r=r_0} = \frac{p_0 e^{j\omega t}}{z_0^2} \sum_{m=0}^{\infty} \frac{j^m P_m(\vartheta)(2m+1)}{D_m(z_0)\, e^{-j\delta_m(z_0)}}, \tag{9-14a}$$

Substituting $p_0 = j\omega\rho \frac{A_0}{4\pi x} \cdot e^{jkx}$, we find:

$$(p_i + p_s)_{r=r_0} = j \frac{A_0 \rho c e^{j(\omega t + kx)}}{4\pi r_0^2 \cdot kx} \sum_{m=0}^{\infty} \frac{j^m P_m(\vartheta) \cdot (2m+1)}{D_m(z_0)\, e^{-j\delta_m(z_0)}}. \tag{9-15}$$

Since the phase in formula (9-13) is measured in the opposite direction to that in formula (9-15), the conclusion follows that both formulae produce values of sound pressure coinciding in amplitude and phase as required by the reciprocity theorem. Figure 79 illustrates the distribution of sound intensity on the surface of the sphere as a function of the angle ϑ for various values of the parameter $z_0 = \frac{2\pi r_0}{\lambda}$. Values of $z_0^2 \frac{|p_i + p_s|^2}{p_0^2}$ are marked off along the ordinate on a logarithmic scale and curves of this function are plotted. These values are calculated by formula (8-75) for the sound intensity of a point source at the pole ($\vartheta = 0$) of a sphere.

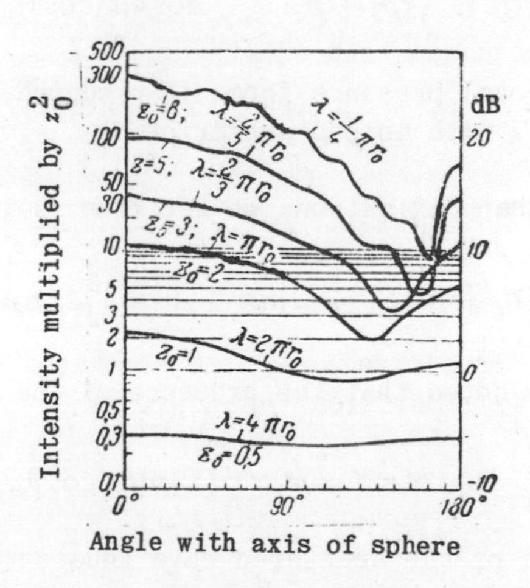

Fig. 79

The Pressure of a Plane Sound Wave on a Fixed Rigid Sphere

Suppose we expand expression (9-14a) for the sound pressure on the surface of a sphere in the form

$$(p_i+p_s)_{r=r_0}=\frac{p_0e^{j\omega t}}{z_0^2}\left[\frac{e^{j\delta_0}}{D_0}+j3\frac{P_1e^{j\delta_1}}{D_1}-5\frac{P_2e^{j\delta_2}}{D_2}-j7\frac{P_3e^{j\delta_3}}{D_3}+\right.$$
$$\left.+9\frac{P_4e^{j\delta_4}}{D_4}+\cdots\right]. \quad (9\text{-}16)$$

Substituting the values D_m and δ_m for small z_0 and bearing in mind that $e^{j\delta_m}\approx 1+j\delta_m$, we discard terms containing z_0 above the power of four and get:

$$(p_i+p_s)_{r=r_0}\approx p_0e^{j\omega t}\left\{\left[1-\frac{5}{9}P_2z_0^2+\left(\frac{P_1}{4}+\frac{9P_4}{525}\right)z_0^4\right]+\right.$$
$$\left.+j\left[\frac{3}{2}P_1z_0+\left(\frac{1}{3}-\frac{7}{60}P_3\right)z_0^3\right]\right\}. \quad (9\text{-}17)$$

The pressure force component in the x direction is $(p_i+$ $+p_s)\cos\vartheta$, per unit area and the total pressure force is

$$F_x\approx-\int_0^\pi(p_i+p_s)_{r=r_0}\cos\vartheta\cdot 2\pi r_0^2\sin\vartheta d\vartheta=$$
$$=2\pi r_0^2e^{j\omega t}\int_0^\pi(p_i+p_s)_{r=r_0}\cos\vartheta d(\cos\vartheta). \quad (9\text{-}18)$$

A non-zero total pressure force is produced only by terms containing P_m with an odd subscript.

As a first approximation, we get from (9-17)

$$(p_i+p_s)_{r=r_0}\approx p_0e^{j\omega t}\left(1+j\frac{3}{2}z_0\cos\vartheta\right).$$

It should be noted that the pressure of the incident wave is

$$p_0e^{jkx}e^{j\omega t}\approx p_0e^{j\omega t}(1+jz_0\cos\vartheta).$$

The reaction of the scattered wave thus contributes half as much as the incident wave to the pressure force. After integration, as a first approximation:

$$F_x \approx -jz_0 \cdot 2\pi r_0^2 p_0 e^{j\omega t} = -j\frac{z_0}{2} S p_0 e^{j\omega t},$$

i.e. at small values of z_0 the pressure force increases in direct proportion to z_0; we put $S = 4\pi r_0^2$.

The mean pressure on a spherical segment of angle ϑ_0* is:

$$p_x = -\frac{p_0 e^{j\omega t}}{z_0} \sum_{m=0}^{\infty} \frac{j^m e^{-j\delta_m (z_0)} [P_{m-1}(\vartheta_0) - P_{m+1}(\vartheta_0)]}{D_m(z_0)[P_{-1}(\vartheta_0) - P_1(\vartheta_0)]} = -p_0 e^{j\omega t}\left[1 + j\frac{3}{4} z_0 (1 + \cos\vartheta_0)\right], \tag{9-19}$$

where $P_{-1}(\cos\vartheta_0) = 1$.

Formula (9-19) indicates a pressure amplitude p_x of the order of p_0 at small values of z_0. If z_0 increases, the amplitude also increases and eventually approximates to $2p_0$, as for a plane wave incident on a rigid wall; if $z_0 = 4$ the pressure is still about 10 per cent less than $2p_0$. Including the terms containing odd Legendre polynomials, the total pressure force from (9-16) and (9-18) is:

$$F_x \approx jp_0 e^{j\omega t} \frac{2\pi r_0^2}{z_0^2}\left[\frac{3e^{j\delta_1}}{D_1}\int_{+1}^{-1} P_1(y)y\,dy - \frac{7e^{j\delta_3}}{D_3}\int_{+1}^{-1} P_3(y)y\,dy + \frac{11e^{j\delta_5}}{D_5}\int_{+1}^{-1} P_5(y)y\,dy + \ldots\right],$$

where $y = \cos\vartheta$.

The integrals appearing in this expression are

$$\int_{+1}^{-1} P_1(y)y\,dy = \int_{+1}^{-1} y^2 dy = -\frac{2}{3}; \quad \int_{+1}^{-1} P_3(y)y\,dy = \int_{+1}^{-1} P_5(y)y\,dy = 0.$$

---

* P.M. Morse, *Vibration and Sound*, New York: McGraw-Hill, (see Sect. 29). 1948.

Consequently,

$$F_x \approx -\frac{2\pi r_0^2 p_0}{z_0^2}\frac{2e^{j\delta_1}}{D_1}e^{j\omega t} = -j2\pi r_0^2 p_0 e^{j\omega t}\cdot\frac{2z_0 e^{j\delta_1}}{\sqrt{4+z_0^4}} \underset{z_0 \ll 1}{\approx} j\frac{Sp_0 e^{j\omega t}}{2} z_0.$$

The quantity

$$\frac{2z_0}{\sqrt{4+z_0^4}} = \frac{z_0}{\sqrt{1+\frac{z_0^4}{4}}}$$

is proportional to z_0 if z_0 is small. It attains a maximum of one if $z_0=\sqrt{2}$ and then begins to decrease according to the law $\approx \frac{2}{z_0}$ (Fig. 80).

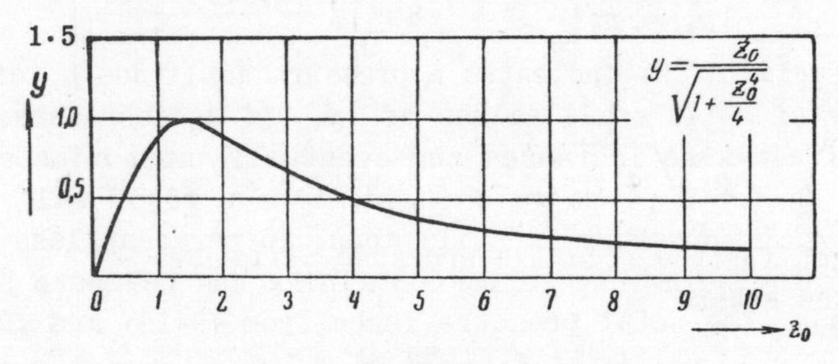

Fig. 80

The pressure difference between two poles of a sphere. A problem of interest in physiological acoustics is the difference in pressure amplitude and phase between a person's two ears when a sound wave is incident from the side. An approximate solution can be obtained by regarding the head as a sphere 18 cm in diameter and calculating the surface pressure by formula (9-14) at the points $\vartheta=0$ and $\vartheta=\pi$. Using (9-17) and bearing in mind that $P_m(0)=1$ and $P_m(-1)=(-1)^m$, the pressure amplitude at $\vartheta=0$ is:

$$p_1 = p_0\left[\left(1-\frac{5}{9}z_0^2+\frac{9}{525}z_0^4+\frac{1}{4}z_0^4\right)+j\frac{3}{2}z_0\left(1-\frac{7}{90}z_0^2+\frac{2}{9}z_0^2\right)\right]. \tag{9-20}$$

and that at $\vartheta = \pi$

$$p_2 = p_0\left[\left(1 - \frac{5}{9}z_0^2 + \frac{9}{525}z_0^4 - \frac{1}{4}z_0^4\right) + j\frac{3}{2}z_0\left(-1 + \frac{7}{90}z_0^2 + \frac{2}{9}z_0^2\right)\right]. \tag{9-21}$$

Putting

$$\alpha = 1 - \frac{5}{9}z_0^2 + \frac{9}{525}z_0^4 \text{ and } \beta = 1 - \frac{7}{90}z_0^2$$

and confining ourselves to small quantities up to z_0^4, we find the absolute values

$$|p_1| \approx p_0\sqrt{\alpha^2 + \frac{9}{4}\beta^2 z_0^2}\left[1 + \frac{z_0^4}{4}\frac{\alpha + 2\beta}{\alpha^2 + \frac{9}{4}\beta^2 z_0^2}\right],$$

$$|p_2| \approx p_0\sqrt{\alpha^2 + \frac{9}{4}\beta^2 z_0^2}\left[1 - \frac{z_0^4}{4}\frac{\alpha + 2\beta}{\alpha^2 + \frac{9}{4}\beta^2 z_0^2}\right].$$

Since

$$p_0\sqrt{\alpha^2 + \frac{9}{4}\beta^2 z_0^2} \approx p_0, \text{ and } \alpha + 2\beta \approx 3$$

we get for the relative pressure difference at the poles of the sphere

$$\gamma = \frac{|p_1| - |p_2|}{p_0} \approx \frac{z_0^4}{2}\cdot\frac{\alpha + 2\beta}{\alpha^2 + \frac{9}{4}\beta^2 z_0^2} \approx \frac{3}{2}z_0^4.$$

Rayleigh*, proceeding from the reciprocity theorem, calculated the relative difference in intensity on the surface of a sphere at the points $\vartheta = 0$ and $\vartheta = \pi$, for $z_0 \ll 1$ and obtained $3z_0^4$. But, strictly speaking, the concept of sound intensity on the surface of a sphere is unacceptable since there is neither a flow of energy nor a velocity component since $(q_i + q_s)_{r=r_0} = 0$. In this case it is necessary to take the quantity $\frac{p_0^2}{2\rho c}$ as the intensity. The rela-

* Lord Rayleigh, *Theory of Sound*. New York: Dover Publications, 1945 (see vol. II, Sect. 328).

tive difference in intensity then is

$$\frac{|p_1|^2-|p_2|^2}{\overline{p}_0^2}=\frac{(|p_1|+|p_2|)(|p_1|-|p_2|)}{\overline{p}_0^2}\approx 3z_0^4,$$

The relative difference in pressure amplitude for a human head at 100 and 200 c/s is

$$f=100\,\text{c/s},\ z_0\approx 0{\cdot}33,\ \gamma\approx 0{\cdot}018;$$
$$f=200\,\text{c/s},\ z_0\approx 0{\cdot}66,\ \gamma\approx 0{\cdot}3.$$

The ear is hardly capable of perceiving a 10 per cent difference in sound pressure. Thus the binaural effect at low frequencies cannot be explained by the difference in sound intensity at the two ears.

The phase difference of the sound at points $\vartheta=0$ and $\vartheta=\pi$ can easily be calculated by formulae (9-20) and (9-21). Apart from terms z_0^3 or more, the tangent of the angle of the phase difference Δ (relative to the phase of the incident wave at the centre of the sphere) at points $\vartheta=0$ and $\vartheta=\pi$ is:

$$\tan\Delta(0)\approx\Delta(0)\approx\frac{\frac{3}{2}z_0\left(1-\frac{7}{90}z_0^2+\frac{2}{9}z_0^2\right)}{1-\frac{5}{9}z_0^2}\approx\frac{3}{2}z_0\left(1+\frac{7}{10}z_0^2\right);$$

$$\tan\Delta(\pi)\approx\Delta(\pi)\approx\frac{-\frac{3}{2}z_0\left(1-\frac{7}{90}z_0^2-\frac{2}{9}z_0^2\right)}{1-\frac{5}{9}z_0^2}\approx-\frac{3}{2}z_0\left(1+\frac{23}{90}z_0^2\right).$$

The phase difference at the points $\vartheta=0$ and $\vartheta=\pi$ is

$$\Delta=\Delta(0)-\Delta(\pi)\approx 3z_0\left(1+\frac{43}{45}z_0^2\right)\approx\frac{3}{2}\left(2r_0k\right).$$

Consequently, if $z_0\ll 1$, the phase difference at the two poles is 1·5 times greater than the phase lead $k\cdot 2r_0$ along a straight path between these points. This conclusion is of interest in estimating the phase difference of sound at two ears when the sound wave is incident at an angle of 90° to the frontal direction, and in certain technical problems associated with sound direction finding.

The Phase Shift of a Plane Sound Wave due to Scattering by a Rigid Sphere

Using formulae (9-3) and (9-6), the total field of the incident and scattered waves can be written in the form:

$$(p_i+p_s)=p_0e^{j\omega t}\sum_{m=0}^{\infty}j^mP_m(\vartheta)(2m+1)\Big[j_m(z)+$$
$$+j\sin\delta_m(z_0)e^{j\delta_m(z_0)}h_m(z)\Big].$$

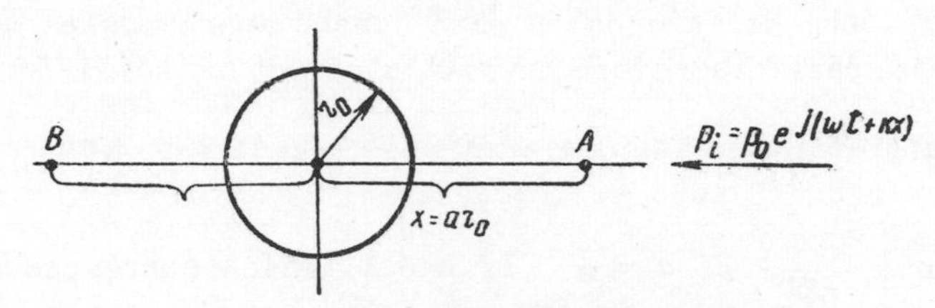

Fig. 81

Suppose we require the pressure at two points A and B (Fig. 81) on the x axis, at distances $+x$ and $-x$ from the centre of the sphere, and put $x=ar_0$, where $a>1$, $kx=z$ and $kr_0=z_0$. Then from (8-21) and (8-28) if $z_0\ll 1$, we have:

$$j_0(z)\approx 1;\ j_m(z)\approx\frac{z^m}{\overline{m}(2m+1)}=\frac{a^mz_0{}^m}{\overline{m}(2m+1)},$$

$$h_m(z)\approx j\frac{\overline{m}}{z^{m+1}}=j\frac{\overline{m}}{a^{m+1}z_0^{m+1}};$$

$$\delta_0(z_0)=\frac{z_0}{3};\ \delta_m(z_0)\approx\frac{-mz_0^{2m+1}}{\overline{m}^2(2m+1)(m+1)}.$$

Performing the calculation up to terms of order z_0^3, we

get:

$$(p_i+p_s)_A \approx p_0 e^{j\omega t}\left[1+jz_0\left(a+\frac{1}{2a^2}\right)\right],$$

$$(p_i+p_s)_B \approx p_0 e^{j\omega t}\left[1-jz_0\left(a+\frac{1}{2a^2}\right)\right].$$

Between points A and B the phase difference is

$$\Delta \approx 2z_0\left(a+\frac{1}{2a^2}\right)=k(2x)\left(1+\frac{1}{2a^3}\right),$$

and the difference in path length of the acoustic ray is

$$\delta \approx \frac{\Delta}{k} \approx 2x\left(1+\frac{1}{2a^3}\right).$$

Thus for points A and B far from the surface of the sphere, the difference in path length approximates to $2x$ and the sphere therefore has little effect on the difference in path length. Thus, $\delta \approx 2x\left(1+\frac{1}{16}\right)$, if $a = 2$, and $\delta \approx$ $\approx 2x\left(1+\frac{1}{250}\right)$ if $a = 5$. If $a = 1$, which corresponds to points A and B being at the poles, $\delta \approx 2r_0\frac{3}{2}=3r_0$.

The Scattering of Sound at a Fluid or Gaseous Sphere (Diffraction at a Flexible Sphere)

The boundary conditions for the scattering of sound at a fluid or gaseous sphere consist of the continuity of the pressure and of the normal velocity component at the boundary of the sphere. Suppose we put p_i and q_{in} for the pressure and normal velocity component of the incident wave in the external medium, p_s and q_{sn} for the scattered wave in the external medium, and $\bar{p}$ and $\bar{q}_n$ for the quantities in the internal medium. In the following, all functions and quantities referring to the internal medium (density, speed of sound) are denoted by a bar on top. The boundary conditions can then be written in the following form:

$$(p_i + p_s)_{r=r_0} = \bar{p}\,|_{r=r_0},$$
$$(q_{in} + q_{sn})_{r=r_0} = \bar{q}_n\,|_{r=r_0}.$$

provided the surface oscillation amplitude of the sphere is very small so that it can be assumed that $r_0 =$ const. Like formulae (9-3) and (9-4) for the scattering of a plane wave of amplitude p_0 incident in the negative x direction on a sphere at the origin, expressions for the pressure and velocity of the incident and scattered waves can be formed as series expansions in spherical functions:

$$p_i = p_0 e^{j\omega t} \sum_{m=0}^{\infty} j^m (2m+1) P_m(\vartheta) j_m(z),$$

$$p_s = e^{j\omega t} \sum_{m=0}^{\infty} a_m P_m(\vartheta) G_m(z) e^{-j\varepsilon_m(z)},$$

$$q_{in} = -\frac{k}{j\omega\rho} p_0 e^{j\omega t} \sum_{m=0}^{\infty} j^m (2m+1) P_m(\vartheta) [-D_m(z) \sin \delta_m(z)],$$

$$q_{sn} = -\frac{k e^{j\omega t}}{j\omega\rho} \sum_{m=0}^{\infty} a_m P_m(\vartheta) D_m(z) e^{-j\left[\delta_m(z) + \frac{\pi}{2}\right]}. \quad (9\text{-}22)$$

In accordance with (8-22) and (8-48), since the solution contains only symmetric spherical harmonics $P_m(\vartheta)$ (Legendre polynominals), we can write for the internal medium:

$$\bar{p} = e^{j\omega t} \cdot \sum_{m=0}^{\infty} \bar{a}_m P_m(\vartheta) j_m(z) = e^{j\omega t} \sum_{m=0}^{\infty} \bar{a}_m P_m(\vartheta) G_m(\bar{z}) \cos \varepsilon_m(\bar{z});$$

$$\bar{q}_n = -\frac{\bar{k} e^{j\omega t}}{j\omega\bar{\rho}} \sum_{m=0}^{\infty} \bar{a}_m P_m(\vartheta) [-D_m(\bar{z}) \sin \delta_m(\bar{z})], \quad (9\text{-}23)$$

where the $\bar{a}_m$ are amplitude coefficients. The boundary conditions for each m separately have the form:

$$p_0 j^m (2m+1) j_m(z_0) - a_m G_m(z_0) e^{-j\varepsilon_m(z_0)} = \bar{a}_m G_m(\bar{z}_0) \cos \varepsilon_m(\bar{z}_0),$$

$$j\frac{p_0}{\rho c} j^m (2m+1) D_m(z_0) \sin \delta_m(z_0) + \frac{a_m}{\rho c} D_m(z_0) e^{-j\delta_m(z_0)} =$$

$$= -j\frac{\bar{a}_m}{\bar{\rho}\bar{c}} D_m(\bar{z}_0) \sin \delta_m(\bar{z}_0).$$

From these equations we find a_m and $\bar{a}_m$:

$$a_m = p_0 j^{m+1}(2m+1) \times$$

$$\times \frac{\frac{\bar{\rho}\bar{c}}{\rho c} D_m \sin \delta_m \cdot \bar{G}_m \cos \bar{\varepsilon}_m - \bar{D}_m \sin \bar{\delta}_m \cdot j_m}{\frac{\bar{\rho}\bar{c}}{\rho c} D_m e^{-j\delta_m} \cdot \bar{G}_m \cos \bar{\varepsilon}_m + j G_m e^{-j\varepsilon_m} \bar{D}_m \sin \bar{\delta}_m}$$

$$\bar{a}_m = p_0 j^{m+1}(2m+1) \times \tag{9-24}$$

$$\times \frac{D_m \sin \delta_m \; G_m e^{-j\varepsilon_m} - jD_m e^{-j\delta_m} \cdot j_m}{D_m e^{-j\delta_m} \cdot \bar{G}_m \cos \bar{\varepsilon}_m + j\frac{\rho c}{\bar{\rho}\bar{c}} G_m e^{-j\varepsilon_m} \bar{D}_m \sin \bar{\varepsilon}_m}.$$

Here the functions with or without a bar on top have arguments $\bar{z}_0$ and z_0 respectively.

To find the first few coefficients a_m for $z_0 \ll 1$ and $\bar{z}_0 \ll 1$ (long waves) we use the following approximate values of D_m, δ_m, G_m and ε_m,

$$\left.\begin{aligned} &D_0 \approx \frac{1}{z^2},\ \delta_0 \approx \frac{z^3}{3},\ G_0 \approx \frac{1}{z},\ \varepsilon_0 \approx z - \frac{\pi}{2},\ j_0 \approx 1, \\ &\qquad e^{-j\delta_0} \approx 1 - j\frac{z^3}{3} \approx 1; \\ &D_1 \approx \frac{2}{z^3};\ \delta_1 \approx -\frac{z^3}{6},\ G_1 \approx \frac{1}{z^2},\ \varepsilon_1 \approx \frac{z^3}{3} - \frac{\pi}{2},\ j_1 \approx \frac{z}{3}; \\ &D_2 \approx \frac{9}{z^4},\ \delta_2 \approx -\frac{2z^5}{135},\ G_2 \approx \frac{3}{z^3},\ \varepsilon_2 \approx \frac{z^5}{5} - \frac{\pi}{2},\ j_2 \approx \frac{z^2}{15}. \end{aligned}\right\}$$

Performing the operations indicated in (9-24), we get:

$$a_0 \approx jp_0 \frac{\frac{z_0^3}{3}\left(1-\frac{\rho c^2}{\overline{\rho c^2}}\right)}{1-\frac{\rho c^2}{\overline{\rho c^2}}\frac{z_0^2}{3}e^{-jz_0}}. \tag{9-25}$$

The quantities $\rho c^2 = \varkappa$ and $\overline{\rho c^2} = \overline{\varkappa}$ are the adiabatic bulk moduli of the external and internal media respectively

$$a_0 \approx jp_0 \frac{\frac{z_0^3}{3}\left(1-\frac{\varkappa}{\overline{\varkappa}}\right)}{1-\frac{\varkappa}{\overline{\varkappa}}\frac{z_0^2}{3}e^{-jz_0}}. \tag{9-26}$$

For a rigid sphere $\frac{\varkappa}{\overline{\varkappa}} \to 0$ and for a_0 we get the expression

$$a_0 \approx jp_0 \frac{z_0^3}{3},$$

which agrees with formula (9-5).

If

$$\frac{\varkappa}{\overline{\varkappa}}\frac{z_0^2}{3} \ll 1 \quad \text{or} \quad z_0 \ll \sqrt{3\frac{\overline{\varkappa}}{\varkappa}}, \tag{9-27}$$

then

$$a_0 \approx jp_0 \frac{z_0^3}{3}\left(\frac{\overline{\varkappa}-\varkappa}{\overline{\varkappa}}\right).$$

As we shall see later, condition (9-27) requires that the frequency ω be small compared with the resonant frequency of pulsation oscillations of the sphere. To the same degree of approximation as in (9-25), we get:

$$\left.\begin{aligned} a_1 &\approx p_0 z_0^3 \frac{\overline{\rho}-\rho}{2\overline{\rho}+\rho}, \\ a_2 &\approx jp_0 \frac{2}{9} z_0^5 \frac{\frac{\overline{\rho}}{\rho}-1}{2+3\frac{\overline{\varkappa}}{\varkappa}}. \end{aligned}\right\} \tag{9-28}$$

The coefficients a_0 and a_1 thus contain a factor z_0^3, whilst a_2 contains z_0^5, i.e. a quantity two orders less than either z_0 or a_1. It is obvious, that the scattered wave is mainly determined by zero and first order terms when $z_0 \ll 1$ and $z_0 \ll \sqrt{3\frac{\bar{\varkappa}}{\varkappa}}$ and from formulae (9-22), (9-26) and (9-28) we find:

$$p_s \approx p_0 e^{j\omega t}\left[j\frac{z_0^3}{3}\,\frac{\bar{\varkappa}-\varkappa}{\bar{\varkappa}}\,G_0(z)e^{-j\varepsilon_0(z)}+z_0^3\,\frac{\bar{\rho}-\rho}{2\bar{\rho}+\rho}G_1(z)e^{-j\varepsilon_1(z)}\cos\vartheta\right].$$

At remote distances $(z \gg 1)$

$$G_0(z)=G_1(z)\approx\frac{1}{z};\quad \varepsilon_0\approx z-\frac{\pi}{2};\ \varepsilon_1\approx z-\pi$$

and

$$p_s \approx p_0 e^{j(\omega t-kr)}\,\frac{k^2r_0^2}{3}\left(\frac{r_0}{r}\right)\left[\frac{\bar{\varkappa}-\varkappa}{\bar{\varkappa}}+3\,\frac{\bar{\rho}-\rho}{2\bar{\rho}+\rho}\cos\vartheta\right].$$

The scattered wave from a flexible sphere at low frequencies is mainly composed of zero and first order radiation like that from a rigid sphere, but there is a different relationship between the components.

The Pulsation of a Flexible Sphere due to a Sound Wave

Here the pulsation corresponds to the zero order term in the expansion of p_s in (9-22). We transform the expression for a_0 (9-26), assuming that $z_0 \ll 1$ so that $e^{-jz_0}\approx 1-jz_0$:

$$a_0\approx -p_0\,\frac{\rho c z_0^2\left(1-\frac{\bar{\varkappa}}{\varkappa}\right)}{\rho c\left[z_0^2+j\left(z_0-\frac{3}{z_0}\,\frac{\bar{\varkappa}}{\varkappa}\right)\right]}=-p_0\rho c\,\frac{z_0^2\left(1-\frac{\bar{\varkappa}}{\varkappa}\right)}{Z_1},\qquad (9\text{-}29)$$

where

$$Z_1=\rho c\left[z_0^2+j\left(z_0-\frac{3}{z_0}\,\frac{\bar{\varkappa}}{\varkappa}\right)\right]=\rho c Z.\qquad (9\text{-}29\text{a})$$

We then calculate the amplitude of the radial velocity component $q_{sn}(r_0)$ and on the surface of the sphere. If $z_0 \ll 1$ from (9-22) and (9-29) we get:

$$\left.\begin{aligned} q_{sn}(r_0) &\approx \frac{ja_0 e^{-j\frac{z_0^3}{3}} e^{j\frac{\pi}{2}}}{\rho c z_0^2} \approx -p_0 \frac{1-\frac{\bar{\varkappa}}{\varkappa}}{Z_1} = -q_0 \frac{1-\frac{\bar{\varkappa}}{\varkappa}}{Z_1}\rho c \\ \text{and} \qquad & \\ q_{in} &\approx -j\frac{p_0}{\rho c}\frac{z_0}{3} = -jq_0\frac{z_0}{3}, \end{aligned}\right\} \quad (9\text{-}30)$$

where $q_0 = \frac{p_0}{\rho c}$ is the particle velocity amplitude in the incident wave. The total radial velocity is mainly determined by the first expression in (9-30), except when $\bar{\varkappa} \gg \varkappa$. In this case $q_{sn} = +jq_0\frac{z_0}{3}$ and the total velocity $q_n(r_0) = 0$. Unless $\bar{\varkappa} \gg \varkappa$, it is clear from the first formula in (9-30) and from (9-29a) that the pulsation amplitude will be a maximum when

$$z_0 = \sqrt{\frac{3\bar{\varkappa}}{\varkappa}}. \qquad (9\text{-}31)$$

This condition corresponds to pulsation resonance of the sphere. For gas bubbles in a fluid of static pressure P, we have:

$$\bar{\varkappa} = \bar{\rho}\ \bar{c}^2 = \bar{\rho}_0\ \bar{c}_0^2 \frac{P}{P_0},$$

where $\bar{\rho}_0$ and $\bar{c}_0$ are the values at 0°C and atmospheric pressure P_0 (for air bubbles in water $\bar{\varkappa}_0 = \bar{\rho}_0\ \bar{c}_0^2 = 1{\cdot}4\times10^6$ dyne/cm^2). From (9-31) we get for the resonant frequency of a gas bubble in a fluid:

$$f_{res} = \frac{c}{2\pi r_0}\sqrt{\frac{3\bar{\varkappa}_0}{\varkappa}} \cdot \sqrt{\frac{P}{P_0}}.$$

For air bubbles in water

$$f_{res} \approx \frac{1{\cdot}5\times10^5}{2\pi r_0}\cdot\sqrt{\frac{3\times1{\cdot}4\times10^6}{2\times10^{10}}}\cdot\sqrt{\frac{P}{P_0}} \approx \frac{340}{r_0}\sqrt{\frac{P}{P_0}} = \frac{680}{2r_0}\sqrt{\frac{P}{P_0}}.$$

Here the effect of surface tension pressure $\left(P'=\frac{2\sigma}{r_0}\right)$ has been neglected since $\sigma=72$ dyne/cm at 18°C for water and therefore the effect of surface tension can safely be ignored for bubbles greater than 10^{-3} cm in radius. If $r_0<\frac{2\sigma}{P}$ the bubbles become unstable and are dissolved in the water since $P'>P$.

Expression (9-29a) can also be written in the form:

$$Z_1=\rho c(z_0^2+jz_0)-j\frac{3\rho c\frac{\bar{x}}{x}}{z_0}=Z_r+Z_e.$$

Thus Z_1 is a certain impedance per unit area; the term $Z_r=\rho c(z_0^2+jz_0)$ is the specific radiation impedance of a pulsating sphere (provided $z_0\ll 1$, see Chapter IV), whilst

$$Z_e=\frac{3\rho c\frac{\bar{x}}{x}}{jz_0}=\frac{3\bar{\rho}\,\bar{c}^2}{j\omega r_0}=\frac{1}{4\pi r_0^2}\cdot\frac{\bar{\rho}\,\bar{c}^2(4\pi r_0^2)^2}{j\omega\left(\frac{4}{3}\pi r_0^3\right)}=\frac{\bar{e}_1}{j\omega}$$

is the specific elastic impedance of a spherical volume $V=\frac{4}{3}\pi r_0^3$. The bulk modulus of the sphere is

$$\bar{e}_1=\frac{3\bar{x}}{r_0}=\frac{3\bar{\rho}\,\bar{c}^2}{r_0}.$$

Analysis of expression (9-30) shows that, in the event of the forced pulsation of a small sphere by a plane wave of pressure amplitude p_0, the surface oscillation velocity q_{sn} is determined by the difference between the compressibilities of the external and internal media and a complex impedance Z_1 consisting of the natural (elastic) impedance Z_e of the sphere and its radiation impedance Z_r.

In forming expression (9-29) it was assumed that $z_0 \ll 1$ and that $\bar{z}_0 = \frac{c}{\bar{c}} z_0 \ll 1$. If $c < \bar{c}$, the second condition is satisfied if the first is; if $c > \bar{c}$, the second condition can be rewritten in the form:

$$\bar{z}_0 = \frac{z_0}{z_{\text{res}}} \sqrt{\frac{3\bar{\rho}}{\rho}} \ll 1.$$

For a gas bubble in water (at $P_0 = 1$ atm) $\sqrt{\frac{3\bar{\rho}}{\rho}} \approx \frac{1}{17}$ and therefore the condition $\bar{z}_0 \ll 1$ leads to the requirement $z_0 \ll 17\, z_{\text{res}}$. It is easy to see that formula (9-29) is applicable up to frequencies several times greater than the resonant frequency, since at the resonant frequency we still get $\bar{z}_0 \approx \frac{1}{17}$, and at a frequency four times greater $\bar{z}_0 \approx \frac{1}{4}$.

It follows from formula (9-30) that the volume flow of the medium across the surface of the sphere is

$$\left|4\pi r_0^2 q_{sn}\right|_{r=r_0} \approx -\frac{\left(1-\frac{\bar{\varkappa}}{\varkappa}\right)4\pi r_0^2}{z_0^2 + j\left(z_0 - \frac{3}{z_0}\cdot\frac{\bar{\varkappa}}{\varkappa}\right)} q_0. \qquad (9\text{-}33)$$

For a gaseous sphere in a fluid the total volume flow of the medium across the surface of the sphere at resonance is:

$$\left|4\pi r_0^2 q_{sn}\right| \approx \left|-q_0\right| \frac{\lambda^2}{\pi}\left(1-\frac{\bar{\varkappa}}{\varkappa}\right) \approx q_0 \frac{\lambda^2}{\pi}.$$

Thus, the volume velocity across the surface of the sphere is $\frac{\lambda^2}{\pi}$ times greater than the flow across 1 cm^2 of the wavefront. This implies that a resonant sphere absorbs energy from an area of the wavefront equal to

$$S' \approx \frac{\lambda^2}{\pi}.$$

This quantity is the *effective scattering cross-section* of a small resonant gas bubble. The same conclusion was reached by Lamb* in a slightly different way for any resonator with small attenuation.

Using the expression $z_{res} = \sqrt{3\frac{\bar{\varkappa}}{\varkappa}}$ and assuming that the natural frequency of a Helmholtz resonator is $\omega_{res}^2 = c^2\frac{K}{V}$, (where K is the conductivity of the neck, approximately equal to $2R$ for a very short neck), it can be assumed that the area $\sigma = \pi R^2$ of the neck of the resonator is equal to the surface $4\pi r_0^2$ of an equivalent sphere; such an assumption is quite acceptable for long waves. Then for the equivalent bulk modulus we get:

$$\bar{\varkappa}' = \frac{\varkappa z_{res}^2}{3} = \frac{\varkappa \omega_{res}^2 r_0^2}{3c^2 V} = \frac{\varkappa R^3}{6V}.$$

Since $R^3 \ll V$ always, we therefore get $\frac{\bar{\varkappa}'}{\varkappa} \ll 1$ and $S' \approx \frac{\lambda^2}{\pi}$. Thus the resonator distorts the acoustic field and absorbs energy like a sphere of bulk modulus $\bar{\varkappa}'$.

According to formula (9-22), the surface pressure on the

* Lord Rayleigh, *Theory of Sound*, New York: Dover Publications 1945 (see vol. II, Sect. 335).

sphere is

$$(p_i+p_s)\underset{r=r_0}{\approx} p_0 e^{j\omega t}\left[\frac{\sin z_0}{z_0}-\frac{\rho c z_0^2\left(1-\frac{\overline{\varkappa}}{\varkappa}\right)}{Z_1}\frac{e^{-jz_0}e^{j\frac{\pi}{2}}}{z_0}\right]\approx$$
$$\approx p_0 e^{j\omega t}\left[1-\rho c\frac{z_0^2\left(1-\frac{\overline{\varkappa}}{\varkappa}\right)}{Z_1}-j\frac{z_0\rho c\left(1-\frac{\overline{\varkappa}}{\varkappa}\right)}{Z_1}\right], \qquad (9\text{-}34)$$

(assuming that $e^{-jz_0}\approx 1-jz_0$). Formula (9-34) is of interest from the point of view of analysing the distortion of acoustic field measurements by sound receivers. Expression (9-34) provides the complete answer in the special case of a small (compared with the wavelength, $z_0 \ll 1$) spherical pressure receiver with an effective bulk modulus $\overline{\varkappa}' < \varkappa$. The following expressions are obtained for the various relationships between z_0 and z_{res}:

$$\left.\frac{(p_i+p_s)}{p_0 e^{j\omega t}}\right|_{r=r_0}=\begin{cases}1+\left(\frac{z_0}{z_{res}}\right)^2\left(1-\frac{\overline{\varkappa}'}{\varkappa}\right)-j\left(\frac{z_0}{z_{res}}\right)^2\left(1-\frac{\overline{\varkappa}'}{\varkappa}\right)z_0\approx 1, \\ \qquad\qquad \text{if } z_0\ll z_{res}\\ \frac{\overline{\varkappa}'}{\varkappa}-j\frac{1}{z_0}\left(1-\frac{\overline{\varkappa}'}{\varkappa}\right)\approx\frac{1}{jz_0}\gg 1, \text{ if } z_0=z_{res}\\ \frac{\overline{\varkappa}'}{\varkappa}+jz_0\left(1-\frac{\overline{\varkappa}'}{\varkappa}\right)\approx jz_0\ll 1, \text{ if } z_0\gg z_{res}\end{cases}$$

$$\text{provided } \frac{z_{res}^2}{3}=\frac{\overline{\varkappa}'}{\varkappa}\ll 1.$$

It is obvious that the receiver reacts correctly to external effects without distorting the pressure of the acoustic field if $z_0 \ll z_{res}$ (a stiffness-controlled receiver). If $z_0 = z_{res}$, the acoustic field is greatly distorted (the pressure on the surface of the receiver is much greater than p_0). The field is also distorted if $z_0 \gg z_{res}$ (a mass-controlled receiver), the pressure on the surface of the receiver being much less than p_0.

At the resonance of a gas bubble in water, if it is borne

in mind that

$$\frac{\overline{\varkappa}}{\varkappa}=\frac{1{\cdot}4\times10^{6}}{2\times10^{10}}\approx0{\cdot}7\times10^{-4}\text{ and } z_0\approx\frac{1}{68}:$$

then from (9-34)

$$(p_i+p_s)_{r=r_0}\approx-jp_0e^{j\omega t}\cdot\frac{1}{z_{\text{res}}}\approx$$

$$\approx 68p_0e^{j\left(\omega t-\frac{\pi}{2}\right)}\ (\text{if } P=1_{\text{a/m}}). \tag{9-35}$$

We will now consider the amplitude of the surface oscillations of the bubble at resonance. From (9-33)

$$|q_{sn}|\approx\frac{q_0}{z^2_{\text{res}}}=\frac{p_0}{\rho cz^2_{\text{res}}}.$$

Since the amplitude is

$$|a|=\frac{|q_{sn}|}{\omega},$$

it follows that

$$\frac{|a|}{r_0}\approx p_0\frac{1}{\varkappa z^3_{\text{res}}}\approx1{\cdot}5\times10^{-5}\cdot p_0.$$

Up to pressures of 10^4 bar it can be assumed that $\frac{|a|}{r_0}\ll1$ and $r_0\approx\text{const}$. But at pressures of the order of 10^6 bar, which are quite common in ultrasonics, the foregoing account of resonance phenomena is no longer valid owing to the motion of the surface of the sphere and the impossibility of defining the boundary conditions on this surface by assuming $r_0=\text{const}$. At large amplitudes the oscillations of a gas bubble are quite complicated and the mass and elasticity become functions of oscillation amplitude.

For long waves $(z_0\ll1)$ the pressure inside the bubble is the same throughout its volume and equal to the surface pressure; at resonance the pressure in the bubble is 68 times greater than that of the incident wave and lags behind it in phase by $\frac{\pi}{2}$.

As mentioned previously, expression (9-35) can be used to ascertain the pressure inside the bubble at resonance only in the case of low amplitudes.

Moreover, expression (9-35) is inaccurate in that a large temperature gradient arises at the boundary of the sphere. Heat exchange between small oscillating gas spheres and the surrounding medium can be important. It can be assumed in practice that the temperature θ_0, of the surrounding medium remains constant, but that there is a small change $\delta\theta$ in that of the gas sphere. Assuming as a first approximation that the process is adiabatic and proceeding from the equation $\theta = BP^{\frac{\gamma-1}{\gamma}}$, we find that the temperature varies according to the law:

$$\frac{\delta\theta}{\theta_0} \approx \frac{\gamma-1}{\gamma}\frac{\delta P}{P_0} - \frac{\gamma-1}{2\gamma^2}\left(\frac{\delta P}{P_0}\right)^2. \tag{9-36}$$

It is apparent from (9-36) that the mean temperature of the gas bubble will be less than that of the surrounding medium owing to the presence of the negative square term. To maintain a lower temperature it is necessary to expend energy continuously in exactly the same way as a refrigerator. This work is done at the expense of the energy stored in the sound wave and thus leads to an increase in sound attenuation.

The increased heat exchange between small spheres and the surrounding medium owing to their greater specific surface even makes use of the adiabatic equations inaccurate. The oscillations inside such spheres will neither be strictly adiabatic, nor strictly isothermal. The figure for the pressure increase at resonance in (9-35) (i.e. the multiplier 68) is the upper limit which would be obtained if no heat exchange were to occur. The actual increase in pressure at resonance is much less. Heat exchange leads to a much greater attenuation due to the gas bubble than that which would be obtained if only the radiation loss were considered*.

For a very rigid sphere $(\bar{\varkappa} \gg \varkappa)$,

$$Z_1 \approx \frac{3\rho c \frac{\bar{\varkappa}}{\varkappa}}{jz_0}$$

and from (9-34) we get:

$$(p_i + p_s)_{r=r_0} \approx p_0 e^{j\omega t}\left[1 - \frac{z_0^2}{3} + j\frac{z_0^3}{3}\right] \approx p_0 e^{j\omega t}.$$

This confirms the previous result, namely, that the distortion of the acoustic field by a rigid sphere is not significant.

Oscillatory Motion of a Fluid or Gaseous Sphere in a Plane Sound Wave Field

The pressure at a point on the surface of a sphere in a plane sound wave $p_i = p_0 e^{j(\omega t + kx)}$, travelling in the negative x direction is:

$$(p_i)_{r=r_0} = p_0 e^{jz_0 \cos\vartheta} \cdot e^{j\omega t} \approx p_0 e^{j\omega t}(1 + jz_0 \cos\vartheta).$$

In this direction the component of the pressure force per unit area is $p_i \cos\vartheta$. The total pressure force of the in-

* H. Pfrim, *Akust. Z.* 5, 202, 1940.

cident wave in the + x direction therefore is

$$F_x = -\int_0^{\pi} (p_i)_{r=r_0} \cdot \cos\vartheta \cdot 2\pi r_0^2 \sin\vartheta \, d\vartheta \approx -j\frac{Sp_i}{3} z_0 \approx -j\omega V\rho q_i,$$

where $q_i = q_0 e^{j\omega t} = \frac{p_0}{\rho c} e^{j\omega t}$ is the particle velocity in the wave, $p_i = p_0 e^{j\omega t}$ and $V = \frac{4}{3}\pi r_0^3$ the volume of the sphere. These expressions hold good if $z_0 \ll 1$.

The force F_x can be regarded as causing motion of the sphere together with the attached mass. The oscillation velocity in the x direction is found from (9-22). If $z_0 \ll 1$ and $\bar{z}_0 \ll 1$, the amplitude of the radial velocity component of the incident wave is:

$$q_{in}(r_0) \approx \frac{p_0}{j\rho c}\left[\frac{1}{z_0^2}\frac{z_0^3}{3} + j3\frac{2}{z_0^3}\left(-\frac{z_0^3}{6}\right)\cos\vartheta\right] = -q_0\left[j\frac{z_0}{3} + \cos\vartheta\right],$$

and that of the scattered wave:

$$q_{sn}(r_0) \approx -q_0\left[\frac{1 - \frac{\bar{\varkappa}}{\varkappa}}{z_0^2 + j\left(z_0 - \frac{3}{z_0}\frac{\bar{\varkappa}}{\varkappa}\right)} - 2\frac{\bar{\rho} - \rho}{2\bar{\rho} + \rho}\cos\vartheta\right] \approx$$
$$\approx -q_0\left[j\frac{z_0}{3}\left(\frac{\varkappa}{\bar{\varkappa}} - 1\right) + 2\frac{\bar{\rho} - \rho}{2\bar{\rho} + \rho}\cos\vartheta\right].$$

The total amplitude of the radial velocity if $z_0 \ll z_{res}$ is:

$$q_n(r_0) = q_{in}(r_0) + q_{sn}(r_0) \approx$$
$$\approx -q_0\left[j\frac{z_0}{3}\frac{\varkappa}{\bar{\varkappa}} + \left(1 - 2\frac{\bar{\rho} - \rho}{2\bar{\rho} + \rho}\cos\vartheta\right)\right]. \qquad (9\text{-}37)$$

The first term in the square brackets determines the *pulsation* amplitude; it is small compared with the second term, which is of order one, only on condition that

$$z_0 < 3\frac{\bar{\chi}}{\chi} = z_{res}^2. \qquad (9\text{-}38)$$

In this case

$$q_n(r_0) \approx -q_0\left(1 - 2\frac{\bar{\rho}-\rho}{2\bar{\rho}+\rho}\cos\vartheta\right). \qquad (9\text{-}39)$$

The velocity amplitude (q_x) in the x direction for the entire sphere as a unit is the value of q_n at $\vartheta = 0$ or $\vartheta = \pi$. It is obviously realistic to discuss the oscillations of the entire sphere as a unit only if the second term in (9-37) is greater than the first. The condition $z_0 < 3\frac{\bar{\chi}}{\chi}$ leads to the conclusion that this is possible for gas bubbles in a fluid (where the second term is of order 2) only at comparatively low acoustic frequencies. For example, it is satisfied for gas bubbles of radius $r_0 =$ $= 0{\cdot}01$ cm ($f_{res} \approx 34$ kc/s) if $f < 1500$ c/s, and for those of radius $r_0 = 0{\cdot}001$ if $f < 15000$ c/s. It is quite different for a balloon filled with hydrogen in air; in this case this particular condition gives:

$$z_0 < 3\frac{\bar{\chi}}{\chi} = 3 \text{ and } z_{res} = \sqrt{3} = 1{\cdot}83.$$

Consequently, the oscillation of a balloon as a unit may be discussed at frequencies equal to or even greater than the resonant frequency.

The quantity z_{res} is very large for solid or fluid particles in suspension in a fluid or gas and the condition $z_0 < z_{res}^2$ is always fulfilled. But in this case q_x is much less than q_0.

From formula (9-39):

$$q_x \approx -q_0\left((1 - 2\frac{\bar{\rho}-\rho}{2\bar{\rho}+\rho}\right) = -q_0\frac{3\rho}{2\bar{\rho}+\rho}. \qquad (9\text{-}40)$$

The velocity of the sphere relative to a medium moving with the velocity $(-q_0)$ is:

$$q'_x = q_x - (-q_0) = q_x + q_0 = 2\frac{\bar{\rho} - \rho}{2\bar{\rho} + \rho} q_0. \qquad (9\text{-}41)$$

The absolute velocities and relative velocities of the type defined in (9-41) for various ratios of the density of the medium to that of the sphere are as follows:

Density ratio	Absolute velocity q_x	Relative velocity q'_x
$\frac{\bar{\rho}}{\rho} \gg 1$	$q_x = 0$	$q'_x = +q_0$
$\frac{\bar{\rho}}{\rho} = 1$	$q_x = -q_0$	$q'_x = 0$
$\frac{\bar{\rho}}{\rho} \ll 1$	$q_x = -3q_0$	$q'_x = -2q_0$

If a sound wave is incident on a very heavy sphere $(\bar{\rho} \gg \rho)$ we get $q_x = 0$, as in the previous case for a rigid fixed sphere. It is of interest to see that the velocity $q_x = 0$ is obtained as a result of adding the velocity of transport of all the medium $(-q_0)$, which is produced by the sound wave, to the relative velocity $q'_x = +q_0$ in the reverse direction, which is caused by the field of the scattered wave.

If $\bar{\rho} = \rho$, the sphere is as it were a part of a homogeneous fluid and moves together with it with the velocity $(-q_0)$ of the incident sound wave. The case $\bar{\rho} = \rho$ can be realised in practice by immersing a loaded spherical shell in a fluid and adjusting the load to make the density of the sphere equal to that of the fluid.

A sphere of very low density is of special interest, e.g. a gas bubble in a fluid. In this case $(\bar{\rho} \ll \rho)$, the relative velocity is twice the velocity of transport of the wave and the absolute velocity is three times the particle velocity of the incident wave.

We will now consider this question in relation to the attached mass. As we have seen, the attached mass of an oscillating sphere is one half the mass of the medium it displaces, i.e.

$$\frac{1}{2}V\rho = \frac{2}{3}\pi r_0^3\rho.$$

The equation of motion of the sphere must necessarily include both the inertial force equal to the product of the mass of the sphere $V\bar{\rho}$ by the acceleration $j\omega q_x$ of the absolute motion, as well as the inertial force equal to the product of the attached mass $\frac{1}{2}V\rho$ by the acceleration $j\omega q'_x$ of the relative motion. The equation of motion takes the form:

$$F_x \approx -j\frac{Sp_0}{3}z_0 = -j\omega V\rho q_0 = j\omega V\left[\bar{\rho}q_x + \frac{\rho}{2}q'_x\right].$$

Bearing in mind that $q'_x = q_x + q_0$, we get from the equation of motion

$$q'_x = 2\frac{\bar{\rho}-\rho}{2\bar{\rho}+\rho}q_0,$$

i.e. expression (9-41) once again. The additional force which causes the relative motion arises owing to the effect of the scattered wave and is equal to the product of the attached mass by the relative acceleration:

$$F'_x = \left(\frac{V\rho}{2}\right)j\omega q'_x = j\omega\left(\frac{V\rho}{2}\right)\cdot 2\cdot\frac{\bar{\rho}-\rho}{2\bar{\rho}+\rho}q_0.$$

If $\bar{\rho} \gg \rho$, then

$$F'_x \approx j\omega\frac{V\rho}{2}q_0,$$

i.e. the additional force is positive (in the opposite direction to the particle velocity in the medium) and equal to the inertance of the attached mass multiplied by the magnitude of the particle velocity of the medium. This force causes motion with the velocity $+q_0$, in the opposite direction to the velocity of the medium and as a result $q_x = 0$.

If $\bar{\rho} = \rho$ then $F'_x = 0$, but if $\bar{\rho} \ll \rho$ then

$$F'_x \approx -j\omega V \rho q_0 = -j\omega \left(\frac{V\rho}{2}\right) 2q_0 = -j\omega \left(\frac{V\rho}{2}\right) q'_x.$$

Therefore the force F'_x is negative, i.e. in the same direction as the particle velocity of the medium. It is obtained by multiplying the impedance of the attached mass $j\omega\left(\frac{V\rho}{2}\right)$ by the relative velocity of the sphere $(-2q_0)$. Since in this case the additional force only causes motion of half the attached mass, it follows that it imparts twice the velocity.

In a homogeneous medium $(\bar{\rho} = \rho)$, it can be seen from (9-40) that this force causes a velocity of the mass $V\rho$, equal to $(-q_0)$.

These are important questions in the study of the oscillation of light particles (e.g. gas bubbles) suspended in fluids and in the analysis of the oscillatory motion of heavier solid or fluid bodies which are buoyantly suspended in a liquid. In the latter case $\bar{\rho}$ is understood to be the mean density of the whole system.

We will now consider whether the foregoing expressions are applicable to the motion of a sphere (having a different density from that of the medium) if the viscosity of the medium is included. Particular attention will be paid to the oscillation of gas bubbles in water.

The amplitude of the resistive force acting on a sphere in a viscous fluid can be calculated by the formula:

$$f_x = C(\pi r_0^2)\frac{\rho q_x'^2}{2},$$

where C is a hydrodynamic coefficient of resistance* which depends on the relative velocity q_x'.

In the case of a gas bubble it is necessary to take into account the inertance of the sphere which in oscillatory motion has the magnitude

$$|F_x'| = \omega\frac{1}{2}\left(\frac{4}{3}\pi r_0^3\rho\right)2q_0 = \omega\left(\frac{2}{3}\pi r_0^3\rho\right)q_x'.$$

Consequently, the ratio of the magnitudes of the inertial and viscous forces is

$$\gamma = \frac{F_x'}{f_x} = \frac{\frac{4}{3}\omega r_0}{Cq_x'} = \frac{\frac{2}{3}\omega d_0}{Cq_x'}. \qquad (9\text{-}42)$$

Formula (9-38), the condition for oscillation to exceed pulsation in amplitude, can be written for the oscillation of a gas bubble in the form, $\frac{z_0}{3}\frac{x}{x} < 2$. Hence

$$\frac{2\omega d_0}{3} < 83, \text{ or } f < \frac{20}{d_0}. \qquad (9\text{-}43)$$

For Reynolds' numbers (Re) less than 1·5, the coefficient $C = \frac{24}{\mathrm{Re}}$ and $Cq_x' = \frac{24\nu}{d_0}$, where ν is the coefficient of kinematic viscosity, and hence from (9-42) we get the condition under which the inertial forces exceed the viscous

---

* L. Prandtl, *Essentials of Fluid Dynamics*, London: Blackie, 1952 (see p. 190).

forces:

$$\gamma = \frac{\frac{2}{3}\omega d_0}{Cq'_x} = \frac{\omega d_0^2}{36\nu} > 1, \quad \text{or} \quad f > \frac{5{\cdot}7\nu}{d_0^2}. \qquad (9\text{-}44)$$

Conditions (9-43) and (9-44) together provide the frequency band in which expressions (9-40) and (9-41) are approximately applicable to the oscillation of bubbles of various diameters. If $\theta = 18°$ and $\nu \approx 10^{-2}$ g cm^{-1} sec^{-1}, we get:

$$\frac{0{\cdot}057}{d_0^2} < f < \frac{20}{d_0}.$$

For the various diameters we have:

$$\begin{aligned} d_0 &= 0{\cdot}1 \text{ cm}, & 6{\cdot}3 < f < 200; \\ d_0 &= 0{\cdot}01 \text{ cm}, & 630 < f < 2000; \\ d_0 &= 0{\cdot}003 \text{ cm}. & 6300 < f < 6700. \end{aligned}$$

Thus, it is possible to use formula (9-40) only for bubbles over 0·003 cm in diameter and then only for frequencies in a narrow band of the audible range. The lower frequency limit falls at high temperatures; at $\theta = 70°$ it is reduced by a factor of 2·5.

The condition Re $< 1{\cdot}5$ is always satisfied for bubbles of the sizes considered here for low oscillation amplitudes ($\dot{q}_x < 0{\cdot}1$ cm/sec); the position is different with large amplitudes. Thus, for a pressure amplitude $p_0 = 2 \times 10^6$ bar ≈ 2 atm, we get $q_0 = 13$ cm/sec and $q'_x = 26$ cm/sec. In this case, Re > 2 for bubbles from 10^{-3} to 10^{-1} cm in diameter; from experimental data for C(Re) it is found that γ can be greater than one only for bubbles over 1·0 cm in diameter in a narrow band of low audio frequencies; thus for $d_0 = 0{\cdot}2$ cm $35 < f < 100$.

For large spherical shells immersed in water and having a mean value $\bar{\rho} < 1$ (positive buoyancy), we can calculate

z_{res} from Love's formula* for thin shells:

$$f_{res} \approx \frac{2}{\pi d_0} \sqrt{\frac{E}{2(1-\sigma)\rho'}},$$

where ρ' is the density of the shell and σ Poisson's ratio. When considering the oscillations of a shell in water it is necessary to include the increase in mass due to the additional mass $M = 4\pi r_0^3 \rho$ of the water. This causes a reduction in the resonant frequency to the value:

$$f'_{res} = f_{res} \sqrt{\frac{1}{1 + \frac{r_0 \rho}{h\rho'}}}.$$

For a steel shell $d_0 = 50$ cm in diameter and $h = 0 \cdot 3$ cm in thickness, the adjusted resonant frequency $f'_{res} = 1540$ c/s. Condition (9-38) provides the upper frequency limit $f < 2500$ c/s, i.e. a higher frequency than f'_{res}. In this case, the mean density $\bar{\rho} = 0 \cdot 28$ and from formula (9-41) we get:

$$q'_x = -0 \cdot 92 q_0 \text{ and } q_x = -1 \cdot 92 q_0.$$

By setting up a seismograph-type device inside the shell and measuring q_x we can then calculate q_0 and the amplitude of the sound pressure $p_0 = \rho c q_0$.

* A. Love, *Mathematical Theory of Elasticity*, p. 300, Cambridge, 1935.

CHAPTER X

RADIATION AND SCATTERING OF SOUND BY A CYLINDER

General Solution of the Wave Equation in Cylindrical Coordinates

The wave equation for the velocity potential, $\nabla^2\Phi = \frac{1}{c^2}\frac{\partial^2\Phi}{\partial t^2}$ becomes $\nabla^2\Psi + k^2\Psi = 0$ on the assumption that $\Phi(x,y,z,t) = \Psi(x,y,z)\cdot e^{j\omega t}$ and in cylindrical polar coordinates this takes the form:

$$\frac{1}{r}\frac{\partial}{\partial r}\left(r\frac{\partial\Psi}{\partial r}\right) + \frac{1}{r^2}\frac{\partial^2\Psi}{\partial\varphi^2} + \frac{\partial^2\Psi}{\partial z^2} + k^2\Psi = 0, \qquad (10\text{-}1)$$

where r, z and φ are the cylindrical polar coordinates of a point (the radius, height and azimuthal angle respectively). Assuming that $\Psi(r,z,\varphi) = Z(z)\cdot G(r,\varphi)$, we separate this equation into two equal constant parts:

$$\frac{1}{r}\frac{\frac{\partial}{\partial r}\left(r\frac{\partial G}{\partial r}\right)}{G} + \frac{1}{r^2}\frac{\frac{\partial^2 G}{\partial\varphi^2}}{G} + k^2 = -\frac{\frac{\partial^2 Z}{\partial z^2}}{Z} = k_z^2,$$

one part of which depends solely on r and φ, and the other on z; k_Z^2 is the separation constant. We thus obtain two differential equations in the functions $G(r,\varphi)$ and $Z(z)$:

$$\frac{\partial^2 Z}{\partial z^2} + k_z^2 Z = 0,$$

$$r\frac{\partial}{\partial r}\left(r\frac{\partial G}{\partial r}\right) + \frac{\partial^2 G}{\partial\varphi^2} + (k^2 - k_z^2)r^2 G = 0.$$

The first equation has the solution

$$Z(z) = A'e^{jk_z z} + B'e^{-jk_z z} = (A' + B')\cos k_z z + \\ + j(A' - B')\sin k_z z.$$

The second is solved by assuming that $G(r, \varphi) = R(r) \cdot F(\varphi)$, and on separation reduces to two differential equations:

$$\left.\begin{aligned} \frac{d^2R}{dr^2} + \frac{1}{r}\frac{dR}{dr} + \left(k^2 - k_z^2 - \frac{m^2}{r^2}\right)R = 0, \\ \frac{d^2F}{d\varphi^2} + m^2F = 0, \end{aligned}\right\} \quad (10\text{-}2)$$

m being a separation constant. The first of these equations is the Bessel equation and has the solution:

$$R(r) = A_m J_m(k_r r) + B_m N_m(k_r r). \quad (10\text{-}3)$$

Here $J_m(k_r r)$ and $N_m(k_r r)$ are Bessel and Neumann functions of order m, whilst the parameter k_r is found from the expression:

$$k_r^2 = k^2 - k_z^2, \quad (10\text{-}3a)$$

where $k = \frac{\omega}{c}$ is the wave number. For the analysis of radiating systems it is better to use Hankel function solutions (see Chapter VIII):

$$R(r) = A'_m H_m^{(1)}(k_r r) + B'_m H_m^{(2)}(k_r r),$$

In this case we have to discard the first term which corresponds to waves converging on the axis (due to the factor $e^{jk_r r}$). But for the analysis of natural oscillations in a cylindrical cavity, it is best to use expression (10-3), where the constant B_m is taken to be zero since $N_m(0) = -\infty$, which is unrealistic physically. The second term in (10-3) has to be retained for cylindrical annular channels or sectors with a rigid cylindrical obstacle at the centre.

The second equation in (10-2) has the solution:

$$F(\varphi)=A_1 e^{jm\varphi}+B_1 e^{-jm\varphi}=A_2\cos m\varphi+B_2\sin m\varphi= \\ =A\cos(m\varphi-\varphi_m),$$

where

$$A=\sqrt{A_2^2+B_2^2} \text{ and } \tan\varphi_m=\frac{B_2}{A_2}.$$

The expression for $F(\varphi)$ is a unique single valued solution only if

$$m=0,1,2,3\ldots$$

For the radiation of sound by waves travelling along the surface of the cylinder in the azimuthal direction, the function $F(\varphi)$ has to be taken in the form $F(\varphi)=Ae^{jm\varphi}$ or $F(\varphi)=Ae^{-jm\varphi}$.

The *m*th order solution of equation (10-1) can be written in the form:

$$\Phi_m(r,z,\varphi,t)=[A_mJ_m(k_rr)+B_mN_m(k_rr)][A'e^{jk_zz}+B'e^{-jk_zz}]\times \\ \times A\cos(m\varphi-\varphi_m)e^{j\omega t}.$$

If the solution is independent of z, then $k_z=0$ and $k_r=k$, and hence the second bracket in this last equation becomes a constant quantity. Since the acoustic pressure and velocity potential are related by the expression $p=j\omega\rho\Phi$, it follows that the general solution of the wave equation for radiation when the process depends only on r and Φ, is written in the form:

$$p(r,z,\varphi,t)=\sum_{m=0}^{\infty}A_mH_m^{(2)}(\zeta)\cos(m\varphi-\varphi_m)e^{j\omega t}= \\ =\sum_{m=0}^{\infty}A_m[J_m(\zeta)-jN_m(\zeta)]\cos(m\varphi-\varphi_m)e^{j\omega t}, \quad (10\text{-}4)$$

where $\zeta=kr$.

The radial velocity is:

$$q_r = -k\frac{\partial\Phi}{\partial\zeta} = -k\frac{\frac{\partial p}{\partial\zeta}}{j\omega\rho} = j\frac{1}{\rho c}\sum_{m=0}^{\infty} A_m\left[J'_m(\zeta) - jN'_m(\zeta)\right] \times$$
$$\times \cos(m\varphi - \varphi_m)\cdot e^{j\omega t}. \tag{10-5}$$

Transforming this expression, we get:

$$q_r = \frac{A_0 C_0(\zeta)}{2\rho c}\, e^{-j\gamma_0(\zeta)} + \sum_{m=1}^{\infty}\frac{A_m C_m(\zeta)}{\rho c} e^{-j\gamma_m(\zeta)} \times$$
$$\times \cos(m\varphi - \varphi_m)\cdot e^{j\omega t}, \tag{10-5a}$$

where

$$\left.\begin{aligned} J'_0(\zeta) - jN'_0(\zeta) &= -j\frac{C_0(\zeta)}{2}e^{-j\gamma_0(\zeta)}, \text{ if } m=0;\\ J'_m(\zeta) - jN'_m(\zeta) &= -jC_m(\zeta)\, e^{-j\gamma_m(\zeta)}, \text{ if } m>0. \end{aligned}\right\} \tag{10-6}$$

The quantities C_0, C_m, γ_0 and γ_m are found from the expressions:

$$\left.\begin{aligned} &\frac{1}{2}C_0\sin\gamma_0 = J_1;\ \frac{1}{2}C_0\cos\gamma_0 = -N_1 \text{ if } m=0;\\ &\left.\begin{aligned} 2C_m\sin\gamma_m &= J_{m+1} - J_{m-1}\\ 2C_m\cos\gamma_m &= -(N_{m+1} - N_{m-1}) \end{aligned}\right\} \text{ if } m>0. \end{aligned}\right| \tag{10-7}$$

A table of the functions $C_m(\zeta)$ and $\gamma_m(\zeta)$ is available in Morse's book *Vibration and Sound* (see Table X, p.449).

Later we will form approximate expressions for the acoustic field for large and small values of the argument $\zeta = kr$. The limiting values of the functions contained in the foregoing expressions for p and q are as follows:

$$
\left.\begin{aligned}
&J_m(\zeta) \underset{\zeta \gg m}{\approx} \sqrt{\frac{2}{\pi\zeta}} \cos\left(\zeta - \frac{2m+1}{4}\pi\right); \\
&N_m(\zeta) \underset{\zeta \gg m}{\approx} \sqrt{\frac{2}{\pi\zeta}} \sin\left(\zeta - \frac{2m+1}{4}\pi\right); \\
&H_m^{(2)}(\zeta) \underset{\zeta \gg m}{\approx} \sqrt{\frac{2}{\pi\zeta}}\, e^{-j\left(\zeta - \frac{2m+1}{4}\pi\right)}; \\
&C_0(\zeta) \underset{\zeta \gg 0}{\approx} \sqrt{\frac{8}{\pi\zeta}};\; C_m(\zeta) \underset{\zeta \gg m}{\approx} \sqrt{\frac{2}{\pi\zeta}}; \\
&\gamma_0(\zeta) \underset{\zeta \gg 0}{\approx} \zeta - \frac{\pi}{4};\; \gamma_m(\zeta) \underset{\zeta \gg m}{\approx} \zeta - \frac{2m+1}{4}\pi;
\end{aligned}\right\} \quad (10\text{-}8)
$$

$$
\left.\begin{aligned}
&J_m(\zeta) = \frac{1}{m!}\left(\frac{\zeta}{2}\right)^m - \frac{1}{1!\,(m+1)!}\left(\frac{\zeta}{2}\right)^{m+2} + \\
&\quad + \frac{1}{2!\,(m+2)!}\left(\frac{\zeta}{2}\right)^{m+4} - \ldots; \\
&N_0(\zeta) \underset{\zeta \to 0}{\approx} \left(\frac{2}{\pi}\right)(\ln\zeta - 0{\cdot}1159); \\
&N_m(\zeta) \underset{\zeta \ll m}{\approx} -\frac{(m-1)!}{\pi}\left(\frac{2}{\zeta}\right)^m; \\
&C_0(\zeta) \underset{\zeta \to 0}{\approx} \frac{4}{\pi\zeta};\; C_m(\zeta) \underset{\zeta \ll m}{\approx} \frac{m!}{2\pi}\left(\frac{2}{\zeta}\right)^{m+1}; \\
&\gamma_0(\zeta) \underset{\zeta \to 0}{\approx} \pi\left(\frac{\zeta}{2}\right)^2;\; \gamma_m(\zeta) \underset{\zeta \ll m}{\approx} -\frac{\pi m}{(m!)^2}\left(\frac{\zeta}{2}\right)^{2m}.
\end{aligned}\right\} \quad (10\text{-}9)
$$

Several general relations for the functions J and N are:

$$
\begin{aligned}
&J_0' = -J_1 \\
&J_m' = \frac{1}{2}(J_{m-1} - J_{m+1});\; J_{m-1} + J_{m+1} = \frac{2m}{\zeta} J_m. \quad (10\text{-}10)
\end{aligned}
$$

The Radiation of a Cylinder with an Arbitrary Surface Velocity Distribution (independent of z)

Suppose it is required to find the acoustic field produced by an infinitely narrow strip of angular width $d\alpha$ which lies along the generatrix of a cylinder at the azimuthal angle $\varphi = \alpha$ and vibrates with the velocity amplitude

$U_0(\alpha)$. The surface velocity distribution is:

$$u_0(\varphi-\alpha,t)=\begin{cases} U_0(\alpha)\,e^{j\omega t} & \text{if} \quad -\frac{d\alpha}{2}<\varphi-\alpha<\frac{d\alpha}{2}, \\ 0 & \text{if} \quad \frac{d\alpha}{2}<\varphi-\alpha<2\pi-\frac{d\alpha}{2}. \end{cases}$$

We expand the function $u_0(\varphi-\alpha,t)$ into a Fourier series:

$$u_0(\varphi-\alpha,t)=\frac{U_0(\alpha)\,d\alpha}{\pi}\left[\frac{1}{2}+\sum_{m=1}^{\infty}\cos m(\varphi-\alpha)\right]e^{j\omega t}.$$

The boundary condition $u_0(\varphi-\alpha,t)=q_r(r_0,\varphi,t)$ must be satisfied on the surface of the cylinder. We introduce the difference between the azimuthal angle φ and the strip azimuth into expressions (10-4) and (10-5) for p and q_r so that they contain $\varphi-\alpha$ in place of α. Equating terms with equal subscripts m in the equation $u_0(\varphi-\alpha,t)=q_r(r_0,\varphi,t)$, gives for the coefficients of the series:

$$A_0=\frac{U_0(\alpha)d\alpha\cdot\rho c}{j2\pi\,[J_0'(\zeta_0)-jN_m'(\zeta_0)]}=\frac{U_0(\alpha)\,d\alpha\cdot\rho c}{\pi C_0(\zeta_0)\,e^{-j\gamma_0(\zeta_0)}},$$

$$A_m=\frac{U_0(\alpha)\,d\alpha\cdot\rho c}{j\pi\,[J_m'(\zeta_0)-jN_m'(\zeta_0)]}=\frac{U_0(\alpha)\,d\alpha\cdot\rho c}{\pi C_m(\zeta_0)\,e^{-j\gamma_m(\zeta_0)}},$$

where $\zeta_0=kr_0$. The expression for A_m in terms of C_m and γ_m is valid for all values of m, including $m=0$. The acoustic field of the vibrating strip at the azimuthal angle $\varphi=\alpha$ is

$$p=\rho c\,\frac{U_0(\alpha)\,d\alpha\cdot e^{j\omega t}}{\pi}\sum_{m=0}^{\infty}\frac{\cos m(\varphi-\alpha)}{C_m(\zeta_0)\,e^{-j\gamma_m(\zeta_0)}}\Big[J_m(\zeta)-jN_m(\zeta)\Big],$$

$$q_r=j\,\frac{U_0(\alpha)\,d\alpha\cdot e^{j\omega t}}{\pi}\sum_{m=0}^{\infty}\frac{\cos m(\varphi-\alpha)}{C_m(\zeta_0)\,e^{-j\gamma_m(\zeta_0)}}\Big[J_m'(\zeta)-jN_m'(\zeta)\Big]. \quad (10\text{-}11)$$

At large distances from the cylinder we get by virtue of (10-8):

$$\underset{\zeta\gg m}{p}\approx U_0(\alpha)\,d\alpha\cdot\rho c\,\sqrt{\frac{r_0}{r}}\,e^{j(\omega t-kr)}\cdot\psi(\varphi-\alpha),$$

$$\underset{\zeta\gg m}{q_r}\approx U(\alpha)\,d\alpha\,\sqrt{\frac{r_0}{r}}\cdot e^{j(\omega t-kr)}\cdot\psi(\varphi-\alpha), \quad (10\text{-}12)$$

where

$$\psi(\varphi-\alpha)_{\zeta\gg m}=\sqrt{\frac{2}{\pi^3\zeta_0}}\cdot\sum_{m=0}^{\infty}\frac{\cos m(\varphi-\alpha)}{C_m(\zeta_0)}e^{j\left[\gamma_m(\zeta_0)+\frac{2m+1}{4}\pi\right]}. \tag{10-13}$$

The same relationship $p=\rho c q_r$ exists here between p and q_r as in the case of a plane wave. The function $\psi(\varphi-\alpha)$ determines the amplitude directivity characteristic of a linear source such as the strip and depends on $\zeta_0=\frac{2\pi r_0}{\lambda}$ and the angle $(\varphi-\alpha)$. We shall determine the intensity directivity characteristic of a linear source in due course. It is easy to see from equation (10-13) that, if ζ_0 is small enough, the largest term in the series corresponds to $m = 0$ and the directivity characteristic is independent of the angle $(\varphi-\alpha)$. Provided $\zeta_0\ll 1$ the acoustic pressure and particle velocity q_r produced by a linear source depend only on the radius at large distances.

If many linear sources with amplitudes $U_0(\alpha)d\alpha$ are spread over the surface of the cylinder, the acoustic field may be found by superposition of the fields of the individual sources, using the formulae:

$$p=\frac{\rho c e^{j\omega t}}{\pi}\sum_{m=0}^{\infty}\frac{J_m(\zeta)-jN_m(\zeta)}{C_m(\zeta_0)e^{-j\gamma_m(\zeta_0)}}\int_0^{2\pi}\cos m(\varphi-\alpha)\,U_0(\alpha)d(\alpha),$$

$$q_r=j\frac{e^{j\omega t}}{\pi}\sum_{m=0}^{\infty}\frac{J'_m(\zeta)-jN'_m(\zeta)}{C_m(\zeta_0)e^{-j\gamma_m(\zeta_0)}}\int_0^{2\pi}\cos m(\varphi-\alpha)\,U_0(\alpha)\,d\alpha. \tag{10-14}$$

These expressions also enable us, for instance, to determine the distant acoustic field of a single finite strip occupying the region between $-\alpha_0$ and $+\alpha_0$ and vibrating with constant velocity U_0 whilst the rest of the surface of the cylinder remains stationary. For the far field we

get:

$$p \approx \rho c \sqrt{\frac{r_0}{r}}\, e^{j(\omega t - kr)} \sqrt{\frac{2}{\pi^3 \zeta_0}} \sum_{m=0}^{\infty} \frac{e^{j\left[\gamma_m(\zeta_0) + \frac{2m+1}{4}\pi\right]}}{C_m(\zeta_0)} \times$$

$$\times \int_{-\alpha_0}^{+\alpha_0} \psi(\varphi - \alpha)\, U_0(\alpha)\, d\alpha, \qquad (10\text{-}15)$$

$$q_r \approx \frac{p}{\rho c}\,.$$

By integration we find:

$$p \approx \rho c U_0 \sqrt{\frac{8}{\pi^3 \zeta_0}} \sum_{m=0}^{\infty} \frac{\sin m\alpha_0 \cos m\varphi}{m C_m(\zeta_0)} e^{j\left[\gamma_m(\zeta_0) + \frac{2m+1}{4}\pi\right]}$$

$q_r \approx \frac{p}{\rho c}$. For the term $m = 0$, $\frac{\sin m\alpha_0}{m} = \alpha_0$.

The Sound Intensity and Radiated Power of an Infinitely Long Cylinder

Linear radiator. In the distant field $(2\pi r \gg m\lambda)$, we can avail ourselves of expressions (10-12) and (10-13) for q and q_r and from an expression for the radial component of the intensity vector:

$$J \approx \frac{1}{2}\ \mathrm{Re}\,(p q_r^*) = \frac{\rho c (U_0 d\alpha)^2}{\pi^3 kr} \sum_{m=0}^{\infty} \frac{\cos m\varphi \cdot \cos n\varphi}{C_m(\zeta_0) C_n(\zeta_0)} \times$$

$$\times \cos\left[\gamma_m(\zeta_0) - \gamma_n(\zeta_0) + \frac{m-n}{2}\pi\right]. \qquad (10\text{-}16)$$

The intensity vector J has only a radial component at large distances.

The directivity characteristics for the intensity of a linear radiator, as calculated by formula (10-16), are shown in figure 82 (taken from Morse's book) for $\zeta_0 = 0{\cdot}4$, 1 and 3.

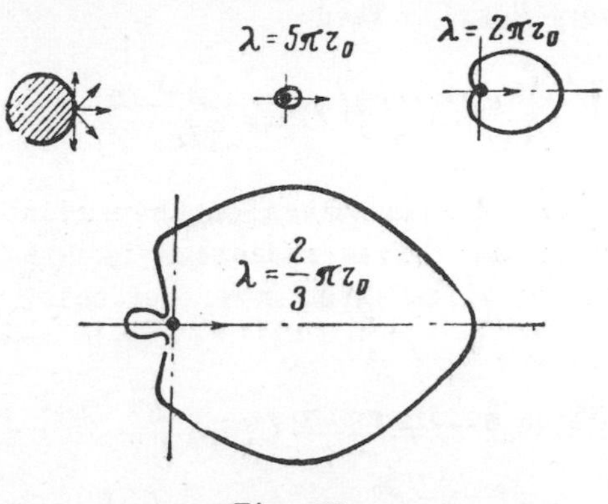

Fig. 82.

The total radiated power per unit length of the cylinder is found by integration of (10-16) from 0 to 2π

$$\Pi = \int_0^{2\pi} Jr d\varphi = \frac{\rho c (U_0 d\alpha)^2}{\pi^2 k}\left[\frac{2}{C_0^2(\zeta_0)} + \sum_{m=1}^{\infty}\frac{1}{C_m^2(\zeta_0)}\right]. \quad (10\text{-}17)$$

For long waves, using (10-9), we get:

$$\Pi \approx \frac{\rho\omega}{4}\cdot\frac{(U_0 r_0 d\alpha)^2}{2}.$$

Radiator in the form of a strip. Consider a strip occupying the region $-\alpha_0$ to $+\alpha_0$, and oscillating with constant velocity U_0 along the normal. Expressions (10-16) and (10-17) then take the form:

$$J = \frac{4\rho c U_0^2}{\pi^3 kr}\sum_{m=0}^{\infty}\frac{\sin m\alpha_0 \sin n\alpha_0 \cos m\varphi \cos n\varphi}{mn\, C_m(\zeta_0)\, C_n(\zeta_0)} \times$$

$$\times \cos\left[\gamma_m(\zeta_0) - \gamma_n(\zeta_0) - \frac{m-n}{2}\pi\right],$$

$$\Pi = \frac{4\rho c U_0^2}{\pi^2\omega}\left[\frac{2\alpha_0^2}{C_0^2(\zeta_0)} + \sum_{m=1}^{\infty}\frac{\sin^2 m\alpha_0}{m^2 C_m^2(\zeta_0)}\right].$$

The approximate expressions (10-8) can be used for C_m

if ζ_0 is very small. Then

$$J \approx \frac{\rho\omega r_0^2\alpha_0^2}{4\pi r} U_0^2 = \frac{\rho\omega S_1'^2}{8\pi r} \cdot \frac{U_0^2}{2},$$

where $S_1' = 2\alpha_0 r_0$ is the area of the radiator per unit length of cylinder. This radiation is non-directional. If $\zeta_0 \ll 1$, the total radiated power per unit length of the strip is:

$$\Pi \approx 2\pi r J = \frac{\rho\omega r_0^2\alpha_0^2}{2} U_0^2 = \frac{\rho\omega S_1'^2}{4} \cdot \frac{U_0^2}{2} =$$

$$= \frac{\rho\omega}{4} \frac{(S_1'U_0)^2}{2} = \frac{\rho\omega}{4} \frac{\dot{X}_0^2}{2} = \frac{1}{2} R_{01}' U_0^2,$$

where

$$R_{01}' = \frac{\rho\omega S_1'^2}{4} = \frac{\alpha_0 S_1' \rho c}{2} \zeta_0, \qquad (10\text{-}18)$$

and $X_0 = S_1' U_0$ is the volume velocity per unit length of the strip. The quantity R_{01}' is the radiation resistance (per unit length) of a vibrating strip of angular width $2\alpha_0$, on the surface of the cylinder. For long waves it is proportional to the square of the area, as in the case of the sphere, but unlike that of the sphere it is proportional to the first and not the second power of the frequency.

Pulsating Cylinder

The acoustic pressure of a pulsating cylinder is determined by the first term of the series in formula (10-4):

$$p(r,t) = A_0 [J_0(\zeta) - jN_0(\zeta)] e^{j\omega t}.$$

The radial particle velocity is

$$q_r = -k \frac{\frac{\partial p}{\partial \zeta}}{j\omega\rho} = -\frac{A_0 k}{j\omega\rho} [J_0'(\zeta) - jN_0'(\zeta)] e^{j\omega t}.$$

If $r=r_0$, the radial particle velocity in the surrounding medium must be equal to the surface pulsation velocity $U_0e^{j\omega t}$. Using expression (10-11), we get:

$$A_0=\frac{2\rho c U_0}{C_0(\zeta_0)}e^{j\gamma_0(\zeta_0)}.$$

The impedance per unit length of a pulsating cylinder (of area per unit length $S_1=2\pi r_0$) is:

$$Z_{01}=\frac{S_1 p(r_0,t)}{q_r(r_0,t)}=\frac{2S_1\rho c e^{j\gamma_0(\zeta_0)}}{C_0(\zeta_0)}[J_0(\zeta_0)-jN_0(\zeta_0)]. \quad (10\text{-}19)$$

Since, according to equation (10-7),

$$e^{+j\gamma_0}=\cos\gamma_0+j\sin\gamma_0=\frac{2N_0'}{C_0}-j\frac{2J_0'}{C_0},$$

and according to equation (10-10)

$$J_0'=-J_1 \text{ and } N_0'=-N_1,$$

it follows that

$$Z_{01}=\frac{4S_1\rho c}{C_0^2}[(J_1N_0-J_0N_1)+j(J_0J_1+ N_0N_1)]=R_{01}+jY_{01}, \quad (10\text{-}20)$$

where

$$R_{01}=\frac{4S_1\rho c}{C_0^2}[J_1N_0-J_0N_1] \text{ and } Y_{01}=\frac{4S_1\rho c}{C_0^2}[J_0J_1+N_0N_1].$$

Expressions (10-20) can be utilized for analysis of long cylindrical receivers as used in hydroacoustics.

For long waves* $(\zeta_0\ll 1)$

$$C_0(\zeta_0)\approx\frac{4}{\pi\zeta_0},\ J_0(\zeta_0)\approx 1-\frac{\zeta_0^2}{4}\approx 1,\ N_0(\zeta_0)\approx\frac{2}{\pi}\ln\zeta_0-0{\cdot}074\approx$$

$$\approx\frac{2}{\pi}\ln\zeta_0,\ J_1(\zeta_0)\approx\frac{\zeta_0}{2},\qquad N_1(\zeta_0)\approx-\frac{2}{\pi\zeta_0},$$

---

* E. Jahnke and F. Emde, *Tables of Functions*, New York: Dover Publications 1945 (see pp. 126 ff.).

and we get:

$$R_{01} \approx \frac{S_1}{2} \rho c \pi \zeta_0 (1 - \zeta_0^2 \ln \zeta_0) \approx \frac{S_1 \pi \rho c}{2} \zeta_0,$$

$$Y_{01} \approx - S_1 \omega \rho r_0 \ln \zeta_0 = S_1 \omega \rho r_0 \ln \frac{1}{\zeta_0} = S_1 \rho c \zeta_0 \ln \frac{1}{\zeta_0}.$$

It can be seen by comparing this expression with (10-18) that when $\zeta_0 \ll 1$ the radiation resistance per cm^2 of a pulsating cylinder is similar to that of a pulsating strip.

The resistance and reactance of an element of height h of an infinitely long pulsating cylinder for long waves are as follows:

$$\left.\begin{aligned} R_0 &= hR_{01} \approx \frac{\pi}{2} S \rho c \zeta_0 = \frac{\rho \omega S^2}{4}, \\ Y_0 &= hY_{01} \approx \omega 2\pi r_0^2 h\rho \ln \frac{1}{\zeta_0} = \omega \left[M_0 2 \ln \frac{1}{\zeta_0} \right] = \omega M, \end{aligned}\right\} \quad (10\text{-}21)$$

where $S = 2\pi r_0 h$ is the area of the radiating surface, $M_0 = \pi r_0^2 h\rho$ is the mass of the medium displaced by the cylindrical element, $M = M_0 2 \ln \frac{1}{\zeta_0}$ is the "attached" mass.

An interesting expression is thus obtained:

$$\frac{M}{M_0} \underset{\zeta_0 < 1}{\approx} 2 \ln \frac{1}{\zeta_0} = \ln \frac{1}{\zeta_0^2}.$$

In the case of long waves the attached mass of a pulsating cylinder increases indefinitely with decreasing ζ_0, whereas that of a sphere tends to a constant quantity, namely, $(M = 3M_0)$.

The reactance of a small pulsating cylinder (small compared with the wavelength) is larger than its resistance. In fact, from equation (10-21) (without the subscripts);

$$\frac{Y}{R} \underset{\zeta_0 \ll 1}{\approx} \frac{2}{\pi} \ln \frac{1}{\zeta_0}.$$

Hence, if $\zeta_0 = 0{\cdot}001$, then $\frac{Y}{R} \approx 4{\cdot}4$, and if $\zeta_0 = 0{\cdot}01$, then $\frac{Y}{R} \approx 2{\cdot}9$. The ratio $\frac{Y}{R}$ for a pulsating sphere is even larger at low values of $z_0 = kr_0$. For instance, from formula (4-10) it follows that if $z_0 \ll 1$, then

$$\frac{Y}{R} \approx \frac{1}{kr_0} = \frac{1}{z_0}.$$

Thus, if $z_0 = 0{\cdot}001$, $\frac{Y}{R}$ is approximately 1000 and if $z_0 = 0{\cdot}01$, $\frac{Y}{R} \approx 100$. Using the asymptotic expressions (10-8) and (10-10) we get, for $\zeta_0 \gg 1$:

$$R \underset{\zeta_0 \gg 1}{\rightarrow} S\rho c; \qquad Y \underset{\zeta_0 \gg 1}{\rightarrow} 0.$$

The curves in Fig. 83 refer to quantities $\frac{R}{\rho c}$, $\frac{Y}{\rho c}$ and $\frac{M}{M_0}$ as calculated by the exact formulae (10-20) with the aid of tables of Bessel functions.

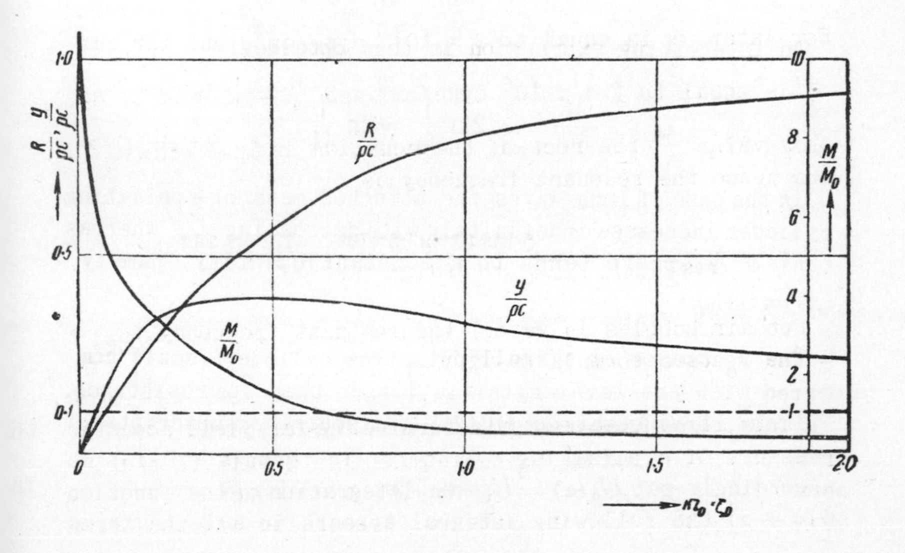

Fig. 83

We will now consider the resonant frequency of a gaseous cylinder in a fluid on condition that $\zeta_0 \ll 1$. The elasticity (bulk modulus) of the cylinder is

$$E = \frac{\rho_0 c_0^2 S^2}{V},$$

where $V = \pi r_0^2 h$, $S = 2\pi r_0 h$ and ρ_0 and c_0 represent, respectively, the density and speed of sound of the gas. The attached mass M is equal to $V\rho.\, 2\ln\frac{1}{\zeta_0}$ and the resonant frequency is

$$\omega_{res} = \sqrt{\frac{E}{M}} = \sqrt{\frac{\rho_0 c_0^2 S^2}{2V^2\rho \ln\frac{1}{\zeta_0}}} = \frac{c}{r_0}\sqrt{\frac{4\rho_0 c_0^2}{\rho c^2 \ln\frac{1}{\zeta_0^2}}}.$$

But since $\frac{\omega_{res}}{c} r_0 = \zeta_0$, the transcendental equation in ζ_0 takes the form

$$\zeta_0^2 \ln\frac{1}{\zeta_0^2} = 4\frac{\rho_0 c_0^2}{\rho\, c^2} = 4\,\frac{\varkappa_0}{\varkappa}.$$

For water, $\varkappa$ is equal to 2×10^{10} dyne/cm^2, but for air $\varkappa_0$ is equal to $1{\cdot}4 \times 10^6$ dyne/cm^2 and $\frac{\varkappa_0}{\varkappa} = 0{\cdot}7 \times 10^{-4}$. At this value $\frac{\varkappa_0}{\varkappa}$ the root of the equation is $\zeta_0 \approx 5{\cdot}15 \times 10^{-3}$, and hence the resonant frequency is

$$f_{res} = \frac{c}{2\pi r_0}\zeta_0 = \frac{5{\cdot}15\times10^{-3}\times1{\cdot}5\times10^5}{2\pi r_0} = \frac{122}{r_0} = \frac{244}{d_0}.$$

For air bubbles in water, the resonant frequency f_{res} = $= 680/d_0$ (see formula (9-32)).

It is also of interest to determine the far field acoustic pressure of a pulsating cylinder. In formula (10-15) we accordingly put $U_0(\alpha) = U_0$. On integration of the function $\psi(\varphi - \alpha)$, the following integral appears in all the terms in the series 10-15:

$$\int_{-\pi}^{+\pi} \cos m(\varphi-\alpha)\,d\alpha = -\frac{\sin m(\varphi-\pi)}{m} + \frac{\sin m(\varphi+\pi)}{m}.$$

This integral will be zero for any non-zero value of m, but if $m = 0$ it will equal $-(\varphi-\pi)+(\varphi+\pi)=2\pi$. Thus the only term remaining in the series (10-15) on integration is that corresponding to $m = 0$ and hence

$$p \approx \rho c \sqrt{\frac{r_0}{r}}\, e^{j(\omega t-kr)} \cdot \sqrt{\frac{2}{\pi^3 \zeta_0}} \cdot \frac{e^{j\left[\gamma_0(\zeta_0)+\frac{\pi}{4}\right]}}{C_0(\zeta_0)} 2\pi U_0,$$

$$q_r \approx \frac{p}{\rho c}.$$

If $\zeta_0 < 1$ we get:

$$p \approx \rho c \sqrt{\frac{r_0}{r}} \cdot \sqrt{\frac{\pi \zeta_0}{2}}\, U_0 e^{j\frac{\pi}{4}} \cdot e^{j(\omega t - kr)}; \quad q_r \approx \frac{p}{\rho c}.$$

The intensity of sound at large distances is

$$J \approx \frac{1}{2} |p| \cdot |q_r|_{\zeta_0 \ll 1} = \rho c \frac{r_0}{r} \pi \zeta_0 \frac{u_0^2}{2}.$$

The total radiated power per unit length of the cylinder is

$$\Pi = 2\pi r J = \frac{\rho\omega S_1^2}{4} \cdot \frac{U_0^2}{2} = R_{01} \frac{U_0^2}{2} = \frac{\rho\omega}{4} \cdot \frac{(S_1 U_0)^2}{2} = 2\rho\pi^3 r_0^2 f \frac{U_0^2}{2}.$$
$$\zeta_0 \ll 1$$

The radiation resistance is given by the expression

$$R_{01} = \frac{\rho\omega S_1^2}{4} = 2\rho\pi^3 r_0^2 f,$$

which corresponds with that obtained previously (10-18) for a pulsating band of width $2\alpha_0$ if $\zeta_0 \ll 1$. This result indicates that for long waves the radiation resistance is independent of the configuration of the radiating surface. In both cases the radiated power is solely a function of the volume velocity $X_0(S_1 U_0)$ of the radiator. Although complicated wave phenomena may occur near the variously shaped pulsating elements, nevertheless the resultant configuration of the acoustic field at large distances is the same in all cases, the intensity being purely radial and independent of angle.

Oscillating Cylinder (Dipole Radiation)

Consider a rigid cylinder which vibrates as a unit with the velocity $u = U_0 e^{j\omega t}$, in the direction $\varphi = 0$ Expressions can be formed for the acoustic pressure and radial velocity in accordance with formulae (10-4), (10-5) and (10-9). The boundary condition on the surface of the cylinder requires the radial component of the oscillation velocity $U_0 e^{j\omega t} \cos\varphi$ to be equal to $q_r(\varphi)|_{r=r_0}$. The series in equation (10-5) therefore reduces to a single term with the subscript $m = 1$ and hence (assuming that $\varphi_m = 0$):

$$A_1 = \frac{-j\rho c U_0}{J_1'(\zeta_0) - jN_1'(\zeta_0)} = \frac{\rho c U_0}{C_1(\zeta_0)} e^{j\gamma_1(\zeta_0)}. \qquad (10\text{-}22)$$

For p and q_r from (10-5) we get:

$$\begin{aligned} p &= \frac{\rho c U_0 e^{j\omega t}}{C_1(\zeta_0)\, e^{-j\gamma_1(\zeta_0)}} [J_1(\zeta) - jN_1(\zeta)] \cos\varphi, \\ q_r &= \frac{jU_0 e^{j\omega t}}{C_1(\zeta_0)\, e^{-j\gamma_1(\zeta_0)}} [J_1'(\zeta) - jN_1'(\zeta)] \cos\varphi = \\ &= U_0 e^{j\omega t} \cdot \frac{e^{j[\gamma_1(\zeta_0) - \gamma_1(\zeta)]}}{C_1(\zeta_0)} C_1(\zeta) \cos\varphi. \end{aligned} \qquad (10\text{-}23)$$

At large distances from the cylinder, using (10-9) we find:

$$p_{\zeta > 1} \approx \frac{\rho c U_0 e^{j\gamma_1(\zeta_0)}}{C_1(\zeta_0)} \cdot \sqrt{\frac{2}{\pi k r}} \cdot e^{j\left(\omega t - kr + \frac{3\pi}{4}\right)} \cdot \cos\varphi,$$

$$q_{r_{\zeta > 1}} \approx \frac{U_0 e^{j\gamma_1(\zeta_0)}}{C_1(\zeta_0)} \cdot \sqrt{\frac{2}{\pi k r}} \cdot e^{j\left(\omega t - kr + \frac{3\pi}{4}\right)} \cdot \cos\varphi.$$

The intensity of the sound in the radial direction is:

$$J=\frac{1}{2}\left|p\right|\cdot\left|q_r\right|=\frac{2\rho c\cos^2\varphi}{\pi krC_1^2(\zeta_0)}\cdot\frac{U_0^2}{2}.$$

The directivity characteristic of the intensity of an oscillating cylinder (dipole) is determined by the function $\cos^2\varphi$ and therefore has the shape of a figure eight. The total radiated power per unit length of the cylinder is

$$\Pi=\int_0^{2\pi}Jr\,d\varphi=\rho c\frac{2}{kC_1^2(\zeta_0)}\frac{U_0^2}{2}=R_1\frac{U_0^2}{2}.$$

The radiation resistance per unit length is

$$R_1=\frac{2\rho c}{kC_1^2(\zeta_0)}\underset{\zeta_0\ll 1}{\approx}\frac{\rho\pi^2\omega^3r_0^4}{2c^2}=\frac{\rho\omega^3S_1^4}{16\pi^2c^2},$$

where

$$S_1=2\pi r_0.$$

An expression for the coefficient $A_1(\zeta_0)$ may be obtained in a way different from formula (10-14) by assuming that the distribution function for the velocity $U_0(\alpha)$ is $U_0(\alpha)=U_0\cos\alpha$. Then

$$p=\frac{\rho cU_0e^{j\omega t}}{\pi}\sum_{m=0}^{\infty}\frac{J_m(\zeta)-jN_m(\zeta)}{C_m(\zeta_0)e^{-j\gamma_m(\zeta_0)}}\int_0^{2\pi}\cos m(\varphi-\alpha)\cos\alpha\,d\alpha;$$

$$q_r=j\frac{U_0e^{j\omega t}}{\pi}\sum_{m=0}^{\infty}\frac{J'_m(\zeta)-jN'_m(\zeta)}{C_m(\zeta_0)e^{-j\gamma_m(\zeta_0)}}\int_0^{2\pi}\cos m(\varphi-\alpha)\cos\alpha d\alpha.$$

The integral contained in these formulae reduces to the form

$$-\frac{1}{2}\Bigg|_0^{2\pi}\left\{\frac{\sin[m\varphi-(m-1)\alpha]}{m-1}+\frac{\sin[m\varphi-(m+1)\alpha]}{m+1}\right\}.$$

Since the first term in this expression is zero for any value of m, and likewise the second for any m except $m = 1$, therefore

$$\int_0^{2\pi} \cos m(\varphi - \alpha)\cos\alpha d\alpha = -\frac{1}{2}\Bigg|_0^{2\pi}\left[\frac{\sin m\varphi\cos(m-1)\alpha}{m-1} - \right.$$

$$\left. - \frac{\cos m\varphi\sin(m-1)\alpha}{m-1}\right]_{m=1} =$$

$$= -\frac{1}{2}\left[\sin m\varphi\frac{\cos(m-1)2\pi}{m-1} - \cos m\varphi\frac{\sin(m-1)2\pi}{m-1} - \right.$$

$$\left. - \sin m\varphi\frac{\cos(m-1)\cdot 0}{m-1} + \cos m\varphi\frac{\sin(m-1)\cdot 0}{m-1}\right]_{m=1}.$$

The first and third terms in the brackets are equal but opposite in sign, the fourth is zero, and the second is equal to $(2\pi\cos\varphi)$ if $m=1$; thus

$$\int_0^{2\pi} \cos m(\varphi - \alpha)\cos\alpha\, d\alpha = \pi\cos\varphi,$$

and we get:

$$p = \rho c\, U_0 e^{j\omega t}\frac{J_1(\zeta) - jN_1(\zeta)}{C_1(\zeta_0)\, e^{-j\gamma_1(\zeta_0)}}\cos\varphi\ ;$$

$$q_r = jU_0 e^{j\omega t}\frac{J_1'(\zeta) - jN_1'(\zeta)}{C_1(\zeta_0)\, e^{-j\gamma_1(\zeta_0)}}\cos\varphi.$$

These expressions are identical to those obtained earlier (10-23).

The total reaction of the acoustic field on the cylinder in the direction of oscillation (per unit length) is

$$\Psi_1 = \int_0^{2\pi} p(r_0)\, r_0\cos\varphi d\varphi = \rho c U_0 e^{j\omega t} r_0\frac{J_1(\zeta_0) - jN_1(\zeta_0)}{C_1(\zeta_0)\, e^{-j\gamma_1(\zeta_0)}}\int_0^{2\pi}\cos^2\varphi d\varphi =$$

$$= \pi r_0 \rho c U_0 e^{j\omega t}\frac{J_1(\zeta_0) - jN_1(\zeta_0)}{C_1(\zeta_0)\, e^{-j\gamma_1(\zeta_0)}}.$$

The impedance of the oscillating cylinder per unit length

is

$$Z_1 = \frac{\Psi_1}{U_0 e^{j\omega t}} = \pi r_0 \rho c \; \frac{[J_1(\zeta_0) - jN_1(\zeta_0)]\,[\cos\gamma_1(\zeta_0) + j\sin\gamma_1(\zeta_0)]}{C_1(\zeta_0)}.$$

Using formulae (10-7), we get:

$$Z_1 = \frac{\pi r_0 \rho c}{2C_1^2(\zeta_0)}[J_1 - jN_1][-(N_2 - N_0) + j(J_2 - J_0)] = R_1 + jY_1.$$

For the resistance and reactance we have:

$$R_1 = \frac{\pi r_0 \rho c}{2C_1^2}\left[N_1(J_2 - J_0) - J_1(N_2 - N_0)\right] = \frac{\pi r_0 \rho c}{C_1^2}\left[N_1\left(J_2 - \frac{J_1}{\zeta_0}\right) - J_1\left(N_2 - \frac{N_1}{\zeta_0}\right)\right],$$

$$Y_1 = \frac{\pi r_0 \rho c}{2C_1^2}[J_1(J_2 - J_0) + N_1(N_2 - N_0)] = \frac{\pi r_0 \rho c}{C_1^2}\left[N_1\left(N_2 - \frac{N_1}{\zeta_0}\right) + J_1\left(J_2 - \frac{J_1}{\zeta_0}\right)\right]. \tag{10-24}$$

Here J_0 and N_0 are expressed in terms of the functions J_2, J_1 and N_2, N_1 by using expressions (10-10).

For long waves

$$\underset{\zeta_0 \ll 1}{R_1} \approx \frac{\pi r_0 \rho c}{4}\pi^2\zeta_0^4\left[\left(-\frac{2}{\pi\zeta_0}\right)\left(\frac{\zeta_0^2}{8} - \frac{1}{2}\right) - \frac{\zeta_0}{2}\left(-\frac{2}{\pi\zeta_0^2}\right)\right] \approx \frac{\rho\pi^2\omega^3 r_0^4}{2c^3},$$

$$\underset{\zeta_0 \ll 1}{Y_1} \approx \frac{\pi r_0 \rho c}{4}\pi^2\zeta_0^4\left[\left(-\frac{2}{\pi\zeta_0}\right)\left(-\frac{4}{\pi\zeta_0^2} + \frac{2}{\pi\zeta_0^2}\right) + \frac{\zeta_0}{2}\left(\frac{\zeta_0^2}{8} - \frac{1}{2}\right)\right] \approx \omega(\pi r_0^2 \rho).$$

The quantity $\pi r_0^2 \rho = M_1$ is the attached mass per unit length. If $\zeta_0 \ll 1$, this is equal to the mass of the medium displaced by the cylinder. Curves are plotted in Fig.84 for the quantities $R_1' = \frac{R_1}{\pi r_0 \rho c} = \frac{R_1}{\frac{1}{2}S_1 \rho c}$ and $Y_1' = \frac{Y_1}{\frac{1}{2}S_1 \rho c}$ For short waves, using the asymptotic expressions (10-8), we get:

$$R_1 \underset{\zeta_0 \gg 1}{\approx} \frac{1}{2} S\rho c \frac{4}{\pi\zeta_0}\left[\sin^2\left(\zeta_0 - \frac{3\pi}{4}\right) + \cos^2\left(\zeta_0 - \frac{3\pi}{4}\right)\right]\frac{\pi\zeta_0}{4} = \frac{1}{2}S\rho c,$$

$$Y_1 \underset{\zeta_0 \gg 1}{\approx} \frac{1}{2} S\rho c \frac{4\dfrac{2}{\pi\zeta_0}}{4\dfrac{2}{\pi\zeta_0}}\left[\cos\left(\zeta_0 - \frac{3\pi}{4}\right)\sin\left(\zeta_0 - \frac{3\pi}{4}\right) - \right.$$

$$\left. - \sin\left(\zeta_0 - \frac{3\pi}{4}\right)\cos\left(\zeta_0 - \frac{3\pi}{4}\right)\right] = 0 .$$

The resistance and reactance of an oscillating (dipole) cylinder cannot be ignored when studying the effect of the surrounding medium on the vibration of a string. In a gas this effect is not large and only entails a small correction to the natural frequency of the string, but in a liquid the effect is rather more important.

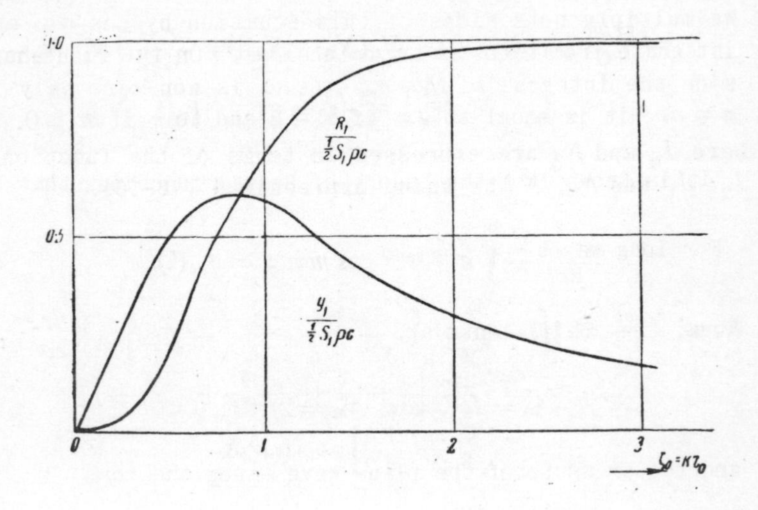

Fig. 84.

The Scattering of a Plane Wave at a Rigid Fixed Cylinder

Under this heading we will describe the method proposed

by Morse* with a few slight changes and corrections.

A plane wave incident in the positive x direction transverse to the axis of the cylinder can be described thus:

$$p_i = p_0 e^{j(\omega t - kx)} = p_0 e^{j\omega t} \cdot e^{-jkr\cos\varphi} = p_0 e^{j\omega t} \cdot e^{-j\zeta\cos\varphi}, \quad (10\text{-}25)$$

where φ is measured from the wave direction, and r is distance from the axis of the cylinder. This plane wave can be represented as a series of cylindrical waves. Suppose we put:

$$e^{-j\zeta\cos\varphi} = \sum_{m=0}^{\infty} A'_m(r) \cdot \cos m\varphi.$$

We multiply both sides of this equation by $\cos n\varphi$ and integrate from 0 to 2π on both sides. On the right-hand side the integral of $\cos m\varphi \cdot \cos n\varphi$ is non-zero only if $m = n$; it is equal to 2π if $m = 0$ and to π if $m > 0$.

It is known from the theory of Bessel functions that

$$\frac{1}{2\pi j^{-m}} \int_0^{2\pi} e^{-j\zeta\cos\varphi} \cos m\varphi d\varphi = J_m(\zeta).$$

Thus, the coefficients are

$$A_0 = J_0(\zeta) \text{ and } A'_m = 2j^{-m} J_m(\zeta),$$

and the pressure of the plane wave takes the form

$$p_i = p_0 e^{j\omega t}\left[J_0(\zeta) + 2\sum_{m=1}^{\infty} j^{-m} J_m(\zeta) \cos m\varphi\right]. \quad (10\text{-}26)$$

Using formulae (10-7) and (10-10), the radial velocity of the incident wave is

---

* P.M. Morse, *Vibration and Sound*, New York: McGraw-Hill, 1948 (see Sect. 29).

$$q_{ir} = -k\frac{\frac{\partial p}{\partial \zeta}}{j\omega\rho} = \frac{p_0 e^{j\omega t}}{j\rho c}\Big\{J_1(\zeta) + \\ + \sum_{m=1}^{\infty} j^{-m}\Big[J_{m+1}(\zeta) - J_{m-1}(\zeta)\Big]\Big\}\cos m\varphi =$$

$$= \frac{p_0 e^{j\omega t}}{j\rho c}\left[\frac{1}{2}C_0(\zeta)\sin\gamma_0(\zeta) + 2\sum_{m=1}^{\infty} j^{-m}C_m(\zeta)\sin\gamma_m(\zeta)\cos m\varphi\right]$$

The incidence of this plane wave on the surface of the cylinder produces a scattered wave. Let us suppose that it is produced in the form of a divergent cylindrical wave. Its acoustic pressure p_s and radial velocity q_{sr} can be determined by formulae (10-4) and (10-5a). The resultant radial velocity on the surface of the cylinder must be zero, i.e. $(q_i + q_{sr})_{r=r_0} = 0$. Consequently,

$$\frac{p_0 e^{j\omega t}}{j\rho c}\left[\frac{1}{2}C_0(\zeta_0)\sin\gamma_0(\zeta_0) + 2\sum_{m=1}^{\infty} j^{-m}C_m(\zeta_0)\sin\gamma_m(\zeta_0)\cos m\varphi + \right. \\ \left. + \frac{A_0 C_0(\zeta_0)\,e^{-j\gamma_0(\zeta_0)}}{2\rho c} + \sum_{m=1}^{\infty}\frac{A_m C_m(\zeta_0)\,e^{-j\gamma_m(\zeta_0)}}{\rho c}\cos m\varphi\right] = 0,$$

whence we find the coefficients $A_m(\zeta_0)$ (the amplitudes of scattered waves of various orders m):

$$A_0 = jp_0 e^{j\gamma_0(\zeta_0)}\sin\gamma_0(\zeta_0) \text{ and } A_m = j2p_0 j^{-m}\cdot e^{j\gamma_m(\zeta_0)}\sin\gamma_m(\zeta_0).$$

The acoustic pressure and radial velocity of the scattered wave at large distances from the cylinder are

$$p_{s_{\zeta\gg 1}} \approx -p_0\sqrt{\frac{2}{\pi}\cdot\frac{r_0}{r}}\cdot\Psi_s(\varphi,\zeta_0)\,e^{j(\omega t - kr)};\quad q_{sr}\approx\frac{p_s}{\rho c},$$

where

$$\Psi_s(\varphi,\zeta_0) = \frac{1}{\sqrt{\zeta_0}}\left[\sin\gamma_0(\zeta_0)\,e^{j\gamma_0(\zeta_0)} + 2\sum_{m=1}^{\infty}\sin\gamma_m(\zeta_0)\,e^{j\gamma_m(\zeta_0)}\cos m\varphi\right].$$

The directivity characteristic for the intensity of the scattered wave is determined by the function $|\Psi_s(\varphi,\zeta_0)|^2$. Directivity characteristics for $\zeta_0 = 1{\cdot}3$ and 5 are shown in Fig. 85 (taken from Morse's book).

With long waves there is not much scattering of sound and what little there is goes mainly backwards, in the direction opposite to that of the incident wave. But as the wave becomes shorter, more and more energy is scattered forwards and the directivity characteristic becomes a complicated shape with a number of lobes.

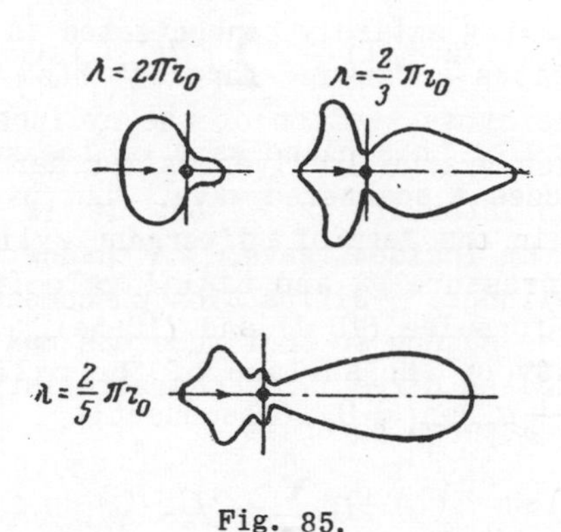

Fig. 85.

For long waves only the first two terms ($m = 0$ and 1) of the series are required in the expression for Ψ_s. A simple formula is obtained for the intensity of the scattered sound:

$$J_s \underset{\zeta_0 \ll 1}{\approx} \left(\frac{\pi\omega^3 r_0^4}{8c^3 r}\right)(1 - 2\cos\varphi)^2 J_0,$$

and the total scattered power is

$$\Pi_s = \int_0^{2\pi} J_s r d\varphi \underset{\zeta_0 \ll 1}{\approx} \frac{3\pi^2\omega^3 r_0^4}{4c^3} J_0 = \frac{6\pi^5 r_0^4}{\lambda^3} J_0,$$

where $J_0 = \frac{p_0^2}{2\rho c}$ is the intensity of the incident plane wave.

The scattered power is inversely proportional to the cube of λ for a cylinder, and not to its inverse fourth power as in the case of a sphere (see (9-10)).

The limiting case of short waves cannot be analysed effectively by simple series expansions in functions $\cos m\varphi$. More refined methods of analysis have indicated that for short waves half the scattered energy (equal to $2r_0J_0$ per unit of cylinder length) is scattered according to the laws of geometric reflection, the bulk of it at all angles in the opposite direction to the incident wave. The other half is practically entirely concentrated in the direction $\varphi=0$. It creates a "shadow-forming" beam which is restricted to the cross section of the cylinder in the near zone, but which gradually diverges further away from the cylinder; its intensity is J_0, but it is in anti-phase relative to the incident wave. A shadow is thus formed behind the cylinder. Diffraction phenomena occur at the boundary of the shadow so that numerous maxima and minima are present in the directivity characteristic.

The total scattered power is

$$\Pi_s \underset{\zeta_0 \gg 1}{\longrightarrow} 4r_0J_0.$$

It is double that of the incident plane wave on the cross-section of the cylinder.

Morse mentions the following expression for the intensity of the scattered wave (at large distances) on the condition that $\zeta_0 \gg 1$:

$$\frac{J_s}{J_0}=\frac{r_0}{2r}\sin\frac{\varphi}{2}+\frac{1}{2\pi kr}\cot^2\frac{\varphi}{2}\sin^2(kr_0\sin\varphi) + \text{rapidly varying terms}$$

The first term represents the intensity of the reflected wave and the second that of the shadow-forming wave concentrated within the angle $\varphi=\frac{\pi}{\zeta_0}=\frac{\lambda}{2r_0}$. The average of the rapidly varying terms over any substantial angular range is zero.

The Pressure of a Sound Wave on a Cylinder

By virtue of formulae (10-4) and (10-26), the total pressure on the surface of the cylinder is:

$$p(r_0)=p_i(r_0)+p_s(r_0)=$$

$$=p_0e^{j\omega t}\left\{\left[J_0+2\sum_{m=1}^{\infty}j^{-m}J_m\cos m\varphi\right]+\left[je^{j\gamma_0}\sin\gamma_0(J_0-jN_0)+\right.\right.$$

$$\left.\left.+2\sum_{m=1}^{\infty}j^{1-m}e^{j\gamma_m}\sin\gamma_m(J_m-jN_m)\cos m\varphi\right]\right\}=$$

$$=p_0e^{j\omega t}\left\{J_0+je^{j\gamma_0}\sin\gamma_0(J_0-jN_0)+\right.$$

$$\left.+2\sum_{m=1}^{\infty}j^{-m}\left[J_m+je^{j\gamma_m}\sin\gamma_m(J_m-jN_m)\right]\cos m\varphi\right\}.$$

Substituting

$$\sin\gamma_0=-\frac{2J'_0}{C_0}\text{ and }\sin\gamma_m=-\frac{J'_m}{C_m}$$

and considering that

$$C_0=2je^{j\gamma_0}(J'_0-jN'_0)\text{ and }C_m=je^{j\gamma_m}(J'_m-jN'_m),$$

the expression for $p(r_0)$ simplifies to

$$j2p_0e^{j\omega t}\sum_{m=0}^{\infty}\frac{j^{-m}e^{j\gamma_m}}{C_m}\left[J_m(J'_m-jN'_m)-J'_m(J_m-jN_m)\right]\cos m\varphi.$$

But since the expression in square brackets is always equal to $\frac{2}{\pi\zeta_0}$,

$$p(r_0)=j\frac{4p_0e^{j\omega t}}{\pi\zeta_0}\sum_{m=0}^{\infty}\frac{\cos m\varphi}{C_m(\zeta_0)}e^{j\left[\gamma_m(\zeta_0)-\frac{m\pi}{2}\right]}. \qquad (10\text{-}27)$$

If the azimuth is read off from the direction $\varphi = \pi$, then $\cos m\varphi$ in this formula is replaced by $\cos m\varphi \cdot e^{jm\pi}$ so that we get:

$$p(r_0) = \frac{4p_0 e^{j\omega t}}{\pi\zeta_0} e^{j\frac{\pi}{4}} \sum_{m=0}^{\infty} \frac{\cos m\varphi}{C_m(\zeta_0)} e^{j\left[\gamma_m(\zeta_0) + \frac{2m+1}{4}\pi\right]}. \quad (10\text{-}28)$$

The dependence on the angle φ is the same as in expression (10-12) for a linear element at the angle φ, provided the azimuth of the linear element is taken as $\alpha = 0$. For complete identity between expressions (10-27) and (10-28) we have to put

$$p_0 = U_0 d\alpha\rho c \sqrt{\frac{r_0}{r}} e^{-jkr} \cdot e^{-j\frac{\pi}{4}} \cdot \sqrt{\frac{2}{\pi^3\zeta_0}} \cdot \frac{\pi\zeta_0}{4},$$

which corresponds to the pressure amplitude of a plane wave produced by a linear element of a very long cylinder of radius r_0 (see formulae (10-12) and (10-13)) for $\zeta_0 \ll 1$. As in the case of a sphere, we have another instance in which the reciprocity principle is observed (see Chapter IX). A remote (linear) source having a certain volume velocity produces the same sound pressure on the surface of a cylinder at the azimuthal angle φ (measured from the radius to the source) as an indentical linear source having the same volume velocity and being located on the surface of the cylinder at the same azimuthal angle would produce on the line occupied by the first source. Thus, the curves in Fig. 85 also show the distribution of the square of the acoustic pressure on the surface of a cylinder for the case of a plane wave, incident on the cylinder.

For long waves the pressure $p(r_0)$ given by expression (10-28) becomes:

$$p(r_0) = j\frac{4p_0 e^{j\omega t}}{\pi\zeta_0}\left[\frac{\pi\zeta_0}{4} + \frac{\pi\zeta_0^2}{2} e^{-j\frac{\pi}{2}} \cdot \cos\varphi + \frac{\pi\zeta_0^3}{8} e^{j\pi} \cos 2\varphi + \dots\right] =$$
$$= jp_0\left[1 - j2\zeta_0 \cos\varphi - \frac{\zeta_0^2}{2} \cos 2\varphi + \dots\right].$$

The total resultant force in the x direction per unit length of the cylinder is:

$$F_x = r_0 \int_0^{2\pi} p(r_0) \cos \varphi d\varphi.$$

But since the integral is zero unless $m = 1$, therefore

$$F_x = j \frac{4p_0 e^{j\omega t}}{\pi \zeta_0} \cdot \frac{\pi r_0 e^{j\left[\gamma_1(\zeta_0) - \frac{\pi}{2}\right]}}{C_1(\zeta_0)} = \frac{4 r_0 e^{j\gamma_1(\zeta_0)}}{\zeta_0 C_1(\zeta_0)} p_0 e^{j\omega t} =$$

$$= \begin{cases} 2\pi r_0 \zeta_0 p_0 e^{j\omega t} \quad \text{if } \zeta_0 \ll 1, \\ \frac{2r_0 \sqrt{2\pi}}{\sqrt{\zeta_0}} e^{j\left(\zeta_0 - \frac{3\pi}{4}\right)} p_0 e^{j\omega t} = \sqrt{4 r_0 \lambda} \cdot e^{j\left(\zeta_0 - \frac{3\pi}{4}\right)} p_0 e^{j\omega t} \quad \text{if } \zeta_0 \gg 1. \end{cases}$$

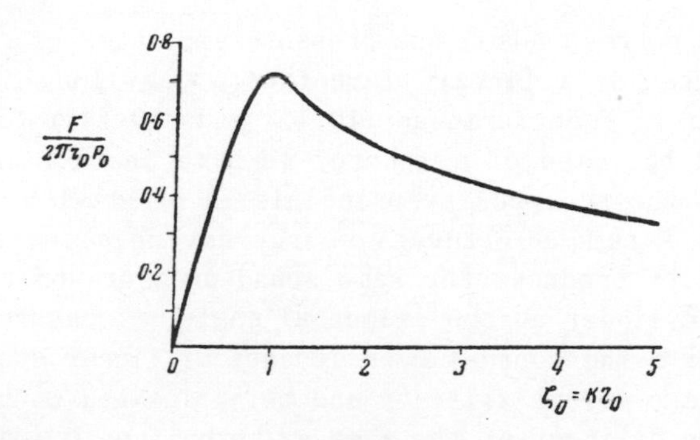

Fig. 86.

Figure 86 shows the quantity $\frac{F}{2\pi r_0 p_0}$ as a function of ζ_0. As in the case of a sphere, the pressure is proportional to ζ_0, at low frequencies, i.e. it corresponds to the pressure drop over the width of the cylinder. If $\zeta_0 = 1$ the pressure attains a maximum and then begins to decline in proportion to $\frac{1}{\sqrt{\zeta_0}}$. The effect of acoustic pressure on a cylinder is to some extent like that of sound on the ribbon of a ribbon microphone. It can be assumed that a ribbon microphone will operate approximately like a pressure gradient microphone if $2\pi a < \lambda$, where a is the width of the ribbon.

CHAPTER XI

RADIATION BY A PLANE PISTON

The Acoustic Field of a Piston

We define our "piston" as an absolutely rigid plane surface, having an arbitrarily shaped perimeter, which vibrates along the normal to its surface. In Rayleigh's* analysis of piston radiators it is assumed that the piston is a perfect fit in an aperture in a plane infinite baffle. The baffle is assumed to be "stationary", i.e. the normal surface velocity is assumed to be zero. In general, the normal velocity may be distributed according to an arbitrary law on the surface of the piston; the simplest case is that of constant surface velocity (this, in fact, exactly corresponds to the meaning of the term "piston"). The radiation of a piston with no baffle has been studied by Gutin**.

The radiation of a piston can be analysed by a general method if the velocity potential and its normal derivative are known on the bounding surface***.

Suppose that in a certain region R with the bounding surface S two functions φ and ψ satisfy the Helmholtz equation:

$$\begin{aligned} \nabla^2 \varphi + k^2\varphi &= 0, \\ \nabla^2 \psi + k^2\psi &= 0, \end{aligned} \qquad (11\text{-}1)$$

---

* Lord Rayleigh, *Theory of Sound*, New York: Dover Publications 1945 (see vol. II, Sect. 302).

** L.Ya. Gutin, *Zhur. tekh. fiz.* 7, 1096, 1937.

*** H. Lamb, *Hydrodynamics*, Cambridge, 1945 (see Sect. 290).

and that these and their second order derivatives are unique, finite and continuous. According to Green's theorem

$$\iiint_V (\varphi \nabla^2 \psi - \psi \nabla^2 \varphi) dV = \iint_S \left(\psi \frac{d\varphi}{dn} - \varphi \frac{d\psi}{dn}\right) dS \qquad (11\text{-}2)$$

where $\frac{d}{dn}$ represents the derivative with respect to the internal normal. The left-hand side of (11-2) is zero in accordance with equations (11-1). Suppose we let ψ be the potential of a point source $\psi = \frac{e^{-jkr}}{r}$ and φ be the velocity potential inside the region having the bounding surface S (strictly speaking φ and ψ define only the spatially-dependent part of the velocity potential if the time dependence is taken in the form $e^{j\omega t}$). The function ψ satisfies the wave equation, but it becomes infinite at the point $r = 0$ so that equation (11-2) is inapplicable at this point. We require the value of the velocity potential at point A, which we take as origin of a system of spherical coordinates. We select as the integration surface in Green's formula the surface S together with the

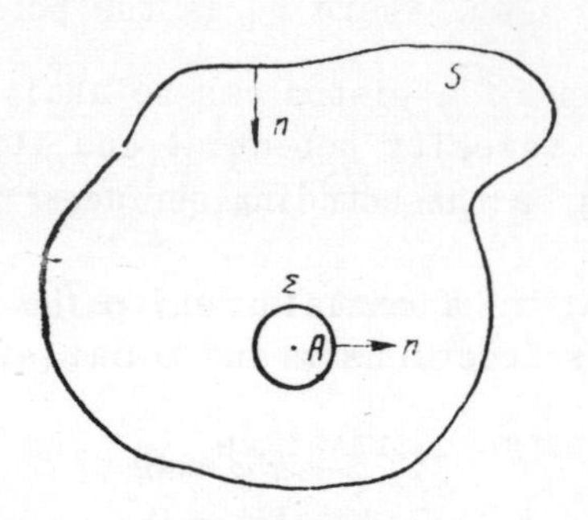

Fig. 87.

surface Σ of a small sphere with its centre at point A (Fig. 87). The point $r = 0$ is then removed from the volume

V and by formula (11-2) (since the left-hand side is zero we find:

$$\iint_{\Sigma}\left[\frac{e^{-jkr}}{r}\cdot\frac{\partial\varphi}{\partial n}-\varphi\frac{\partial}{\partial n}\left(\frac{e^{-jkr}}{r}\right)\right]d\Sigma=$$
$$=-\iint_{S}\left[\frac{e^{-jkr}}{r}\cdot\frac{\partial\varphi}{\partial n}-\varphi\frac{\partial}{\partial n}\left(\frac{e^{-jkr}}{r}\right)\right]dS. \qquad (11\text{-}3)$$

On the surface of the sphere Σ

$$\frac{\partial}{\partial n}\left(\frac{e^{-jkr}}{r}\right)=\frac{\partial}{\partial r}\left(\frac{e^{-jkr}}{r}\right)=-\frac{1+jkr}{r^2}e^{-jkr}.$$

The surface element $d\Sigma$ is equal to $r^2 d\Omega$, where Ω is the solid angle subtended by $d\Sigma$. Consequently,

$$\iint_{\Sigma}\frac{e^{-jkr}}{r}\frac{\partial\varphi}{\partial n}d\Sigma=\int_{\Sigma}re^{-jkr}d\Omega\underset{r\to 0}{\longrightarrow}0,$$
$$-\iint_{\Sigma}\varphi\frac{\partial}{\partial n}\left(\frac{e^{-jkr}}{r}\right)d\Sigma=\int_{\Sigma}\varphi(1+jkr)e^{-jkr}d\Omega\underset{r\to 0}{\longrightarrow}4\pi\varphi_A.$$

If $r\to 0$, the first integral tends to zero, but the second tends to $4\pi\varphi_A$, where φ_A is the potential at point A. Then

$$\varphi_A=-\frac{1}{4\pi}\iint_{S}\frac{e^{-jkr}}{r}\left(\frac{\partial\varphi}{\partial n}\right)_S dS+\frac{1}{4\pi}\iint_{S}\varphi_s\frac{\partial}{\partial n}\left(\frac{e^{-jkr}}{r}\right)dS. \qquad (11\text{-}4)$$

Thus the velocity potential at any point within the surface S is expressible in terms of its value on the surface S, φ_s and its normal derivative $\left(\frac{\partial\varphi}{\partial n}\right)_s$ on the surface S.

Transforming expresssion (11-4) by the Fourier integral, we obtain the known Kirchhoff formula which expresses the potential in terms of the retarded surface potential $\varphi_s\left(t-\frac{r}{c}\right)$ and its normal derivative on surface S.

Formula (11-4) provides a solution of the boundary problem if both the velocity distribution $\left(\frac{\partial\varphi}{\partial n}\right)_s$, and the potential φ_s distribution are known. But it is impossible to specify both these quantities on the surface S independently since in defining one of them we automatically prescribe the other. Generally speaking, expression (11-4) is a useful solution of the boundary value problem only in certain special cases when it can be transformed so that it is no longer dependent on both φ_s or $\left(\frac{\partial\varphi}{\partial n}\right)_s$.

It is important to note that expression (11-4) defines the field at point A as the resultant effect of point sources with a surface density $\left(\frac{\partial\varphi}{\partial n}\right)_s$ and dipole sources with the density φ_s on the surface S. Since φ_s is equal to $\frac{p_s}{j\omega\rho}$, where p_s is the acoustic pressure, the second term in (11-4) depends on the pressure distribution p_s over the surface S.

Formula (11-3) is applicable to a region V' between a surface S and a sphere Σ' of infinite radius. Suppose we make φ_s and $\frac{\partial\varphi}{\partial n}$ both zero on the surface of the sphere Σ' and assume that there are no sources of sound at infinity or in the volume V'. The left-hand side of (11-3) then vanishes. On the external side of the surface S, suppose we put φ'_s and $\left(\frac{\partial\varphi'}{\partial n'}\right)_s$ respectively for the velocity potential and its derivative with respect to the external normal n' (i.e. with respect to the internal normal for the region V'). We then get:

$$0 = -\frac{1}{4\pi}\iint_S \frac{e^{-jkr}}{r}\left(\frac{\partial\varphi'}{\partial n'}\right)_s dS + \frac{1}{4\pi}\iint_S \varphi'_s \frac{\partial}{\partial n'}\left(\frac{e^{-jkr}}{r}\right) dS \,. \quad (11\text{-}5)$$

By adding equations (11-4) and (11-5) and taking into account that $\frac{\partial}{\partial n'} = -\frac{\partial}{\partial n}$, we find:

$$\varphi_A = -\frac{1}{4\pi}\iint_S \frac{e^{-jkr}}{r}\left(\frac{\partial\varphi}{\partial n} + \frac{\partial\varphi'}{\partial n'}\right)_S dS + \\ +\frac{1}{4\pi}\iint_S (\varphi - \varphi')_S \frac{\partial}{\partial n}\left(\frac{e^{-jkr}}{r}\right) dS. \tag{11-6}$$

Here the quantity $\left(\frac{\partial\varphi}{\partial n} + \frac{\partial\varphi'}{\partial n'}\right)_S$ is the total volume velocity (strength) per unit area of the source distribution on S; the total local strength of the pulsation is proportional to the sum of the outward normal velocity components on both sides of the element dS. The quantity $(p - p')_S = j\omega\rho(\varphi - \varphi')_S$ is determined by the jump in pressure across the surface S. Equation (11-6) leads to solutions of the boundary value problem in certain special cases which will now be considered.

Suppose that the surface S is a plane and that the quantities φ'_S and $\frac{\partial\varphi'}{\partial n'}$ are symmetrically distributed about this plane on both sides, i.e. that at every point

$$\varphi_S = \varphi'_S \quad \text{and} \quad \left(\frac{\partial\varphi}{\partial n}\right)_S = \left(\frac{\partial\varphi'}{\partial n'}\right)_{S'}.$$

Then (11-6) becomes

$$\varphi_A = -\frac{1}{2\pi}\iint \left(\frac{\partial\varphi}{\partial n}\right)_S \frac{e^{-jkr}}{r} dS, \tag{11-7}$$

the integral being taken over only one side of the plane S. The total velocity $\left(\frac{\partial\varphi}{\partial n} + \frac{\partial\varphi'}{\partial n'}\right)_S$ along the normal must be zero in the plane of symmetry at those points where there are no sources. Outside the region of sources the plane of symmetry can be replaced by a rigid wall (baffle) and integral (11-7) can be confined to that part of the plane where $\frac{\partial\varphi}{\partial n} \neq 0$. It is also obvious that with a rigid wall we are justified in confining the calculations to the acoustic field on one side of the plane S, the nature of the field on the other side being irrelevant.

It is absolutely essential to remember that in deriving formula (11-4) we assume that no sources are present at infinity. Since the surface S extends to infinity in expression (11-7), it is necessary to bear in mind that *the part of the plane S which has non-zero velocities* $\left(\frac{\partial\varphi}{\partial n}\right)_S$, must also have finite dimensions. Otherwise, the integral in (11-7) may be divergent.

If the surface S is a pulsating plane piston, the outward normal velocity amplitude on both sides being q_0, then $q_0 = -\left(\frac{\partial\varphi}{\partial n}\right)_S$, and we get the formula

$$\varphi_A = \frac{q_0}{2\pi} \iint\limits_S \frac{e^{-jkr}}{r} dS. \qquad (11\text{-}8)$$

Suppose that the plane of symmetry outside the piston is occupied by a rigid baffle. Formula (11-8) then provides a solution for the acoustic field of a piston vibrating in an aperture in an infinite baffle.

The quantity

$$d\varphi = -\frac{1}{2\pi}\left(\frac{\partial\varphi}{\partial n}\right)_s \frac{e^{-jkr}}{r} dS$$

represents the velocity potential of a point source with strength $\left(\frac{\partial\varphi}{\partial n}\right)_s dS$, radiating into a solid angle 2π. Formula (11-7) shows that the potential at point A is obtained by adding the potentials $d\varphi$ of the individual point sources over the area S, with the retarded phase, expressed by the factor e^{-jkr}) taken into account. Expression (11-8) thus corresponds in meaning to Huygens' principle.

Suppose that the surface S is an infinitely thin sheet with zero internal volume (e.g. an infinitely thin disc or conical sheet). For vibration of the entire surface as one unit, the sum of the normal components of velocity on both sides $\left(\frac{\partial\varphi}{\partial n}+\frac{\partial\varphi'}{\partial n'}\right)_S=\left(\frac{\partial\varphi}{\partial n}-\frac{\partial\varphi}{\partial n}\right)_S$ is zero and in this case formula (11-6) gives:

$$\varphi_A=\frac{1}{4\pi}\iint\limits_S(\varphi-\varphi')_S\frac{\partial}{\partial n}\left(\frac{e^{-jkr}}{r}\right)dS. \tag{11-9}$$

Thus, the velocity potential φ_A depends solely on the dipole sources $(\varphi-\varphi')_S$, and the moment of the dipole layer per unit area depends on the pressure difference $(p-p')_S=j\omega\rho(\varphi-\varphi')_S$. Formula (11-9) can be used if the distribution of the acoustic pressure on the surface S is known; but, in general, and in particular for a disc or cone (loudspeaker) which vibrates as one unit with a given velocity, the pressure distribution is not known and it cannot be expressed simply in terms of the oscillation velocity. In such cases formula (11-9) obviously is of no direct use in solving the problem.

Formula (11-6) can be applied to the rotational noise of an airscrew (propeller). The pressure of the screw on the air can be calculated from aerodynamic formulae at all points on the surface, the resultant and the resultant moment of these pressure forces being the thrust and the rotational torque, respectively, of the airscrew; the pressure distribution is not symmetric, it being greater on the thrust side (downstream). The first term in formula (11-6) depends on the displacement of the air by the body of the screw during rotation; this also is easy to include. In this case the fluctuating dipole and velocity sources are all known in the form of rotating perturbations. This method was used by Gutin* to analyse the rotational noise of an airscrew (see Chapter VIII).

---

* L.Ya. Gutin, *Zhur. tekh. phys.* VI, 6, 899, 1936; 12, 76, 1942.

The Impedance of a Circular Disc Piston

Formula (11-8) enables us to calculate the velocity potential on the surface S of the piston face itself. The pressure at some point on this face depends on the combined effect of the individual elements dS of the face. It is obvious that the pressure distribution is symmetric about the centre of this face and solely dependent on the distance u between the element dS_1 in question and the centre

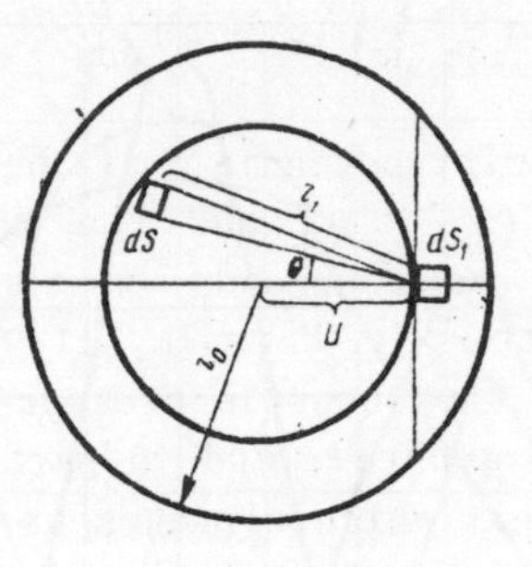

Fig. 88.

(Fig. 88). Putting r_1 for the distance between this particular element and the other elements dS, we get:

$$p(u) = j\omega\rho \frac{q_0}{2\pi} \iint_S \frac{e^{-jkr_1}}{r_1} dS = B \iint_S \frac{e^{-jkr_1}}{r_1} dS, \qquad (11\text{-}10)$$

where

$$B = j\omega\rho \frac{q_0}{2\pi}.$$

The pressure force on the element dS_1 is equal to $p(u)dS_1$, and the total pressure force Ψ on the entire surface is found by integration over the face:

$$\Psi = B \iint_S dS_1 \iint_S \frac{e^{-jkr_1}}{r_1} dS. \qquad (11\text{-}11)$$

It is a complicated mathematical problem to calculate the integral

$$V = \iint_S \frac{e^{-jkr}}{r_1} dS,$$

for the pressure distribution over the piston face. The calculations have however been made for certain values of kr_0 by Maclachlan* and Stenzel**. The curves in Fig. 89 illustrate the distribution of the relative pressure amplitude $p_0'/q_0\rho c$ over the piston face for various values of kr_0. The part of the integral which covers the area of the circle of radius u is fairly simple to calculate; further, it is shown by Rayleigh*** that we can manage to calculate the total force Ψ by integration over the area of the internal circle of radius u alone.

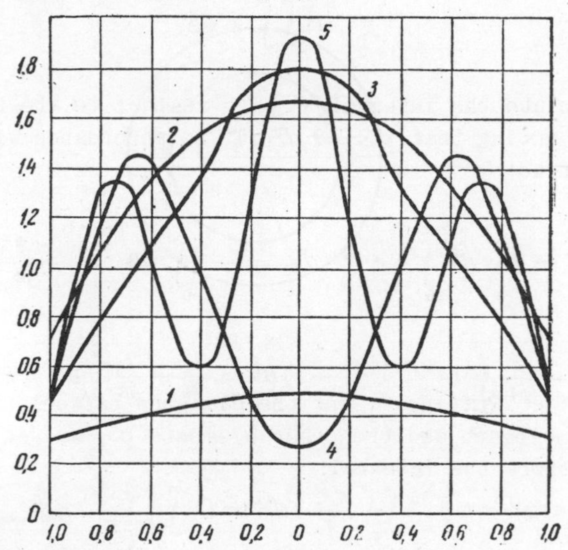

1 — $kr_0 = 0{,}5$; 2 — $kr_0 = 2$; 3 — $kr_0 = 4$; 4 — $kr_0 = 6$; 5 — $kr_0 = 10$

Fig. 89

In the integration for V we first integrate over all elements dS, inside the circle of radius u (Fig. 88). We call the function obtained at this stage V'. If we now

---

* N.W. McLachlan, *Loudspeakers*, Oxford University Press, 1934.

** H. Stenzel, *Leitfaden zur Berechnung der Schallvorgänge*. Berlin, new edition, 1958.

*** Lord Rayleigh, *Theory of Sound*, New York: Dover Publications, (see vol. II, Sect. 302), 1945.

integrate BV' over all dS_1 we obtain that portion of the entire integral (11-11) due to elements dS nearer to the origin than each dS_1. This is, in other words, that portion of Ψ due to elements dS_1 farther from the origin than each dS. But because of the symmetry of the integrand with respect to the coordinates of dS and dS_1 This portion is also equal to the contribution to Ψ of elements dS farther from the origin than each dS_1. Hence Ψ is just equal to twice the integral of BV' over all dS_1 that is:

$$\Psi = 2B \iint_S V' dS_1. \tag{11-12}$$

We calculate the integral V' with respect to the internal circle, noting that $dS = r_1 dr_1 d\theta$. In accordance with Fig. 88, we find:

$$V' = 2\int_0^{\frac{\pi}{2}} d\theta \int_0^{2u\cos\theta} e^{-jkr_1} dr_1 = -2\int_0^{\frac{\pi}{2}} d\theta \Big|_0^{2u\cos\theta} \frac{e^{-jkr_1}}{jk} =$$

$$= -\frac{2}{jk} \int_0^{\frac{\pi}{2}} (e^{-j2ku\cos\theta} - 1)\, d\theta = \frac{\pi}{jk} - \frac{2}{jk} \int_0^{\frac{\pi}{2}} e^{-jku\cos\theta}\, d\theta.$$

We transform the integral:

$$\int_0^{\frac{\pi}{2}} e^{-jy\cos\theta}\, d\theta = \int_0^{\frac{\pi}{2}} \cos(y\cos\theta)\, d\theta - j\int_0^{\frac{\pi}{2}} \sin(y\cos\theta)\, d\theta,$$

where $y = 2ku$. It is known from the theory of Bessel functions*, that,

$$\int_0^{\frac{\pi}{2}} \cos(y\cos\theta)\, d\theta = \frac{\pi}{2} J_0(y), \tag{11-13}$$

---

* V.I. Smirnov, *A Course of Advanced Mathematics*, Moscow, Gostekhizdat, 1956 (vol.III, ch. VI).

where $J_0(y)$ is a zero order Bessel function. The second integral is expressible in terms of the zero order Struve function* (which is not an integral of the Bessel equation):

$$\int_0^{\frac{\pi}{2}} \sin(y\cos\theta)\,d\theta = \frac{\pi}{2} S_0(y). \qquad (11\text{-}14)$$

Using expressions (11-13) and (11-14) we get:

$$V'(y) = \frac{\pi}{jk} - \frac{\pi}{jk} J_0(y) + \frac{\pi}{k} S_0(y) = \frac{\pi}{k} S_0(y) - j\frac{\pi}{k}\left[1 - J_0(y)\right].$$

Incidentally, the acoustic pressure at the element dS_1 cannot be calculated from the expression $BV'(2ku)$, since the integral V' extends only over the internal circle (of radius u) and does not take into account the effect of the external ring. Substituting the expression for V' into formula (11-12) and taking a ring of radius u and width du as the area element,

$$dS_1 = 2\pi u du = \frac{\pi}{2k^2}(2ku)\,d(2ku) = \frac{\pi}{2k^2} y dy,$$

we find the total pressure force Ψ on the piston:

$$\Psi = 2B\int\int V' dS_1 = \frac{B\pi^2}{k^3}\int_0^{z_0} [S_0(y) - j(1 - J_0(y)]\,y dy,$$

where $z_0 = kr_0$.

The integrals of zero-order Struve and Bessel functions are expressible in terms of first order functions, and the functions $J_1(x)$ and $S_1(x)$ can be expanded into series:

---

* E. Jahnke and F. Emde, *Tables of Function*. New York: Dover Publications, 1945 (see p.211).

$$\left.\begin{aligned} J_1(x) &= \frac{x}{2}\left[1 - \frac{\left(\frac{x}{2}\right)^2}{1.2} + \frac{\left(\frac{x}{2}\right)^4}{1.2.2.3} - \frac{\left(\frac{x}{2}\right)^6}{1.2.3.2.3.4} + \ldots\right], \\ S_1(x) &= \frac{2x^2}{3\pi}\left[1 - \frac{x^2}{3.5} + \frac{x^4}{3.5.5.7} - \frac{x^6}{3.5.7.5.7.9} + \ldots\right]. \end{aligned}\right\} \quad (11\text{-}15)$$

These series are useful for calculations at low values of x (i.e. if $x < 2$). If $x \ll 1$, the expression in brackets can be assumed equal to unity. After integration the expression for Ψ becomes:

$$\Psi = \frac{B\pi^2}{k^3}\left[(2z_0)S_1(2z_0) - j\frac{(2z_0)^2}{2} + j(2z_0)J_1(2z_0)\right] = \\ = \frac{\omega\rho\pi q_0 e^{j\omega t}}{2k^3}\left[\frac{(2z_0)^2}{2} - (2z_0)J_1(2z_0) + j(2z_0)S_1(2z_0)\right].$$

The impedance of the piston is

$$Z = \frac{\Psi}{q} = \frac{\omega\rho\pi}{k^3}\left[\frac{(2z_0)^2}{2} - (2z_0)J_1(2z_0) + j(2z_0)S_1(2z_0)\right] = \\ = S\rho c\left[\left(1 - 2\frac{J_1(2z_0)}{2z_0}\right) + j\frac{2S_1(2z_0)}{2z_0}\right] = \\ = R(z_0) + jY(z_0) = S\rho c\,[R'(z_0) + jY'(z_0)]. \quad (11\text{-}16)$$

The resistance and reactance are:

$$R'(z_0) = \left[1 - 2\frac{J_1(2z_0)}{2z_0}\right] = \frac{z_0^2}{2}\left[1 - \frac{z_0^2}{6} + \frac{z_0^4}{72} - \ldots\right], \quad (11\text{-}17)$$

$$Y'(z_0) = \frac{2}{2z_0}S_1(2z_0) = \frac{8z_0}{3\pi}\left[1 - \frac{4z_0^2}{15} + \frac{16z_0^4}{525} - \ldots\right]. \quad (11\text{-}18)$$

The quantities $R'(z_0)$ and $Y'(z_0)$ represent the *dimensionless impedance of the piston radiator*. The dimensionless impedance depends solely on the parameter:

$$z_0 = \frac{2\pi r_0}{\lambda}.$$

The series for $R'(z_0)$ and $Y'(z_0)$, are quite convenient for calculating the impedance if z_0 is less than 2; if z_0 is larger resort must be had to tables of Bessel and Struve functions.

In the extreme case of long waves ($z_0 \ll 1$) we get:

$$\left.\begin{aligned} R &= S\rho c R' \approx S\rho c \frac{k^2 r_0^2}{2} = \frac{\rho\omega^2 S^2}{2\pi c}, \\ Y &= S\rho c Y' \approx S\rho c \frac{8kr_0}{3\pi} = \omega \frac{8}{3} \rho r_0^3 = \omega M; \end{aligned}\right\} \quad (11\text{-}19)$$

where M represents the attached mass of the piston

$$M \approx \frac{8}{3} \rho r_0^3. \quad (11\text{-}20)$$

The radiation resistance of a pulsating sphere for $z_0 \ll 1$ is $\frac{\rho\omega^2 S^2}{4\pi c}$, and that of a hemisphere (in a baffle) $\frac{\rho\omega^2 S^2}{2\pi c}$. Thus the power radiated by a pulsating hemisphere is equal to that radiated by a piston of equal area in an infinite baffle (given equal velocity amplitudes). *For long waves the radiation resistance of all radiators is the same regardless of their shape and the radiated power is determined by the square of the total volume velocity* $(Sq_0)^2$ *regardless of the shape of the radiator.*

A different result is obtained for the attached mass. For a pulsating hemisphere of the same area as a piston ($2\pi R_0^2 = \pi r_0^2$, i.e. if $R_0 = \frac{r_0}{\sqrt{2}}$), the attached mass is, if $kR_0 \ll 1$

$$M' \approx \frac{1}{2} 3 \left(\frac{4}{3} \pi R_0^3 \rho \right) = \frac{\pi}{\sqrt{2}} \rho r_0^3.$$

Therefore,

$$\frac{M}{M'} = \frac{\frac{8}{3} \rho r_0^3}{\frac{\pi}{\sqrt{2}} \rho r_0^3} = \frac{8\sqrt{2}}{3\pi} \approx 1{,}2,$$

i.e. the attached mass of a piston is 20 per cent greater than that of a hemisphere of equal area.

In the case of short waves, $z_0 \gg 1$, series (11-7) and

(11-18) are inapplicable and use must be made of asymptotic representations of the functions $J_1(z_0)$ and $S_1(z_0)$. It follows from Rayleigh's calculations* that

$$\left.\frac{J_1(2z_0)}{2z_0}\right|_{z_0\to\infty} \to \frac{1}{2z_0} \quad \text{and} \quad \left.\frac{2S_1(2z_0)}{2z_0}\right|_{z\to\infty} \to \frac{2}{\pi z_0}.$$

At the limit of very large z_0 we get:

$$R_{z_0\to\infty} \to S\rho c;\ Y_{z_0\to\infty} \to 0;\ M_{z_0\to\infty} \to 0. \quad (11\text{-}20a)$$

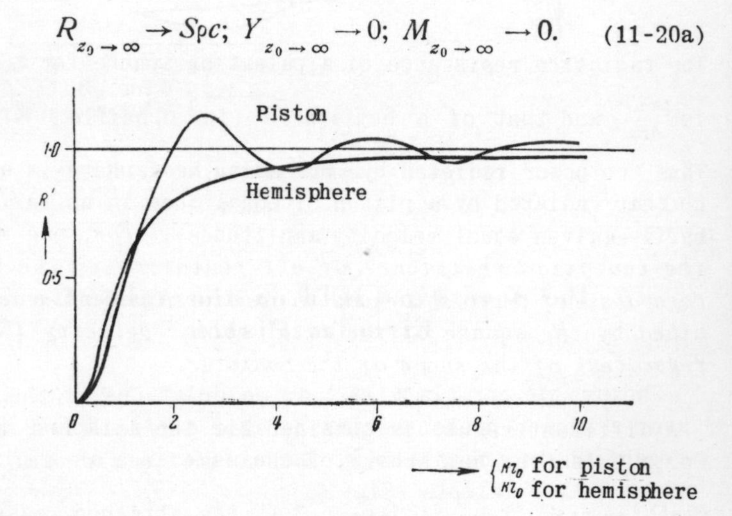

Fig. 90

It can be seen from Figs. 90 and 91 that the functions $R'(z_0)$ and $Y'(z_0)$ (if z_0 is large) tend to the limit through oscillations of gradually diminishing amplitude. For short waves ($z_0 \ll 1$) the impedance of a piston corresponds to the radiation resistance of a plane wave, i.e. ρc per unit area.

---

* Lord Rayleigh, *Theory of Sound*, New York: Dover Publications, 1945 (see vol. II, Sect. 302).

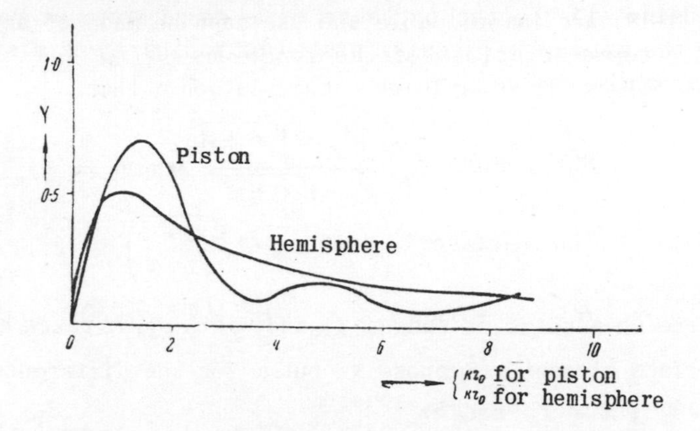

Fig. 91

The Acoustic Field on the Axis of a Circular Piston

The use of formula (11-7) in calculations of the field near a piston presents considerable difficulties, but an exception is the field on the axis of a circular disc, which is very simple (Fig. 92).

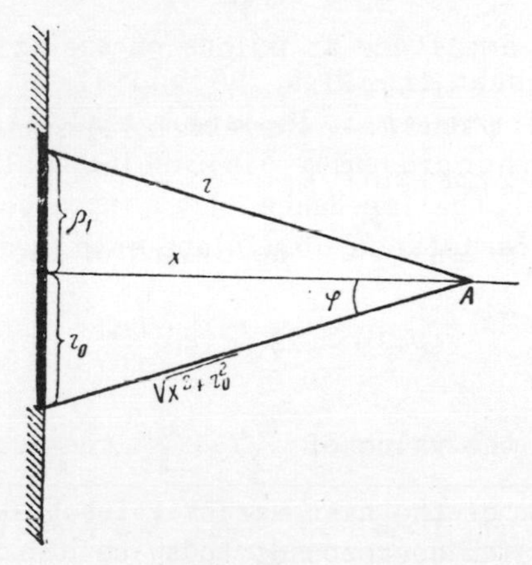

Fig. 92.

Using (11-8), the pressure of a sound wave at point A on the axis of a circular piston of radius r_0, a distance x from the centre, is:

$$p(x,t)=j\omega\rho\frac{q_0e^{j\omega t}}{2\pi}\int_0^{r_0}\frac{e^{-jk\sqrt{x^2+\rho_1^2}}}{\sqrt{x^2+\rho_1^2}}2\pi\rho_1 d\rho_1= \\ =q_0\rho c e^{j\omega t}\left(e^{-jkx}-e^{-jk\sqrt{x^2+r_0^2}}\right), \tag{11-21}$$

where an annulus of radius ρ_1 and width $d\rho_1$ is taken as the surface element. Suppose we put α for the difference between $\sqrt{x^2+r_0^2}$ and x:

$$\alpha=\sqrt{x^2+r_0^2}-x=x\left[\sqrt{1-\frac{r_0^2}{x^2}}-1\right]\approx \\ \approx x\left(1+\frac{r_0^2}{2x^2}\right)-x\approx\frac{r_0^2}{2x}, \text{ if } x\gg r_0 \tag{11-22}$$

The quantity α varies from r_0 (if $x=0$) to 0 (if $x=\infty$. If $x\gg r_0$ it can be assumed approximately that $\alpha\approx\frac{r_0^2}{2x}$. Using expression (11-22), we find:

$$p(x,t)=q_0\rho c e^{j(\omega t-kx)}(1-e^{-jk\alpha})= \\ =q_0\rho c e^{j(\omega t-kx)}(1-\cos k\alpha+j\sin k\alpha).$$

The pressure amplitude at points on the axis is

$$p_0(x)=q_0\rho c\,|\sqrt{\cos^2 k\alpha-2\cos k\alpha+1+\sin^2 k\alpha}\,|= \\ =2q_0\rho c\left|\sin\frac{k\alpha}{2}\right|. \tag{11-23}$$

The acoustic pressure at the centre of the disc is

$$p_0(0)=2q_0\rho c\left|\sin\frac{kr_0}{2}\right|.$$

Depending on the value of $\frac{kr_0}{2}=\frac{\pi r_0}{\lambda}$,the acoustic pressure at the centre of the disc varies between 0 and the quantity $2q_0\rho c$, which corresponds to twice the pressure of a plane wave with velocity amplitude q_0. If $\frac{kr_0}{2}$ is equal to $n\pi$, i.e. if $r_0 = 2n\frac{\lambda}{2}$, then the pressure $p_0(0)$ at the centre is equal to 0, but if $\frac{kr_0}{2}$ is equal to $\left(n+\frac{1}{2}\right)\pi$, i.e. if $r_0 = (2n+1)\frac{\lambda}{2}$, then $p_0(0) = 2q_0\rho c$. In the first case an even number of half-wave Fresnel zones is formed on the surface of the disc and their effects at the centre mutually cancel out, but in the other case there is an odd number of these zones and the maximum occurs at the centre.

It likewise follows from (11-23) that the acoustic pressure $p_0(x)$ on the axis has a number of maxima equal to $2q_0\rho c$, and minima equal to zero depending on x. The minima occur when

$$\frac{ka}{2} = n\pi \quad \text{or} \quad a = 2n\frac{\lambda}{2}, \tag{11-24}$$

i.e. when there is an even number ($2n$) of annular Fresnel zones on the surface of the disc from the centre to the perimeter. The maxima occur if

$$\frac{ka}{2} = \left(n+\frac{1}{2}\pi\right) \quad \text{or} \quad a = (2n+1)\frac{\lambda}{2}, \tag{11-24a}$$

i.e. when there is an odd number $(2n+1)$, of such zones, which accounts for the occurrence of minima and maxima.

The radius r_1 of the first Fresnel zone can easily be calculated at great distances x. This is the radius of the circle which is formed by the intersection of the plane of the disc face with the sphere of radius $x+\frac{\lambda}{2}$; it is approximately equal to $r_1 \approx \sqrt{x\lambda}$. The area S of the first Fresnel zone is approximately $\pi x\lambda$. It is important to note that in this case the formation of an even or odd number of Fresnel zones leads exactly, and not approximately, to the occurrence of maxima equal to $2q_0\rho c$, and minima equal to zero.

The distance from the centre of the disc to the maxima and minima is found from expression (11-23) and conditions (11-24):

$$x_m = r_0 \left[\frac{r_0}{m\lambda} - \frac{m}{4}\frac{\lambda}{r_0}\right], \qquad (11\text{-}25)$$

where m is equal to $2n + 1$ for the maxima and to $2n$ for the minima ($n = 0, 1, 2, 3, \ldots$). We get the most distant maximum from the centre of diaphragm at $n = 0$, i.e. if $m = 1$:

$$x_0 = \frac{r_0^2}{\lambda} - \frac{\lambda}{4}. \qquad (11\text{-}26)$$

If $r_0 \gg \lambda$, then $x_0 \approx \frac{r_0^2}{\lambda}$.

In between this maximum and the centre of the diaphragm there can be a number of other maxima and minima. It will be seen from formula (11-25) that it is a necessary condition for positive values of x for the minima that

$$\frac{r_0^2}{2n\lambda} - 2n\frac{\lambda}{4} > 0 \quad \text{or} \quad n < \frac{r_0}{\lambda}. \qquad (11\text{-}27)$$

Thus the nearest whole number less than $\frac{r_0}{\lambda}$, gives the number of minima between zero and the most distant maximum x_0. The minima gradually come closer together towards the face of the disc.

The distance between the last and penultimate maximum is found from expression (11-25):

$$\Delta = r_0\left(\frac{2}{3}\frac{r_0}{\lambda} + \frac{\lambda}{2r_0}\right) = \frac{2}{3}\left(\frac{r_0}{\lambda}\right)^2 \lambda \left[1 + \frac{3}{4}\frac{1}{\left(\frac{r_0}{\lambda}\right)^2}\right] \approx \frac{2}{3}\frac{r_0^2}{\lambda}.$$

The distance between the nearest minima to the face (if $r_0 \gg \lambda$)can also be found from the same expression if, in accordance with (11-27), we put $m_1 \approx 2\frac{r_0}{\lambda}$ and $m_2 \approx 2\left(\frac{r_0}{\lambda} - 1\right)$.

$$\Delta' \approx r_0 \left[\frac{1}{2\left(\frac{r_0}{\lambda} - 1\right)} + \frac{1}{2}\frac{\lambda}{r_0} \right] = \lambda \left[\frac{\frac{r_0}{\lambda}}{2\left(\frac{r_0}{\lambda} - 1\right)} + \frac{1}{2} \right] \approx \lambda.$$

For the case which is to be considered below where $\frac{r_0}{\lambda} = 5$, the distance Δ' between the nearest two minima is approximately $1{\cdot}1\ \lambda$. The maxima are spaced farther and farther apart with increasing distance from the face and the distance Δ between the last two maxima is greater than λ by a factor of $\frac{2}{3}\left(\frac{r_0}{\lambda}\right)^2$; in the following example $\Delta \approx 16\ \lambda$. The distribution of the pressure amplitude $p_0(x)$ on the axis is illustrated in Fig. 93 for $r_0 = 5\lambda$. The dotted line in this diagram refers to the amplitude of the fluctuating component of the particle velocity in the x direction at various distances from the disc.

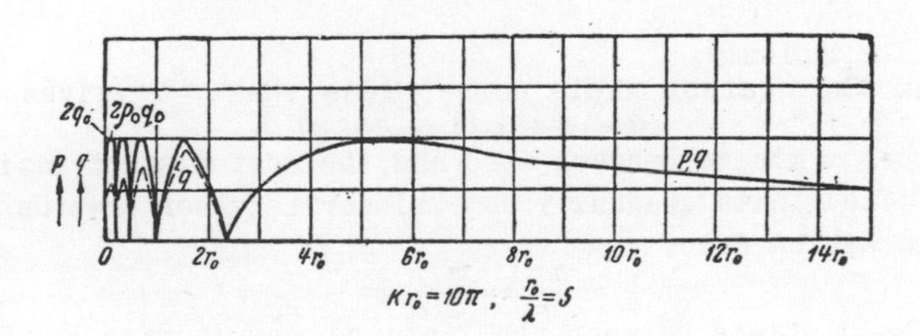

Fig. 93

The fluctuating velocity in the x direction is found from the expression:

$$q(x,t) = -\frac{1}{j\omega\rho}\frac{\partial p}{\partial x} = q_0 e^{j(\omega t - kx)}\left[1 - \frac{x e^{jkx}}{\sqrt{x^2 + r_0^2}} e^{-jk\sqrt{x^2 + r_0^2}}\right].$$

We introduce the auxiliary angle φ (Fig. 92), and since

$$\sqrt{x^2+r_0^2}=x+\alpha=\frac{x}{\cos\varphi} \text{ and } \frac{r_0}{x}=\tan\varphi,$$

it follows that

$$\alpha=r_0\tan\frac{\varphi}{2}.$$

The velocity amplitude is expressed thus:

$$|q|=q_0\frac{\left|\sqrt{x^2+\frac{x^2}{\cos^2\varphi}-2\frac{x^2}{\cos\varphi}\cos k\alpha}\right|}{\frac{x}{\cos\varphi}}=$$

$$=q_0\left|\sqrt{1+\cos^2\varphi-2\cos\varphi\cos k\alpha}\right|=$$

$$=q_0\left|\sqrt{1+\cos^2\varphi-2\cos\varphi\cos\left(kr_0\tan\frac{\varphi}{2}\right)}\right|.$$

The maximum velocity amplitude $|q|_{\max}=q_0(1+\cos\varphi)$ is obtained when

$$\tan\frac{\varphi}{2}=\frac{m\pi}{kr_0}=\frac{m}{2}\frac{\lambda}{r_0}=\frac{2n+1}{2}\frac{\lambda}{r_0},$$

and the minimum

$$|q|_{\min}=q_0(1-\cos\varphi)$$

when

$$\tan\frac{\varphi}{2}=\frac{m\pi}{kr_0}=\frac{m}{2}\frac{\lambda}{r_0}=\frac{2n}{2}\frac{\lambda}{r_0}.$$

Remote maxima, for which the angle φ is small, are approximately equal to $2q_0$, and the minima are nearly zero. The angle φ tends to 90° on coming nearer to the disc, and the maxima and minima tend to q_0 in value. The distances between the centre of the face and the maxima and minima of the velocity amplitude are found from the expression:

$$x_m = \frac{r_0}{\tan\varphi} = r_0 \frac{1-\tan^2\frac{\varphi}{2}}{2\tan\frac{\varphi}{2}} = r_0\left[\frac{r_0}{m\lambda} - \frac{m}{4}\frac{\lambda}{r_0}\right],$$

which coincides with (11-25). Therefore the extreme values of the acoustic pressure and particle velocity occur at the same distances from the centre of the face (Fig. 93).

It is clear from this analysis that the component of the intensity vector in the x direction is also zero at those points where p and q are zero, and that at points in the vicinity of the maxima of p and q the flow of energy becomes almost four times greater than that quantity $\frac{1}{2}p_0q_0 = \frac{1}{2}\rho c q_0^2$, which would occur in a plane wave with particle velocity amplitude q_0 and pressure amplitude $p_0 = \rho c q_0$. Hence it is clear that the streamlines of energy flux from the face are not straight lines parallel to the x axis; the energy flux flows round the minimum points, passes them and concentrates at the maxima. These relations will be more obvious when we have fully dealt with the near field of a piston in the next section.

In accordance with formula (11-26), the most distant maximum is a distance $x_0 = \frac{r_0^2}{\lambda} - \frac{\lambda}{4}$ from the face. If $\frac{ka}{2} \ll 1$ or $x \gg \pi\frac{r_0^2}{\lambda}$, it is then quite accurate to assume that

$$\sin\frac{ka}{2} \approx \frac{ka}{2} = \frac{\pi}{2}\frac{r_0^2}{\lambda x}.$$

The acoustic pressure then is

$$p(x,t) \approx 2q_0\rho c\frac{\pi}{2}\frac{r_0^2}{\lambda x}e^{j(\omega t - kx)} = \frac{\pi r_0^2}{x\lambda}q_0\rho c e^{j(\omega t - kx)} =$$
$$= \pi\frac{S}{S_1}q_0\rho c e^{j(\omega t - kx)},$$

where S_1 is the area of the first Fresnel zone. The acoustic pressure on the axis in the distant zone diminishes in inverse proportion to the distance x; its amplitude is less by a factor of $\pi \frac{S}{S_1}$ than that of a plane wave with velocity amplitude q_0, where $\frac{S}{S_1}$ is the ratio of the area of the piston face to that of the first Fresnel zone.

If the radius of the face is increased indefinitely, we eventually come to the case of sound radiation by an infinite oscillating plane and we must obviously get the acoustic field of a plane wave. By applying formula (11-21) to this case, the acoustic pressure is

$$p(x,t) = q_0 \rho c e^{j(\omega t - kx)} - q_0 \rho c e^{j\omega t} \cdot e^{-j\infty}.$$

The first term correctly expresses the acoustic pressure of a plane wave generated by the oscillations of a plane with velocity amplitude q_0. The second term has an absolute value of $q_0 \rho c$ and an *indeterminate* phase. This term is not realistic physically and in any case is indeterminate. In the derivation of formula (11-18) for the acoustic pressure of a plane piston, it was required that no sound sources should be present at infinity. By increasing the radius of the piston to infinity we have introduced sources at infinity and therefore it is not surprising that an indeterminate result has been obtained.

The Near Field of a Piston Radiator

The near field of a piston is given by formula (11-8), which is applicable to all distances, but if the points under investigation are not on the axis great difficulties arise in the calculations and resort must be had to complicated series. The necessary calculations have been performed by Stenzel* and presented in graphical form as contours of equal acoustic relative pressure $p/q_0\rho c$ (see Fig. 94, 95 and 96) for

$$kr_0 = 4,\ (r_0 = \frac{2}{\pi}\lambda);\ kr_0 = 6,\ (r_0 = \frac{3}{\pi}\lambda) \text{ and } kr_0 = 10,\ (r_0 = \frac{5}{\pi}\lambda).$$

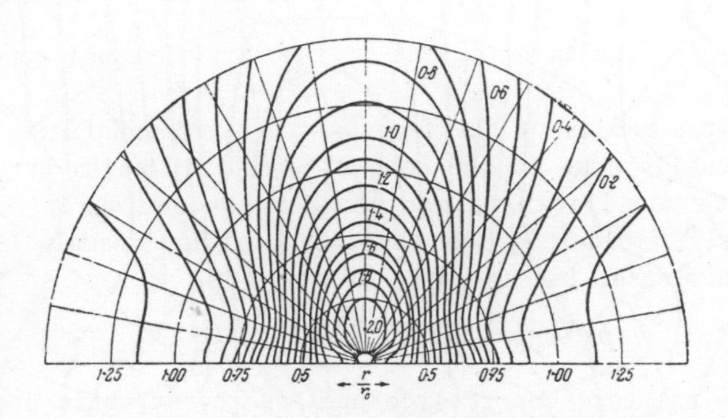

Fig. 94

Zones of minimum and maximum pressure on and alongside the axis are clearly visible on the diagrams; the points on the axis with pressure 0 and $2\rho c q_0$ correspond to the previously calculated minima and maxima (formulae (11-24) and (11-24a)). It is also apparent from these diagrams that if there is zero energy flux at points of zero pressure on the axis, then in the vicinity of a zone of minimum pressure there occur regions of high pressure in which the energy flux (intensity) vector is greater than the mean and so directed that the flux flows round the zone of minimum pressure in order to concentrate later in the zone of maximum pressure on the axis. The pressure on the surface of the piston also has a number of maxima and minima in concentric circles; the smaller the ratio $\frac{\lambda}{r_0}$, the more there are of them in number.

* H. Stenzel, *Leitfaden zur Berechnung der Schallvorgänge*, Berlin, 1958.

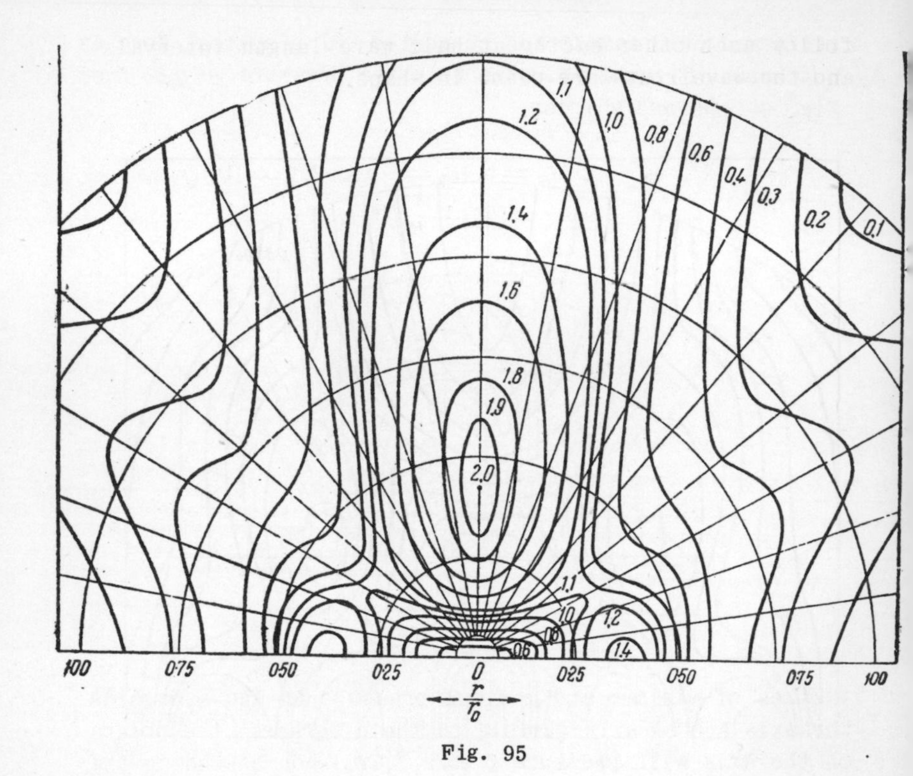

Fig. 95

While we are on the subject of near fields, it is as well to say a few words about the widely-held opinion that the radiation of a piston is practically a plane wave if $r_0 \gg \lambda$. It is on this idea, for instance, that Pierce's ultrasonic interferometer method is based. Here the reflector which produces the standing waves is always placed in the near zone. Despite the fact that the points of maxima and minima on the axis obviously alternate in the near zone at intervals other than half wavelengths, nevertheless varying the distance between the reflector and the radiator still produces maxima and minima of current in the valve circuit at exactly half wavelength intervals. The same sort of thing occurs in the visualization of standing waves from quartz plates as observed by Töpler's method, for the maxima and minima of illumination in the visible pattern follow each other eactly at half wave length intervals and the wavefronts are plane in shape.

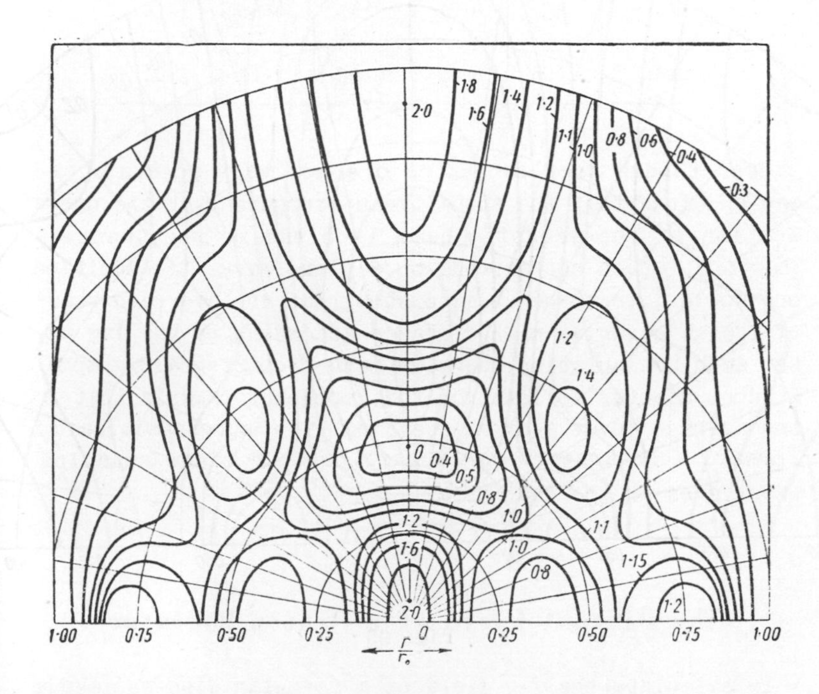

Fig. 96

It is to be supposed in these cases that a "determining" role is played by the mean acoustic pressure over the section transverse to the axis. As we have seen (see(11-20a)), if $r_0 \gg \lambda$ $(kr_0 \gg 1)$ the impedance at the piston face tends to the quantity $S\rho c$ and the mean pressure over the area is $\varsigma_0 \rho c$. The same result apparently would be obtained to a good degree of approximation for cross sections at small distances from the face. No analysis of this problem has as yet been made however. Calculation of the mean pressure using the curves in Fig. 95 provides an estimate of $\bar{p}$ for cross-sections at various distances (x) from the face; these estimates are given in Table 11.

TABLE 11

x/r_0	0	0·31	0·52	0·85	1·16
p/p_0	1·05	0·92	0·90	1·14	1·01

Even though such estimates are not very accurate, we can conclude that the actual mean pressure over the cross section of the acoustic beam is close to the quantity $p_0 = \rho c q_0$, which corresponds to a plane wave. In addition one would like to be able to show that the averaged phase of the wave varies with distance according to the law kx, but such a calculation cannot be made from Stenzel's graphs. It does however follow from the foregoing remarks that on the average (over a cross-section) the superposition of forward and backward waves must produce plane standing waves even in the near zone.

The Distant Field of a Piston Radiator

To calculate the far field of a circular disc we take a rectangular system of coordinates (Fig. 97) and assume that the point A at which the field is sought lies in the plane xz at a large distance r so that the lines AO and AP from point A to separate points on the piston face can be assumed parallel; suppose that these lines are at the angle ϑ to the axis of the disc z. The acoustic field of all points at the angle ϑ to the axis and at the same distance r will be identical by virtue of the axial symmetry.

We draw a plane perpendicular to the radius-vector r intersecting the line AP from point A to surface element dS at point Q, which is the same distance r from point A as the centre of the disc O. The distance between points P

and A is:

$$r_1 = r + \Delta r = r + PQ = r + x \sin \vartheta = r + u \sin \vartheta \cos \psi,$$

where x is the abscissa of point P, u its distance from the centre, and ψ the angle between the x axis and the line OP. The area of the element dS is $u du d\psi$.

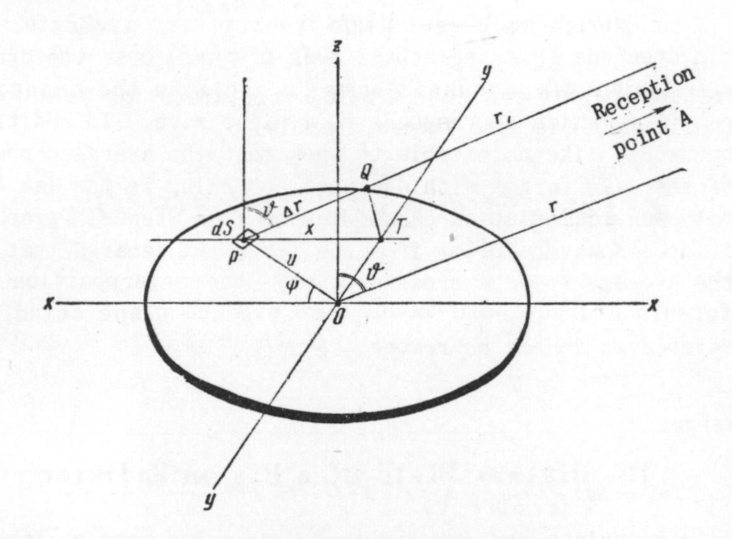

Fig. 97.

We find the velocity potential at point A by adding together the potentials of all the surface elements dS. Since $p = j\omega\rho\Phi$, it follows that the acoustic pressure at point A is:

$$p(\vartheta) = j\omega\rho \frac{q_0}{2\pi} \int\int_S \frac{e^{-jkr_1}}{r_1} dS$$

(apart from the exponential term $e^{j\omega t}$). But since $\Delta r \ll r$, it can be assumed in the denominator that $r_1 = r =$ const. The same approximation cannot be made in the exponent because:

$$e^{-jkr} = e^{-jkr_1} \cdot e^{-jk\Delta r}.$$

The factor $e^{-jk\Delta r}$ significantly affects the phase of the individual integration elements since $k\Delta r$ varies with position on the face, and Δr may have any value between 0 and, as in the case of short waves, many times λ.

Inserting the limits of integration for u and ψ we get:

$$p(\vartheta) = j\omega\rho \frac{q_0 e^{-jkr}}{r} \int_0^{r_0} u du \int_0^{2\pi} e^{-jku \sin\vartheta \cos\psi} \cdot d\psi.$$

Putting $ku \sin\vartheta = z'$ and $kr_0 \sin\vartheta = z'_0$, and using relations from Bessel function theory, namely,

$$\int_0^{2\pi} e^{-jz' \cos\psi} \cdot d\psi = \int_0^{2\pi} e^{jz' \cos\psi} \cdot d\psi = 2\pi J_0(z')$$

and

$$\int_0^{z'_0} J_0(z') z' dz' = z'_0 J_1(z'_0),$$

we get:

$$p(\vartheta) = j\omega\rho \frac{q_0 e^{-jkr}}{(k \sin\vartheta)^2 r} \int_0^{z'_0} J_0(z') z' dz' = j\omega\rho \frac{(\pi r_0^2) q_0 e^{-jkr}}{\pi r} \frac{J_1(z'_0)}{z'_0}.$$

The pressure amplitude is

$$p_0(\vartheta) = \omega\rho \frac{\pi r_0^2 q_0}{2\pi r} \left[2 \frac{J_1(z'_0)}{z'_0}\right]. \qquad (11\text{-}28)$$

The function $2 \frac{J_1(z'_0)}{z'_0}$ (Fig. 98) has a maximum equal to unity at $z'_0 = 0$, i.e. in the axial direction ($\vartheta = 0$). The pressure directivity characteristic of the piston, which is defined by the ratio $p_0(\vartheta)/p_0(0)$ where $r =$ const. is:

$$\Phi(\vartheta) = 2 \frac{J_1(z'_0)}{z'_0}. \qquad (11\text{-}29)$$

If $z'_0 < 2$ it can be calculated by the rapidly convergent series:

$$\Phi(\vartheta)=1-\frac{\left(\frac{z'_0}{2}\right)^2}{1.2}+\frac{\left(\frac{z'_0}{2}\right)^4}{1.2.2.3}-\frac{\left(\frac{z'_0}{2}\right)^6}{1.2.3.3.4.5}+\ldots \quad (11\text{-}29a)$$

If $z'_0 \ll 1$, then $\Phi(\vartheta)$ is approximately equal to 1. This implies that the pressure amplitude is independent of ϑ:

$$p_0(\vartheta)\approx\omega\rho\frac{\pi r_0^2 q_0}{2\pi r}.$$

The directivity characteristic then is a sphere of unit radius. The radiated power is:

$$\Pi\Big|_{z_0\ll 1}\approx\frac{1}{2}(2\pi r^2)\frac{p_0(\vartheta)^2}{\rho c}=\frac{1}{2}\cdot\frac{\rho\omega^2 S^2}{2\pi c}q_0^2=\frac{1}{2}Rq_0^2,$$

where

$$R=\frac{\rho\omega^2 S^2}{2\pi c}.$$

is the radiation resistance. This expression for R has already been obtained from the general formulae for the impedance of a piston (see formula 11-9)).

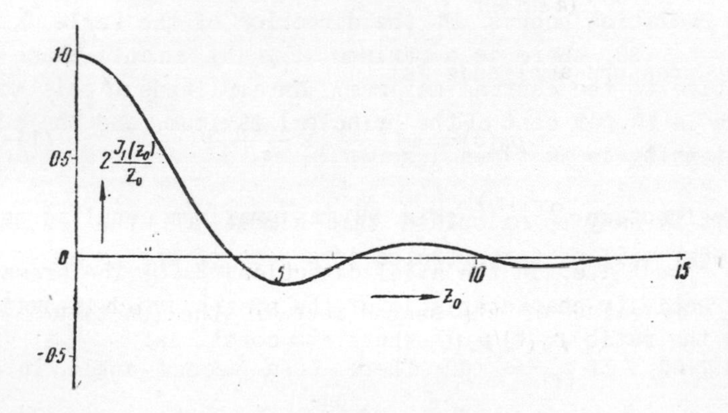

Fig. 98

Figure 99 shows sections in an axial plane of the directivity characteristics for various values of $z_0 = kr_0$. For $z_0 = \frac{\pi}{4}$; $(\lambda = 8r_0)$ the section of the characteristic is still almost a circle. With increasing z_0 $\left(z_0 = \frac{\pi}{2} \text{ and } z_0 = \pi\right)$ the characteristic gradually narrows; the acoustic pressure in the direction $\vartheta = 90^\circ$ is already considerably less than that at $\vartheta = 0$. When z_0 is further increased, the directivity characteristic takes the form of a curve with a central maximum and a number of side lobes (see Fig. 99, at bottom). As can be seen from Fig. 98, the function $\Phi(\vartheta) = 2\frac{J_1(z_0')}{z_0'}$, has a number of zeroes, the first of which, z_{01}' is equal to 3·83 and hence for the sine of the corresponding angle ϑ_1 we get:

$$\sin\vartheta_1 = \frac{z_{01}'}{kr_0} = 0{\cdot}61\frac{\lambda}{r_0}. \tag{11-30}$$

For small angles, we have approximately

$$\vartheta_1 \approx 0{\cdot}61\frac{\lambda}{r_0} \quad \text{or in degrees} \quad \vartheta_1^\circ \approx 35\frac{\lambda}{r_0}. \tag{11-30a}$$

No radiation occurs in the direction of the angle ϑ_1. If $z_0' = 5\cdot33$, there is a maximum of $p_0(\vartheta)$ (in anti-phase relative to the central maximum). The amplitude of this maximum is 13 per cent of the principal maximum, and the sound intensity is 59 times less.

It is easy to calculate that almost all the radiated energy will be concentrated in a cone of vertex angle 0·7 ϑ_1. The value of the second root of the function $2\frac{J_1(z_0')}{z_0'}$ is 7·02. If $z_{02}' = 7\cdot02$, there is a second angle in the characteristic at which no radiation is present; it is found from the expression $\sin\vartheta_2 = \frac{z_{02}'}{kr_0}$. With a further increase in z_0' a second radiation maximum occurs, smaller than the first. Figure 99 shows (the lower curve) the directivity characteristic for the case $kr_0 = 5\pi$, $(\lambda = 0{\cdot}4r_0)$; besides the principal maximum it has three side lobes. The pattern of maxima and minima in rings round the axial direction corresponds exactly to the Fraunhofer diffraction pattern of an illuminated circular aperture.

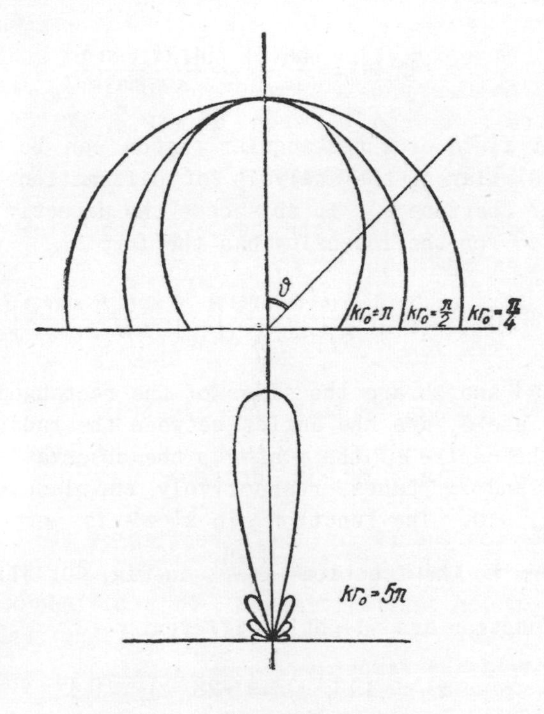

Fig. 99

An acutely directional beam of sound can be obtained only if $\lambda \ll r_0$. Thus, an angular width $\vartheta_1 = 10^\circ$ requires that $\lambda \approx \frac{r_0}{3{\cdot}5}$. This can be achieved by increasing the dimensions of the piston or by increasing the frequency. For example, a rather large radiator $(r_0 = 17{\cdot}5$ cm) is required at 30 kc/s in water ($\lambda \approx 5$ cm). A dynamic loudspeaker in baffle having a cone 15 cm in radius produces highly directional radiation at 5 kc/s, the main beam angular width being 16°, but this is not usually desirable in practice since good audibility is provided only in the axial direction.

The directivity characteristic for the intensity of a circular piston is:

$$\Phi^2(\vartheta) = \frac{4J_1^2(z_0')}{(z_0')^2} = \frac{4J_1^2(kr_0 \sin\vartheta)}{k^2 r_0^2 \sin^2\vartheta}.$$

The far field of a rectangular piston can be analysed in a way similar to the analysis of diffraction by a rectangular aperture*. In this case the directivity characteristic for the intensity has the form:

$$\Phi_0(\vartheta_x, \vartheta_y) = \left[\frac{\sin(kA\sin\vartheta_x)}{kA\sin\vartheta_x}\right]^2 \cdot \left[\frac{\sin(kB\sin\vartheta_y)}{kB\sin\vartheta_y}\right]^2, \quad (11\text{-}31)$$

where $2A$ and $2B$ are the sides of the rectangular piston, and ϑ_x and ϑ_y are the angles between the radius-vector r from the centre of the plate to the observation point and the yz and zx planes, respectively, the plate being in the plane $z = 0$. The function $\sin z'/z'$ is very similar in its form to the function $\frac{J_1(z')}{z'}$, in Fig. 98. The zeroes of this function are slightly different:

$$z_{01}' = 3{\cdot}14;\ z_{02}' = 6{\cdot}28;\ z_{03}' = 9{\cdot}42.$$

Thus the maxima and minima when either $\sin\vartheta_x$ or $\sin\vartheta_y$ is zero follow one another at roughly the same angular distances as in the case of a circular disc; in particular, the angle of the first minimum is

$$\sin\vartheta_1' \simeq \vartheta_1' = 0{\cdot}50\frac{\lambda}{A}.$$

Analysis of expression (11-31) shows that the diffraction maxima are most pronounced in the yz and zx planes.

---

* M. Born, *Optik*, Berlin: Springer, 1933.

In intermediate directions the intensity at the maxima is considerably less. The diffraction pattern thus has a cruciform character.

A useful notion in acoustic engineering is that of a coefficient of acoustic energy concentration β, which is defined as the ratio of the sound intensity $J(0)$ at a point on the axis of the piston (or horn) to that mean intensity $\bar{J}$ at the same point which would have been obtained if all the power had been radiated uniformly in all directions. From (11-28), since

$$2\frac{J_1(z_0')}{z_0'}\Big|_{\vartheta\to 0}\to 1$$

we have:

$$J(0)=\frac{1}{2}\cdot\frac{p_0^2(0)}{\rho c}\approx\frac{\omega^2\rho r_0^4 q_0^2}{8cr^2}.$$

Using (11-17), we get:

$$\bar{J}=\frac{\frac{1}{2}R'\pi r_0^2\rho c q_0^2}{4\pi r^2}=\frac{\left(1-2\frac{J_1(2z_0)}{2z_0}\right)\pi r_0^2\rho c q_0^2}{8\pi r^2},$$

where $z_0=kr_0$.

Therefore

$$\beta=\frac{J(0)}{\bar{J}}=\frac{z_0^2}{1-2\frac{J_1(2z_0)}{2z_0}},$$

If $z_0\gg 1$ (short waves), the expression in the denominator tends to zero and the concentration coefficient β becomes very large:

$$\beta=z_0^2=(kr_0)^2.$$

Thus β is equal to 246 for a radiator 30 cm in diameter at 25 kc/s ($\lambda=6$ cm) in hydroacoustics. If $z_0\ll 1$, using

(11-17) we have:

$$\beta \approx 2.$$

This is quite understandable because if $z_0 \ll 1$, the sound from a piston in a baffle is uniformly distributed over the angle 2π, whereas in the case of radiation in all directions it is uniformly distributed over an angle 4π.

The Acoustic Field and Impedance of Oscillatory (Dipole) and Pulsating Pistons with No Baffle

The velocity potential of an oscillating (dipole) piston with no baffle ceases to be symmetric about the plane of the piston. Such symmetry made it possible for us to form a simple expression (11-8) for the velocity potential provided the surface oscillation velocity of the piston were known.

When there is no baffle, the problem could still be solved by formula (11-9) if the pressure distribution over the piston face were known, but as there is no way to determine it in advance, this method is not feasible.

The acoustic field of an *oscillating* circular piston (dipole) has been discussed by Hanson, using ellipsoidal functions.* He proposed an expression for the velocity potential in the form of a series:

$$\varphi = \frac{1}{k} \sum_{n=1,3,5\ldots} j^n \frac{2C_n}{l_n} \cdot \frac{D_n + j\frac{\pi}{2}C_n}{D_n^2 + \frac{\pi^2}{4} C_n^2} \varepsilon_n E_n(\cos\theta), \qquad (11\text{-}32)$$

where C_n, D_n, l_n and ε_n are functions of the argument $z_0 = kr_0$, which are also expressed in the form of series

* E.T. Hanson, *Phil. Trans.* (A) 232, 223, 1933.

for which the first terms were calculated. The ellipsoidal functions $E_n(\cos\theta)$ depend on the variable θ, which is the parameter of a family of confocal hyperboloids (Fig. 100). At great distances, θ tends to ϑ, where ϑ is the angle between the axis of the piston and a line drawn from its

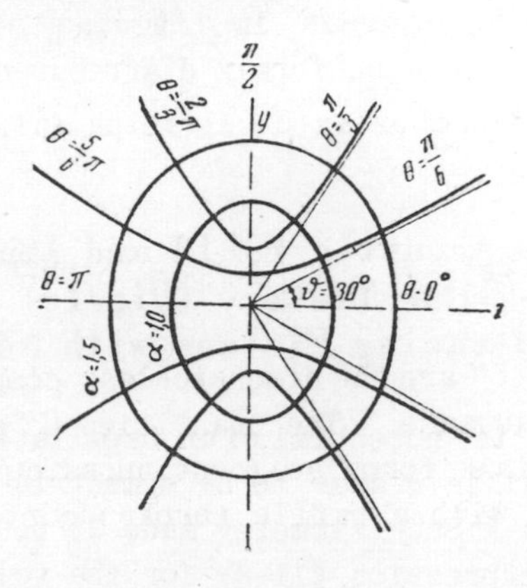

Fig. 100

centre to a remote point. Later Gutin* corrected important errors in Hanson's calculations for the quantities C_n, D_n, l_n and ε_n. Gutin's formulae enable us to calculate the impedance quite accurately up to values $z_0 = 4$. If $z \ll 1$ we can confine ourselves to the first term in expression (11-32) when analysing the far field. In this case the directivity characteristic is given by:

$$E_1(\cos\vartheta) = P_1(\cos\vartheta) - \gamma_{13}P_3(\cos\vartheta) + \gamma_{15}P_5(\cos\vartheta),$$

where $\gamma_{13} = -\frac{z_0^2}{25}$, and $\gamma_{15} = \frac{z_0^4}{45\cdot 49}$ (with small correction factors which rapidly tend to unity if $z_0 \leqslant 4$). For odd values of n, $P_n(\cos\vartheta)$ is zero at $\vartheta = \frac{\pi}{2}$ and therefore the directivity characteristic is always the figure

* L. Ya. Gutin, *Zhur. tekh. phys.* 7, 1096, 1937.

eight shape typical of a dipole source. If z_0 is small, the directivity is described by the function $P_1(\cos\vartheta)=\cos\vartheta$.

If $z_0 \ll 1$, the expression for φ takes the form:

$$\varphi \approx \frac{je^{-jkr}}{k^2r} \cdot \frac{2z_0^3}{3\pi}\cos\vartheta,$$

and the impedance of an oscillating (dipole) piston thus is:

$$Z \approx \left[\frac{8}{27\pi^2}z_0^4 + j\frac{4}{3\pi}z_0\right]2\pi r_0^2\rho c = S\rho c\,(R'' + jY''), \qquad (11\text{-}33)$$

where R'' and Y'' are the dimensionless components of resistance and reactance. The quantities R'' and Y'', as calculated by Gutin's formulae (continuous curves), and R', Y', for a piston with a baffle (broken curves) are plotted in Fig. 101.

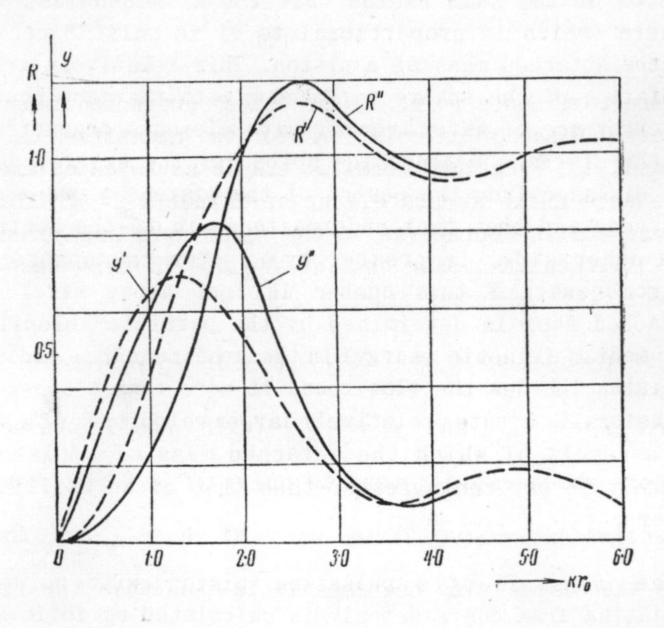

Fig. 101

It is of interest to compare the resistance and reactance of an oscillating circular piston with the corresponding quantities for an oscillating sphere of equal radius at low frequencies. For the sphere, if $z_0 \ll 1$, we have (see Chapter IV, (4-16)):

$$R_{\text{sph}} \approx 4\pi r_0^2 \rho c \frac{z_0^4}{12} \text{ and } Y_{\text{sph}} \approx S\rho c \frac{z_0}{6} = \omega \cdot \frac{1}{2}\left(\frac{4}{3}\pi r_0^3 \rho\right).$$

Thus, provided the sphere and piston are of equal radius, we have:

$$\frac{R_{\text{sph}}}{R_{\text{pist}}} = \frac{9\pi^2}{16} = 5{\cdot}6 \text{ and } \frac{Y_{\text{sph}}}{Y_{\text{pist}}} = \frac{M_{\text{sph}}}{M_{\text{pist}}} = \frac{\pi}{4},$$

where M_{sph} is the attached mass of the sphere and M_{pist} is that of the piston. Consequently, the radiation of an oscillating sphere is 5·6 times greater than that of a piston of the same radius, but the attached mass of a sphere (which is proportional to Y) is only 78 per cent of the attached mass of a piston. This relatively greater radiation of the sphere is bound up with the fact that the interference of waves from opposite elements, characterized by the distance between the poles for the sphere, and by the distance from the centre of the piston on one side to its edge and then back underneath again to the centre on the other side, is greater by $\frac{\pi}{2}$ for the sphere (the fourth power of this number is just about six). The attached mass is determined by the particle velocity of the medium (kinetic energy) in the zone near the radiator. A piston impedes the flow round it more than a sphere and it naturally creates relatively larger velocities of motion, as a result of which the attached mass of a piston is roughly 25 per cent greater than that of an oscillating sphere.

The impedance of a pulsating piston with no baffle radiating from one side only is calculated as follows. It is supposed that the piston pulsates symmetrically on both sides and simultaneously oscillates along the axis. The velocity amplitudes of the two vibrations are identical and equal to unity. We thus obtain in effect double oscillation velocity on one side of the piston and none on the other. This in fact corresponds to a piston which is radiating from one side. The velocity potentials φ_1 and φ_2 are known for these special cases and the required potential φ of such a unilaterally radiating piston (of unit velocity amplitude) is $\frac{\varphi_1+\varphi_2}{2}$. In order to calculate the impedance of a pulsating piston in a baffle, we have to integrate the pressure $p=j\omega\rho\varphi$ over the surface of one side of the piston ($S=\pi r_0^2$). On the other hand, in order to calculate the impedance of an oscillating (dipole) piston by formula (11-33), it is necessary to perform integration over both sides of the disc, i.e. $S=2\pi r_0^2$. To calculate the impedance of a *unilaterally-pulsating* piston it is only necessary to take into account the field on one side (the radiating side) and therefore it is only necessary to take half the impedance (11-33) of an oscillatory (dipole) piston. If $z_0 \ll 1$ we get:

$$Z=\frac{1}{2}\left[\frac{z_0^2}{2}+j\frac{8z_0}{3\pi}+\frac{8z_0^4}{27\pi^2}+j\frac{4z_0}{3\pi}\right]\pi r_0^2\rho c \approx \approx S\rho c\left[\frac{z_0^2}{4}+j\frac{2z_0}{\pi}\right]. \tag{11-34}$$

Thus the radiation resistance of a pulsating piston with no baffle is half that which would be obtained if a baffle were present (see formula (11-19)), owing to the doubling of the solid angle of the space in which radiation takes place. The attached mass is

$$M \underset{z_0 \ll 1}{\approx} \frac{S\rho c\frac{2z_0}{\pi}}{\omega}=2\rho r_0^3. \tag{11-35}$$

If $z_0 \ll 1$, the attached mass M of a piston in a baffle is 8/3 ρr_0^3, (see (11-19)) i.e. it is greater by a factor of 4/3.

It is these values of the components of impedance that

should be used to study the radiation of sound from the open end of a tube or from the mouth of a horn. The correction for the apparent elongation of the tube due to the attached mass is obviously $\left(\frac{2}{\pi}\right)r_0 \approx 0{\cdot}63 r_0$.

INDEX